OCEAN ENGINEERING INFORMATION SERIES Vol. 3

COASTAL/ESTUARINE POLLUTION

An Annotated Bibliography

by

Evelyn Sinha, Ph.D.

OCEAN ENGINEERING INFORMATION SERVICE

P. O. Box 989, La Jolla, California 92037

OCEAN ENGINEERING INFORMATION SERIES Vol. 3

COASTAL/ESTUARINE POLLUTION

An Annotated Bibliography

by

Evelyn Sinha, Ph.D.

OCEAN ENGINEERING INFORMATION SERVICE

P. O. Box 989, La Jolla, California 92037

TABLE OF CONTENTS

ABSTRACT

    This bibliography contains 631 INFORMATIVE ABSTRACTS of literature providing substantial scientific and technological information on: the detection, identification, measurement and analysis of parameters of pollution and pollutants; sources of pollution; coastal and estuarine processes; effects of pollution; water quality management and waste heat utilization. A bibliography of bibliographies, separate identification of theses, books, patents and detailed subject and author indexes are included. Represented are sources found in 111 journals, some 32 national and international conferences and symposia, governmental research and development reports, institutional studies and industrial contract reports. Intended as a guide in interdisciplinary studies of pollution in the coastal zone. Coverage 1965 to May 1970.

Sinha, Evelyn. Coastal/Estuarine Pollution - an annotated bibliography. Ocean Engineering Information Series Vol. 3, 1970, 87 pages plus x. $15.00 prepaid (U. S. Dollars). Published by: Ocean Engineering Information Service, P. O. Box 989, La Jolla, California 92037.

ACKNOWLEDGMENT

We acknowledge the invaluable library assistance of George
Vdovin and Barbara Begg. Thanks are also due to Jessie B.
Roehling and Sandy McCosh for their assistance. Special thanks
are due to Bonnie McCosh for her editorial assistance in
preparation of the manuscript.

CODE FOR JOURNALS CITED

J-1 Water Pollution Control Federation Journal
J-2 Marine Biological Association Journal (UK)
J-3 ASCE Sanitary Engineering Division. Journal
J-4 Water and Sewage Works
J-5 Environmental Science and Technology
J-6 Science
J-7 Nature (London)
J-8 Institute of Petroleum Journal (London)
J-9 Journal of Applied Chemistry
J-11 Journal of Soil and Water Conservation
J-12 Water Research
J-13 Water Treatment and Examination
J-14 California Fish and Game
J-15 World Health Organization. Bulletin
J-16 Water Resources Research
J-17 Engineering Geology
J-18 ASCE Hydraulic Division. Journal
J-19 Candian Journal of Microbiology
J-20 Journal of Marine Research
J-21 Chemistry and Industry
J-22 Scientific American
J-23 American Fisheries Society. Transactions
J-24 Boston Society of Engineering Journal
J-25 Chesapeake Science
J-26 Progressive Fish Culturist
J-27 Nuclear Applications and Technology
J-28 Georgia Academy of Science Bulletin
J-29 Houille Blanche
J-30 American Water Works Journal
J-31 Applied Microbiology
J-32 Canada. Fisheries Research Board. Journal
J-33 Australian Journal of Marine and Freshwater Research
J-34 Netherlands Journal of Sea Research
J-35 Indian Journal of Chemistry
J-36 The Geographical Review
J-37 Canadian Journal of Public Health
J-38 Talanta
J-39 Bioscience
J-40 Pesticides Monitoring Journal
J-41 Limnology and Oceanography
J-42 International Journal of Oceanology and Limnology
J-43 Endeavour
J-44 Crustaceana
J-45 Indian Academy of Science. Proceedings
J-46 Environmental Health. (India)
J-47 Chemical Engineering
J-48 CEBEDEAU. Tribune
J-49 Civil Engineering
J-50 Royal Society of New Zealand (General). Transactions
J-51 Journal of Applied Ecology
J-52 Marine Technology Society Journal
J-53 Texas Journal of Science
J-54 Tokyo University Journal of the Faculty of Engineering Series A
J-55 Journal of Hydraulic Research
J-56 Photogrammetric Engineering
J-57 Air and Water Pollution Journal
J-58 Water Resources Bulletin
J-59 Revue Internationale D'Oceanographie Médicale
J-60 Penn Ar Bed
J-61 Trudy Vses gidrobiol Obschch

J-62 Journal of Liverpool Engineering Society
J-63 Institution of Engineers. Journal (India)
J-64 Hydrobiologia
J-65 Health and Laboratory Sciences
J-66 Oceanology. English Edition. Translation by AGU
J-67 Shore and Beach
J-68 Vattenhygiene
J-69 Nuovi Annali di Igiene Microbiologie
J-70 Techniques et Sciences Municipales
J-71 Municipal Engineering (London)
J-72 Zentralblatt fuer Bakteriologie, Parasitenkunde
J-73 Health Physics
J-74 Water & Pollution Control (Journal. Proc. Inst. Sew. Purification)
J-76 Environmental Health (India)
J-77 Cahier Oceanographique
J-78 Deutsche Gewaesserkundliche Mitteilungen
J-79 Journal du Conseil - Conseil International pour l'Exploration de la Mer
J-80 Consulting Engineer
J-81 Journal of Agriculture and Food Chemistry
J-82 Japanese Society of Scientific Fisheries. Bulletin
J-83 Gesundheitswesen und Desinfekhtion
J-84 Dock and Harbour Authority
J-85 Wasser, Boden und Lufthygien Schr. Reihe. Ver.
J-86 Hokkaido Regional Fisheries Research Laboratory. Bulletin
J-87 Wasserwirtschaft
J-88 Geokhimiya
J-89 Annales de l'Institut Pasteur
J-90 Ecology
J-91 Water and Wastes Engineering
J-92 Radio-Isotopes (Tokyo)
J-93 Institution of Municipal Engineers. Journal (England)
J-94 Effluent Water Treatment. Journal
J-96 Journal of Experimental Marine Biology and Ecology
J-97 DeepSea Research
J-98 Gas u Wass Fach
J-99 Nippon Siusan Gakkaishi
J-100 Naturaliste Canadien
J-101 Water and Water Engineering
J-102 Water (Netherlands)
J-103 Radiological Health Data and Reports
J-104 Tokyo. Institute of Public Health. Bulletin
J-105 Woods Hole Marine Biological Laboratory. Biology Bulletin
J-106 Helgolaender Wissenschaftliche Meeresuntersuchungen
J-107 EOS Transactions. American Geophysical Union
J-108 Cent Etud. Rech biol oceanog. medicale
J-109 Oceanology International
J-110 Ocean Industry
J-111 UnderSea Technology
J-112 Earth and Planetary Science Letters
J-113 Oceans
J-114 Journal of Hygiene

CODE FOR PROCEEDINGS CITED

P-1 Commission Internationale pour l'Exploration Scientific de la Mer Mediterranee, Monaco April 1964 384 p. 40 papers published 1965.

P-2 National Symposium on Estuarine Pollution. Proceedings Aug 1967. Stanford University.

P-3 Symposium on Radioecology. 2nd National 1967 Ann Arbor. Published 1969.

P-4 Symposium International Atomic Energy Agency. Proceedings 1966.

P-5 Symposium on Estuarine Fisheries: American Fish. Soc. Special Publication No. 3. 1966. (See also J-23 95(4)).

P-6 International Seaweed Symposium. Proceedings 1965.

P-7 International Conference Radiation Protection. Rome 1966. Published 1968.

P-8 International Conference. Water Pollution Research. Prague Sept 1968. Fourth.

P-9 International Conference Water Pollution Research. Munich Sept 1966. Third. (Some published as abstracts only in J-1 38(3) 1966.

P-10 International Conference Water Pollution Research. Tokyo 1964. Second. Published 1965.

P-11 Internation Conference on Water for Peace 1967. (1968).

P-12 North American Wildlife and Natural Resources Conference. San Francisco 32nd. Transactions.

P-13 Offshore Technology Conference. Houston, Texas, May 1969.

P-14 Oil on the Sea: Symposium on the scientific and engineering aspects of oil pollution of the sea. Proceedings. Cambridge, Mass. May 1969. MIT and WHOI - cosponsors. Edited by David P. Hoult.

P-15 Ocean Science and Engineering. Transactions. 1965. Joint Conference MTS and ASLO, Washington, D. C. 2 volumes.

P-16 Pollution and Marine Ecology Conference 1967. Olson and Burgess.

P-17 Critical Look at Marine Technology. Marine Technology Society. 4th Annual Conference. Washington, D. C. July 1968.

P-18 International Association for Hydraulic Research. 11th Congress. Leningrad.

P-19 International Colloquim on Mediterrean Ocean. Proceedings. 3rd. (See also J-59)

P-20 Advances in Instrumentation: ISA Annual Conference. Proceedings. Houston, Texas.Vol 24 Part 3, 1969.

P-21 Oceanology International 69. Conference. England 1969.

P-22 Gulf and Caribbean Fisheries Institute Proceedings. 19th Annual Session 1966. Published 1967.

P-23 ASTM. Symposium on Microorganic Matter in Water. 71st Annual. held June 1968 at San Francisco, California.

P-24 American Petroleum Institute. Division of Production. Spring Meeting. Pacific Coast District. Los Angeles, May 1969.

P-25 National Symposium. Ocean Sciences & Engineering of the Atlantic Shelf. Marine Technology Society. Trans. 1968.

P-26 Marine Temperature Measurement. Marine Technology Society. Symposium.

P-27 International Seaweed Symposium. 6th.1969. Madrid.

P-28 International Harbour Congress. 5th. June 1968.

P-30 Biological Aspects of Thermal Pollution

P-30b Engineering Aspects of Thermal Pollution

P-32 Symposium on Water quality criteria to protect aquatic life. In: American Fisheries Society. Transactions. Special Publication No. 4. J-23 96(1) Suppl. 1967.

P-33 Marine, Estuarine, and Riparian Pollution Disasters and their consequences. Ocean Resources Subcommittee.

P-34 ASCE Coastal Engineering. Santa Barbara Conference. Oct 1965.

Aerojet General Corp., El Monte, Calif.
American Fisheries Society
A.I.Ch.E. American Institute of Chemical
  Engineers
American Littoral Society
American Water Resources Conference. New York
Arthur D. Little, Inc., Cambridge, Mass.
Australia. Victoria Fisheries and Wildlife
  Department
Battelle Memorial Institute. Pacific Northwest
  Laboratory, Richland, Wash.
California. Dept. of Fish and Game
California. State Water Quality Control Board
Chesapeake Bay Institute. The Johns Hopkins Univ.
Engineering-Science Inc., Arcadia, Calif.
Federal Water Pollution Control Administration,
  Edison, N. J.
FWPCA. Office of Estuarine Studies
FWPCA. Northwest Region. Corvalis, Oregon
FWPCA. Philadelphia, Penn.
FWPCA. Southwest Region. San Francisco, Calif.
Florida. Bureau of Sport Fisheries and Wildlife
Great Britain. Ministry of Agriculture, Fisheries
  and Food
Gosud. Kom. Ispol. Atomn Energii, Moscow, SSSR
Harvard University. Water Program
Hydronautics Inc., Laurel, Md.
IIT Research Institute. Technology Center,
  Chicago, Ill.
International Atomic Energy Agency
Interstate Commission on the Potomac Basin, Vir.
Lamont Geological Observatory
London. Board of Trade
London. Cabinet Office
London. Water Pollution Steering Committee
Maryland. Baltimore Regional Planning Council
Maryland. Wye Institute (Queen Anne's County)
Mass. Inst. Tech., Cambridge. Fluid Mechanics Lab.
Mississippi State Univ. Water Resources
  Research Institute
NASA
New York. State Conservation Dept.
New York. Water Resources and Marine Sciences
  Center
North Carolina Water Resources Research Inst.,
  Raleigh, N. C.
Northeastern University, Boston, Mass. Dept. of
  Civil Engineering
Northeast Marine Health Service Laboratory,
  D.H.E.W. Narragansett, R. I.
Ocean Engineering Information Service, La Jolla,
  Calif.
Office of Saline Water Research and Development
Robert A. Taft Sanitary Engineering Center
Scotland. Marine Lab., Aberdeen
Stanford University. Remote Sensing Labs.
U. K. Atomic Energy Authority
U. S. Atomic Energy Commission
U. S. Dept. of the Interior. Office of Water
  Resources Research
U. S. Dept. of the Interior. Water Resources
  Science Information Center
U. S. Fish and Wildlife Service

U. S. Geological Survey
U. S. Naval Civil Engineering Lab., Port Hueneme,
  Calif.
U. S. Naval Radiological Defense Lab., San Fran-
  cisco, Calif.
U. S. Public Health Service
Univ. of California. Berkeley. Sanitary Engineering
  Research Lab.
Univ. of California. Institute of Marine Resources
Univ. of Florida. Engineering Dept.
Univ. of Hawaii. Water Resources Research Center
Univ. of Maine
Univ. of Maryland. Solomons. Natural Resources
  Institute
Univ. of New Hampshire
Univ. of North Carolina. Chapel Hill. WRRI
Univ. of Puerto Rico, Mayaguez, Dept. of Marine
  Science
Univ. of Rhode Island, Kingston
Univ. of Texas. Inst. of Marine Science
Virginia Polytechnic Institute. Water Resources
  Research Center
Washington. Water Research Center

RECOMMENDED SECONDARY SOURCES

A. Water Pollution Abstracts - a monthly. published
   in Great Britain. Ministry of Technology.
   Water Pollution Research Branch. Available by
   subscription from H.M.S.

B. Selected Water Resources Abstracts. U. S. Dept.
   of Interior. Water Resources Scientific
   Information Center, Washington, D. C. Twice
   Monthly. $22.00 annual subscription.

C. Journal Water Pollution Control Federation - June
   issue - provides excellent bibliographies of
   literature published during the past year.

D. Oceanic Instrumentation Reporter - a monthly,
   "current awareness". Ocean Engineering
   Information Service, La Jolla, Calif.

(identification by abstract number)

I. DETECTION, IDENTIFICATION, MEASUREMENT AND ANALYSIS OF THE PARAMETERS OF POLLUTION AND POLLUTANTS.

A. BOD, DO, COD
1, 3, 10, 16, 35, 37, 48, 52, 69, 72, 77, 85, 120, 139, 143, 146, 154, 159, 176, 232, 249, 254, 290, 320, 321, 326, 327, 351, 354, 387, 396, 403, 416, (430-432), 452, 460, 461, 466, 486, 494, 504, 523, 529, 534, 539, 542, 545, 552, 567, 575, 576, 595.

B. Plant nutrients
2, 3, 16, 44, 61, 116, 130, 132, 184, 190, 201, 225, 229, 253, 282, 293, 294, 318, 332, 359, 394, 397, 448, 450, 485, 487, 506, 513, 527, 564, 578.

C. Detergents
15, 53, 113, 135, 165, 251, 306, 317, 354, 357, 408, 434, 605, 606.

D. Pesticides
98, 141, 169, 285, 296, 306, 323, 339, 378, 383, 456, 458, 467, 476, 482, 496, 611, 612, 617.

E. Bacteriological Studies. Biological (includes infectious agents)
1, 15, 18, (22-31), 43, 55, 60, (66-68), 70, (73-76), 81, 82, 92, 94, 111, 171, 183, (196-198), 202, 203, 220, 229, 243, 252, 253, 267, 275, 291, 299, 310, 319, 334, 336, 351, 364, 367, 368, (375-377), 382, 386, 387, (392-394), 413, 414, 433, 485, 586, 493, 498, 499, 506, 530, 533, 535, 610, 611, 625.

F. Radioactivity (Tracers in section III, A. 2)
Fallout - 14, 50, 117, 122, 305, 409, 426, 427, 466.
Waste - 11, 13, 32, 44, 56, 91, 105, 106, 108, 109, 117, 142, 144, 160, 161, 163, 164, 166, 173, 182, 186, (191-193), 226, 235, 268, 280, 281, 283, 287, 297, 298, 305, 307, 314, 316, 322, 328, 333, 340, 341, 344, 360, 379, 390, 406, 407, 418, 426, 427, 436, 438, 447, 463, 464, 480, 508, 540, 556, 558, 573, 613, 616.

G. Oil
6, 10, 19, 33, 53, 57, 58, 63, 80, 84, 86, 87, 100, 101, 104, 113, 114, 137, 139, 175, 177, 180, 199, 200, 236, 247, 255, 256, 259, 260, 263, 274, 300, 301, 303, 317, 330, 331, 347, 348, 356, 358, 392, 400, 408, 434, 435, 454, 468, 472, 474, (475-479), 493, 509, 512, 520, 524, 536, 557, 573, 580, 615, 618, 623, 627, 628.

H. Thermal
4, 9, 109, 110, 123, 136, 137, 146, 151, 152, 167, 205, 214, 239, 244, 246, 248, 272, 283, 302, 312, 313, 329, 361, 370, 371, 372, 388, 389, 417, 445, 455, 462, 516, 531, 532, 549, 587, 625, 629, 630.

I. Instruments and Methods
12, 16, 18, 33, 52, 77, 185, 205, 221, (222-225), 228, 242, 257, 258, 276, 278, 279, 293, 294, 298, 309, 325, 342, 346, 347, 356, 363, 365, 369, 374, 398, 399, 407, 416, 447, 454, 467, 473, 489, 502, 503, 517, 528, 554, 556, 558, 560, 565, 568, 585, 588, 609, 610, 623.

II. SOURCES OF POLLUTION

A. Domestic Sewage
7, 15, 18, 20, 26, (28-30), 43, 45, 66, 68, 92, 94, 95, 112, 119, 157, 168, 171, 174, 181, 188, 196, 197, 253, 262, 310, 327, 334, 352, 365, 380, 387, 393, 396, 412, 413, 419, 428, 433, 440, 453, 457, 476, (484-487), 491, 495, 499, 515, 535, 548, 561, 562, 577, 596.

B. Industrial Wastes
30, 46, 48, 59, 132, 139, 181, 206, 209, 224, 273, 286, 308, 334, 403, 457, 460, 476, 484, 486, 515, 523, 551, (574-576), 578, 598.

C. Dredging and other coastal engineering activities
61, 85, 102, 116, 190, 209, 253, 273, 318, 358.

D. See Oil (other sections)

Continued on next page

E. <u>See Radioactivity</u> (other sections)

F. <u>See Thermal Pollution</u> (other sections)

III. COASTAL AND ESTUARINE PROCESSES

A. <u>Paths of pollutants</u>

  1. Dispersion, diffusion, mixing - 17, 34, 36, 45, 46, 52, 61, 65, 119, 130, 133, 140, 154, 156, 158, 161, 163, 164, 188, 189, 193, 206, 208, 211, 214, 219, 226, 234, (237-239), 241, 245, 250, 258, 261, 266, 275, 283, 289, 341, 345, 411, 428, 429, 444.

  2. Tracer Studies - 7, 17, 22, 29, 32, 34, 45, (88-90), 109, 111, 122, 139, 166, 219, 258, 266, 308, 345, 356, 411, 446, 449, 484, 510, 570, 608.

  3. Models - 4, 9, 36, 52, 65, 72, 89, 143, 158, 173, 188, 212, 215, 240, 241, 249, 284, 320, 321, (324-326), 343, 374, 384, (395-397), 404, 405, 425, 430, 431, 469, 488, 494, 500, 534, (541-554), 569, 575, 599.

B. <u>Hydrological and Meteorological influences</u>
   5, 7, 10, 13, 25, 28, 52, 60, 69, 72, 120, 132, 162, 168, 171, 174, 188, 194, 196, 197, 203, 214, 228, 234, 235, 240, 241, 244, 256, 258, 261, 264, 266, 304, 329, 342, 352, 356, 380, 381, 393, 394, 396, 403, 411, 421, 426, 428, 433, 444, 484, 499, 507, 529, 531, 546, 550, 572, 577, 578, 587, 597, (608-610), 619, 621.

C. <u>Sediments and Sedimentation (exchange processes)</u>

  1. Turbidity - suspended matter - 61, 72, 75, 116, 190, 235, 297, 318, 341, 357, 394, 437 460, 492.

  2. Bottom sediments - 44, 68, 69, 118, 121, 161, 164, 190, 201, 213, 218, 228, 232, 280, 281, 286, 287, 291, 295, 305, 344, 401, 407, 418, 434, 437, 438, 441, 460, 487, 490, 530, 534, 540, 573, 578, 585.

  3. Beach sediment - 87, 317, 323, 393, 401

  4. Mud Flats - 46, 295, 490, 539.

  5. Salt marshes - 141, 438, 487, 490, 531, 539, 611

IV. EFFECTS OF POLLUTION

A. <u>Multiple effects - Ecological Systems</u>
   2, 5, 19, 53, 54, 61, 97, 98, 115, 117, 132, 133, (135-137), 183, 236, (244-246), 248, 256, 268, 285, 301, 304, 323, 340, 352, 358, 361, (371-373), 378, 380, 389, 390, 392, 398, 408, 413, 414, 422, 463, 477, 481, 504, 527, 540, 547, 555, 566, 579, 620, 621, 625, 627, 629, 631.

B. <u>Human Health</u>
   82, 97, 160, 177, 186, 268, 271, 433, 436, 465, 551, 603.

C. <u>Fishes</u>
   13, 39, 46, 49, 59, 69, 75, 86, 100, 107, 108, 115, 132, 133, 141, 151, 159, 170, 236, 251, 254, 271, 285, 296, 306, 308, 316, 344, 357, 358, 378, 383, 388, 427, 436, (455-458), 463, 464, 472, 476, 482, 483, 516, 523, 531, 537, 546, 611, 622.

D. <u>Shellfish</u>
   46, (73-76), 91, 94, 99, 100, 108, 124, 133, 160, 218, 251, 252, 271, 306, 311, 316, 339, 354, 364, 368, 376, 378, 392, 403, 410, 414, 441, 443, 456, 465, 468, 480, 505, 506, 523, 533, 540, 564, 581, 582, 610, 611, 612, 627.

E. <u>Birds</u>
   100, 236, 306, 467, 611.

F. <u>Beaches and intertidal organisms, salt marshes, mud flats</u>
   80, 87, 168, 174, 179, 197, 198, 213, 329, 380, 393, 398, 449, 454.

Continued on next page

V. WATER QUALITY MANAGEMENT

A. Prevention and Control
8, 40, 51, 65, 78, 96, 97, 119, 125, (127-129), 131, 138, 153, 158, 177, 195, 204, (207-210), 212, 216, 217, 224, 227, 249, 284, 318, 343, 345, 350, 352, 363, 370, 374, 384, 395, 397, 400, 404, 405, 431, 439, 470, 471, 488, 490, 501, 511, 519, 522, 525, 530, (543-545), 547, 585, 601, 615, 617.

B. Monitoring Systems
41, 51, 78, 137, 157, 166, 216, 264, 335, 336, 401, 405, 478, 479, 496, 526, 528, 560, 562, 563, 570, 571, 583, 584, 589, 619.

C. Special Areas

1. Waste treatment - 19, 48, 93, 95, 157, 195, 249, 262, 292, 303, 335, 384, 412, 491, 514, 520, 582, 620.

2. Outfall design - 62, 94, 111, 112, 157, 174, 188, 189, 198, 226, 288, 336, 385, 412, 419, 440, 453, 497, 515, 526, 577, 620, 621.

3. Oil management - 6, 19, 57, 58, 63, 64, 83, 84, 86, 100, 101, 104, 135, (148-150), 177, 180, 199, 200, 247, 255, 256, 259, 260, 263, 274, 300, 303, 315, 330, 331, 350, 374, 400, 420, 434, 474, 478, 479, 493, 509, 512, 523, 536, 557, (580-582), 618, 624, 626, 628.

4. Waste heat utilization - 9, 123, 126, 136, 205, 239, 272, 312, 313, 361, (370-372), 389, 462, 549, 581, 589, 602, 614, 620.

5. Radioactivity - 163, 173, 265, 283, 360.

D. Instruments/Equipment - Methods/Technology
12, 16, 48, 83, 101, (148-150), 215, 224, 260, 262, 289, 292, 313, 315, 335, 346, 350, 354, 365, 384, 385, 400, 407, 412, 416, 417, 478, 484, 493, 519, 521, 549, 580, 592, 618, 621, 623, 624.

E. Specialized Management Methods/Equipment

1. Remote sensing techniques - 6, 33, 103, 114, 136, 257, 342, 362, 363, 398, 424, 503, 521, 526, 528, 538, 570, 571, 577, 583, 623.

VI. BIBLIOGRAPHY OF BIBLIOGRAPHIES
(more than 50 references in articles and true bibliographies)

6, 30, 38, 70, 90, 151, 155, 205, 227, 246, 267, 285, 302, 304, 337, 342, 371, 413, 414, 448, 455, 478, 479, 498, 503, 521, 524, 537, 547, 579, 615, 619.

VII. THESES AND BOOKS

A. Theses
49, 147, 201, 235, 280, 287, 305, 316, 352, 381, 386, 403, 463, 487, 513, 521, 583, 603.

B. Books (collected works)
129, 131, 224, 249, 259, 269, 270, 313, 369, 389, 402, 417, 421, 436, 572.

VIII. PATENTS

83, 93, 148, 149, 150, 289, 292, 338, 373, 385, 412, 491, 514, 519.

3.0 - 1
Aalto, Johan (1968). POTOMAC ESTUARY - STATISTICS AND PROJECTIONS
--Presents information on water quality and pollution loads in the Upper Potomac Estuary. It was found that the total load is eight times the assimilative capacity required to maintain a DO average of five mg/l. Counts are given for coliforms and fecal coliforms. Ref: *Interstate Commission on the Potomac Basin Winter Meeting, Fredericksburg, Virginia, Feb 29, 1968.*

3.0 - 2
Abbott, Walter (1967). MICROCOSM STUDIES OF EFFECTS OF SINGLE DOSES OF NITRATE AND PHOSPHATE ON ESTUARINE ECOLOGY
--Effect of factorial doses of nitrate (10, 25, 50, 100 μmoles/l) and orthophosphate (1, 10, 50, 100 μmoles/l) were studied using 16 carboy microcrosms of previously demonstrated replicability. The time courses of the effects of the two nutrients on photosynthetic production and on respiration varied. Ultimately, both metabolic parameters show graded responses to varying levels of both nutrients; however, there is no interaction effect of nutrient combination on metabolism. Utilization of the two nutrients occurs independently. Kinetic treatment indicates an overall first-order effect for phosphate consumption, with maximum velocity of 5-6 μmoles/day/l. Nitrate uptake-rate plots show a curvilinear effect, with depression of uptake at high dissolved nitrate levels. Ref: *J-1 39(1):113-122, Jan 1967. 31 refs.*

3.0 - 3
Abbott, Walter (1968). NUTRIENT STUDIES IN HYPERFERTILIZED ESTUARINE ECOSYSTEMS
--Experimental results cast doubt on the generally proposed mechanisms for waste-water enrichment of a receiving body and on the function of exogenous dissolved organic matter in oxygen depletion.
Ref: *P-8 and J-12 (abstract only) 2,:105-106, 1968.*

3.0 - 4
Ackers, Peter (1969). MODELING OF HEATED-WATER DISCHARGES
--Presents a discussion on some of the more practical aspects of the modeling of buoyant effluents, including a comparison of model and prototype observations in several situations. EDWARD E. DRIVER and REX A. ELDER commented on ACKER'S work and comments from the floor were made by HARLEMAN, NAKATANI and others. Ref: *P-30b Chap 6: 177-224, 1969. Refs.*

3.0 - 5
Alfimov, N. N. (1959). DATA ON METHODS OF HYDROBIOLOGICAL ANALYSIS OF COASTAL SEA-WATER PURITY
--On the southern coast of the Crimea green algae predominated in contaminated bays and brown algae in uncontaminated bays; from the proportions of the different algae it is possible to estimate the extent of diffusion of contaminated waters. A list of macrophytes and epiphytic diatoms, indicating contamination at different seasons of the year is given. Ebb tides improve the quality of coastal waters and high tides have the opposite effect; tidal action can have a purifying effect only where there is free water exchange between the polluted area and the open sea. (In Russian)
Ref: *J-61 9,:360-366, 1959.*

3.0 - 6
Alkire, G. C.; Becker, C. D.; Cook, M. W.; Davis, Diana; and Leach, C. E. (1967). OIL SPILLAGE STUDY, LITERATURE SEARCH, AND CRITICAL EVALUATION FOR SELECTION OF PROMISING TECHNIQUES TO CONTROL AND PREVENT DAMAGE.
--A review and evaluation of 761 references to the literature on the state of technology of prevention and control of major oil spillage on water, the restoration of the shoreface and fowl. Operational practices in shipping, offshore oil production practices, and transmission line safety codes are encompassed. Note is taken that oil spills are studied by aerial surveys including spectrophotometric, ultraviolet, infrared, radar and microwave imaging. In regard to chemical treatments, it is indicated that all dispersants and emulsifiers are more or less toxic. Oil may be confined by booms and then either burned or recovered. Technology for reclamation of recovered oils though available is not in general use.
Ref: *Battelle Memorial Institute Pacific Northwest Labs., Richland, Wash. 281 p., Nov 1967. 761 refs.*

3.0 - 7
Allan Hancock Foundation, University of Southern California (1965). INVESTIGATION ON THE FATE OF ORGANIC AND INORGANIC WASTES DISCHARGED INTO THE MARINE ENVIRONMENT AND THEIR EFFECTS ON BIOLOGICAL PRODUCTIVITY
--Contains the results of studies on selected aspects of the biological, chemical, and physical behavior of waste fields in coastal waters, to provide information for use in solving marine waste disposal problems. The aspects investigated included dye patch studies on the dilution and dispersion of a waste field in the sea; dye plume studies on dilution and dispersion under conditions of continuous release; the primary productivity of phytoplankton in a marine waste field; the use of ultraviolet absorption for tracking a sewage field; and suitable methods of chemical analysis. Meteorological influences such as wind speed effects were also considered. Ref: *California State Water Quality Control Board Publication No. 29, 130 p., 1965. $3.75.*

3.0 - 8
Allen, G. W. (1967). BIOLOGISTS VIEWPOINT OF MAN-MADE CHANGES IN ESTUARIES
--No man-made changes in estuaries benefit production and in most cases harm it. Ref: *P-22 p. 69-77, 1967.*

3.0 - 9
Allen, J. Frances (1969). RESEARCH NEEDS FOR THERMAL-POLLUTION CONTROL
--This paper points out that before controls can be effectively instigated, it is essential that pertinent information be available for the development and establishment of controls. The discussion is concerned with research needs of the bio-

logical aspects of thermal-pollution control, including mention of the related physical and chemical environments. Ref: *P-30 p. 382-392, 1969. 11 refs.*

3.0 - 10
Alyakrinskaya, I. O. (1966). EXPERIMENTAL DATA ON THE CONSUMPTION OF OXYGEN IN SEA WATER POLLUTED WITH PETROLEUM
--Reports extensive contamination by petroleum in Novorossiysk Bay. The film on the water surface acts as a barrier to exchange between the water and the atmosphere. Large concentrations reduce the content of dissolved oxygen and increase biochemical oxygen demand and oxydizability. In the summer calms catastrophically high concentrations of pollution occur. Experimental data are tabulated. Ref: *J-66 6(1):71-78, 1966.*

3.0 - 11
Amburgey, J. W. (1968). STUDY OF POLLUTANT DISCHARGES FROM REACTOR OPERATIONS UTILIZING ULTRACENTRIFUGATION TECHNIQUES
--Samples of reactor cooling water from Hanford, Wash., were treated by ultracentrifugation techniques and the suspended solids were separated into groups and examined by chemical and radiochemical techniques. A few radionuclide parent elements, such as chromium, sulphur, and zinc, were found almost entirely associated with the dissolved materials fraction. It is concluded that the suspended solids in the cooling water do not add significantly to the radioactive pollution of the Columbia River. Ref: *U. S. Atomic Energy Commission K-1754, 36 p., 1968.*

3.0 - 12
Anderson, J. B. and Mason, William T., Jr. (1968). COMPARISON OF BENTHIC MACROINVERTEBRATES COLLECTED BY DREDGE AND BASKET SAMPLER
--Benthic macroinvertebrates from the Ohio River at Louisville and Cincinnati and the Wabash River at New Harmony were collected by Petersen dredge and a basket sampler. Data are presented which show the kinds and numbers of organisms collected with each sampler. The Petersen dredge collected more of the organisms which normally inhabit the bottom sediments, such as worms and mollusks. However a larger number and variety of pollution sensitive aquatic insects were obtained with the basket sampler which makes it of great value in water pollution investigations. Ref: *J-1 40(2):252-259, Feb 1968. 6 refs.*

3.0 - 13
Angelovic, J. W.; White, J.C., Jr. and Davis, E.M. (1969). INTERACTIONS OF IONIZING RADIATION, SALINITY, AND TEMPERATURE ON THE ESTUARINE FISH, *FUNDULUS HETEROCLITUS*
--The interactions of salinity, temperature, and ionizing radiation as environmental factors affecting mortality, LD-50 and sodium-22 efflux of the euryhaline fish, *Fundulus heteroclitus*, were determined in a series of experiments. Ref: *P-3 p. 131-141, 1969.*

3.0 - 14
Angino, E. E.; Simek, J. E. and Davis, J. A. (1965). FIXING OF FALLOUT MATERIAL BY FLOATING MARINE ORGANISMS, *SARGASSUM FLUITANS AND S. NATANS*
--Gamma-spectrometric studies on samples of the free-floating marine algae *Sargassum fluitans* and *S. natans* collected from the Gulf of Mexico indicated the presence of the following radioactive isotopes (in decreasing order of fractional concentrations): cerium-144/promethium-144; ruthenium-106/rhodium-106; caesium-137 and zirconium-95/niobium-95; ruthenium-103/rhodium-103; and manganese-54, none of which could be attributed to natural radioactivity in the marine environment but only to the fallout of fission products. The results, which complement those obtained by GLAZUNOV, V.V, PARCHEVSKII, V.P., and FLEISHMAN, D.G., for benthic alga *Cystoseira barbata* from the Black Sea, are now to be compared with those for other samples of *Sargassum* obtained either before nuclear tests or from other areas. Ref: *Texas University. Institute of Marine Science Publication no. 10, p. 173-178, 1965.*

3.0 - 15
Armangau, C. (1968). ON THE VALUE OF ANIONIC DETERGENTS AS TRACERS OF BACTERIAL POLLUTION
--The relative merits of faecal bacteria and anionic detergents as indicators of pollution in the vicinity of a coastal sewage discharge were considered. According to circumstances, the presence of either might be detected when the other appeared to be absent and thus a parallel relationship should be interpreted with caution. Ref: *P-19 and J-59 9,:219-222, 1968.*

3.0 - 16
Armstrong, F. A. J. and Tibbitts, S. (1968). PHOTOCHEMICAL COMBUSTION OF ORGANIC MATTER IN SEA WATER, FOR NITROGEN, PHOSPHORUS AND CARBON DETERMINATION
--The construction of a photochemical reactor using a medium-power mercury arc lamp for oxidation of organic matter in sea water is described. First-order kinetics with rate constants in the range $0.2-4.0 h^{-1}$ were observed for the decomposition of known compounds in distilled water and sea water using a 380 W lamp. Total nitrogen and phosphorus determinations were made for samples from 10 m depth in the English Channel and results are presented. The decomposition of naturally-occurring organic compounds did not follow first-order reaction kinetics. A technique for measuring oxygen consumption during irradiation, which provides a method for determining carbon or measuring total biological oxygen demand, is described. Ref: *J-2 48(1):143-152, Feb 1968.*

3.0 - 17
Asano, Takashi (1967). DISTRIBUTION OF POLLUTIONAL LOADINGS IN SUISUN BAY
--Reports that the California Department of Water Resources conducted a series of dye tracer studies during 1965-1966. The waste dispersive characteristics under various flow regimes and the specific effect of fresh water inflow upon the dispersion and transit of continuously discharged pollutants into the study area were investigated. Ref: *P-2 p. 441-461, 1967.*

3.0 - 18
Aubert, M.; Lebout, H.; and Aubert, J. (1965). METHODS FOR STUDYING MICROBIOLOGICAL POLLUTION NEAR THE OUTLET INTO THE SEA OF A WASTE-WATER OUTFALL AND EXAMINATION OF RESULTS
--The authors outlined the methods and instruments

used by the National Institute of Hygiene, Nice, France, to study the pollution of a marine area by wastes from the land, including a general survey of the currents, both offshore and near the beaches, especially where affected by local rivers; qualitative and quantitative investigations on the solid matter in the region of estuaries and outfalls and further offshore; and a study on the pathogenicity of the waste material and the microscopic pollution carried to bathing waters. The methods used for the determination of total and coliform bacteria, and streptococci are also summarized. Procedure on board ship is outlined. Ref: *P-1 p. 19-23, 1965.*

3.0 - 19
Aubert, M. and Miquelis, E. (1965). TECHNIQUES FOR STUDYING AND RESULTS OF USING A DESTRUCTIVE PRODUCT (P.A.M.6) ON LAYERS OF FUEL OIL FLOATING ON THE SEA
--After discussing the causes and characteristics of pollution of sea water by fuel oil, the effects of such pollution on coastal regions and beaches, and the impossibility of chemical treatment to produce a harmless substance, the authors describe extensive studies using various artificial and natural adsorbant powders to precipitate the surface layer of hydrocarbon on to the sea bed, thus avoiding carriage of pollution onshore. Exceptionally satisfactory results were obtained only with natural marine deposits of the type containing quartz crystals, hyaline quartz, mica, mica schist, hornblende, and amphibole; the process of adsorption and precipitation of hydrocarbon was accelerated by mixing the adsorbent material with activated silica which serves as a wetting agent. The method introduces no toxic materials into the sea, and the precipitated material has no harmful effects on the benthic flora, but, the products of the gradual degradation are taken up by the benthic flora and may even provide certain growth factors. The natural precipitant used, known as P.A.M.6 was applied satisfactorily on a large scale when water contaminated with hydrocarbons had to be pumped out of a boat wrecked in Cannes Harbor in 1962. Ref: *P-1 p. 319-322, 1965.*

3.0 - 20
Aubert, M.; Lebout, H. and Aubert, J. (1965). EFFECT OF MARINE PLANKTON IN DESTRUCTION OF ENTERIC BACTERIA
--Investigations were made to determine the cause and extent of the disinfectant action of sea water on sewage. Methods used are reported. The factor responsible for the antibiotic activity of sea water is not a phage but is thermolabile and apparently biochemical in nature, probably a secretion or a component of the plankton. Ref: *P-10 3,:303-314, 1965.*

3.0 - 21
Aubert, M.; Aubert, J. and others (1966). ORIGIN AND NATURE OF ANTIBIOTIC SUBSTANCES PRESENT IN THE MARINE ENVIRONMENT. I. BIBLIOGRAPHIC STUDY AND ANALYSIS OF PREVIOUS WORKS
--Studies by various investigators to discover the origin and chemical composition of antibiotic substances in sea water have shown that although sea water itself has physico-chemical properties which do not favor the survival of organisms of terrestrial origin, there are also substances with antibiotic properties towards these organisms, released by marine bacteria, animals, and vegetation. Chemical analyses were carried out on some of these substances and they were found to consist mostly of fatty acids, terpenes, hydrocarbons, and chlorophyllides, which were seen to exist in significant quantities in the sea. Ref: *J-59 1,:9-26, 1966. refs.*

3.0 - 22
Aubert, M.; Guizerix, J. and others (1966). STUDY OF BACTERIAL DISPERSION OF WASTE WATERS IN THE SEA BY MEANS OF RADIOACTIVE TRACERS
--A joint study by the French National Institute of Health and Medical Research and the Centre of Nuclear Studies at Grenoble was carried out on the dispersion of terrestrial bacteria at an ocean outfall, the dynamics of self-purification, and the siting of future outfalls. A study was made during dispersion of the concentrations of a radioactive tracer injected instantaneously into sewage from Nice, terrestrial bacteria, and salinity, and a good correlation between them was found. Sewage marked by 1 curie of bromine-82 was injected into open sea free from terrestrial bacteria. At short distances from the point of injection, water, strongly marked by radioactive tracer, no longer contained terrestrial bacteria, which emphasized the importance of the self-purifying power of the sea against these organisms. Ref: *J-59 1,:56-91, 1966.*

3.0 - 23
Aubert, M.; Aubert, J.: Gauthier, M. and Daniel, S. (1966). ORIGIN AND NATURE OF ANTIBIOTIC SUBSTANCES PRESENT IN THE MARINE ENVIRONMENT. II. METHODS OF STUDY AND EXPERIMENTAL TECHNIQUES
--Studies were carried out to investigate the antibiotic activity of individual species. Samples of each species of phytoplankton, each in two different media, were put into a sterilized culture chamber with a temperature of 18° ± 1°C and a daily lighting routine of 12 hours of light followed by 12 hours of darkness. After two weeks, they were divided into culture liquid and cellular extract and analysed bacteriologically by the diffusion method or by study in the liquid medium, and biochemically by paper or column chromatography. Ref: *J-59 1,:27-34, 1966.*

3.0 - 24
Aubert M., Gauthier, M. and Daniel, S. (1966). ORIGIN AND NATURE OF ANTIBIOTIC SUBSTANCES PRESENT IN THE MARINE ENVIRONMENT. III. ANTIBACTERIAL ACTIVITY OF A MARINE DIATOM, *ASTERIONELLA JAPONICA*
--The cellular extracts and liquids of cultures of *Asterionella japonica* were tested by the diffusion method and by dilution in liquid media on *Esch. coli, Staphylococcus aureus 209P and Streptococcus faecalis,* and an anti- *Staphylococcus aureus 209P* activity and an anti-*Streptococcus faecalis* activity were found. A comparative study of activity in liquid media showed a bacteriostatic activity in those incubated at 37°C in darkness, and a bactericidal activity in those incubated at the same temperature in the light. The cultures used were non-axenic but previous studies by other workers showed no difference in activity between axenic and non-axenic cultures. Ref: *J-59 1,:35-43, 1966.*

3.0 - 25
Aubert, M.; Lebout, H.; Aubert, J. and others
(1966).   STUDY OF BACTERIOLOGICAL POLLUTION OFF
THE   MEDITERRANEAN   COAST   OF   FRANCE.   GENERAL
INTRODUCTION. PART I. HYDROLOGICAL AND BACTERIO-
LOGICAL STUDY OF MARINE AREAS SITUATED OFF THE
MARITIME ALPS
--A series of investigations were carried out to
assess   the   effects   of   present   or   proposed   discharges of waste waters into the sea off the Mediterranean coast of France. Tabulated and diagrammatical results are given for the first part of
the investigations, carried out off the Maritime
Alps in a region extending 5 miles out to sea.
The nature and points of discharge of waste waters
and rivers are tabulated. Polluting matter will
affect different parts of the shore depending on
the prevailing wind and the mechanisms of dispersion will depend on the hydrological characteristics and circulation of the sea water at the point
where the pollution is discharged. A table shows
the degree of pollution in the water and on the
land at various sampling points, and also the composition of material deposited at high tide.
Ref: *J-59   3,:11-54, 1966.*

3.0 - 26
Aubert, M. and Aubert, J. (1967).   STUDY ON THE
DIFFUSION OF BACTERIAL POLLUTION IN THE SEA
--The diffusion of waste waters in the sea was
studied by means of studies on currents, by the
use of tracers, and by measurement of self-purification,   and a quantitative expression between
waste water and primary biomass was developed.
Even small amounts of domestic sewage increase the
growth of plankton, and these exert an antibiotic
effect on the bacteria in the contaminated water.
It is concluded that, except with industrial pollution, the marine environment is not affected adversely, and any noticeable pollution is local in
character. Ref: *J-60   6(50):139-149, 1967.*

3.0 - 27
Aubert, M.; Aubert, J.; Gauthier, M. and Pesando,
D. (1967).   STUDY ON THE ANTIBIOTIC PHENOMENA
ASSOCIATED WITH A BLOOM OF PERIDINIANS
--During studies in 1964 on the antibiotic activity of phytoplankton, it was noted that, at certain periods of the year, antibacterial substances
occurred which were thermally stable. More detailed studies were carried out in 1967 showing that
at these periods, the antibiotic substances in the
sea water were thermally stable and resistant to
ageing, and that these properties coincided with a
change in the proportions of phytoplankton species,
with predominance of peridinians,   particularly
Ceratium furca. Results for 1964 and 1967 are tabulated and the antibacterial activities associated
with peridinians and with diatoms are compared;
when the predominant species of phytoplankton
changes,   there are parallel changes in the antibacterial spectra and chemical characteristics of
the sea water, sea water in which peridinians had
predominated had an antagonistic effect on *Asterionella japonica*, which was associated with the
unknown thermally-stable substance. Ref: *J-59
6-7,:43-52, 1967.*

3.0 - 28
Aubert, M.; Aubert, J.; Fruchart, A. et al (1968).
PRESENT STATE OF BACTERIOLOGICAL POLLUTION ALONG

THE FRENCH MEDITERRANEAN COAST
--In studies on the pollution of beaches and inshore waters by sewage discharges along the French
Mediterranean coast, the distribution of faecal
bacteria has been considered in relation to prevailing hydrological and meteorological conditions.
The results of similar studies of the north-, east-
and west-coastal regions of Corsica were also discussed. Ref: *P-19 and J-59   9,:45-72, 1968.
14 refs.*

3.0 - 29
Aubert, J. and Daniel, S.   (1968).   BIOLOGICAL
TRACERS OF WASTE WATER
--Recommendations are made on using bacteria as
tracers to determine the extent of pollution from
existing or proposed coastal outfall   sewers.
Species occuring naturally in sewage would   be
used to indicate dilution and dispersion of existing discharges and of proposed discharges to unpolluted waters, but to investigate future discharges to polluted zones distinctive bacteria
would be introduced in the region of the proposed
outfall. Ref: *P-19 and J-59   9,:223-236, 1968.
14 refs.*

3.0 - 30
Aubert, M.; Aubert, J. and others (1968). FRENCH
COASTS: NATIONAL INVENTORY OF BACTERIAL POLLUTION
OF LITTORAL WATERS. VOLS I AND II.
--The extent of bacterial pollution of French
beaches and coastal waters has been studied at the
Centre d'Etudes et de Recherches de Biologie et
d'Océanographic Médicale, Nice, during the past
six years. The authors review the hazards of disease, particularly from the consumption of contaminated fish and molluscs, owing to pollution by
sewage and industrial waste waters. The fate of
bacteria discharged to the sea is reviewed with
reference to their dispersion and die-off, and
especially to self-purification in the environment
by the antibiotic activity of marine algae and by
other agents. Measures to avoid the immediate pollution of beaches and bathing waters are considered and studies of long-term effects, such as an
increase in marine productivity and the toxic effects of some chemical waste waters, are indicated.
Volume II comprises charts, graphs, and tables
showing the speed and direction of surface currents and the density of bacteria at flow and ebb
tides along the French northern coastline. Volume
I also includes a bibliography of 158 references.
Ref: *J-59 Supplement 1968. Vol. I, 68 p., Vol. II,
124 p. 158 refs.*

3.0 - 31
Aubert, M.; Aubert, J. and others (1968). FRENCH
COASTS: NATIONAL INVENTORY OF BACTERIAL POLLUTION
OF LITTORAL WATERS. VOLS. III AND IV.
--These volumes which complete the set of data
relating to the numbers of bacteria present in
French coastal waters and factors which affect
their distribution give details in charts, diagrams
and tables of conditions existing along the Atlantic and Mediterranean shores. Ref: *J-59 Supplement 1968, Vol. III, 106 p., Vol. IV, 172 p.*

3.0 - 32
Ausset, R. and Farges, L.   (1968).   USE OF
RHODAMINE-B IN THE STUDY OF THE HYDROLOGICAL
CHARACTERISTICS OF A MARINE SITE FOR THE DISCHARGE

OF RADIOACTIVE EFFLUENTS
--Details were given of tracer studies to estimate the dispersion and persistence of a proposed discharge of low-level radioactive waste water from a nuclear plant at La Hague, Normandy. Ref: *P-19 and J-59 9,:167-189, 1968.*

3.0 - 33
Bailey, James S. and White, Peter G. (1969). REMOTE SENSING OF OCEAN COLOR
--Two instruments, the Widerange Image Spectrophotometer (WISP) and the Water Color Spectrometer (WCS) were developed at TRW Systems Inc. for remote sensing of ocean color. The WCS produces a continuous record of the spectral ocean in only one spatial element while the WISP is designed to measure simultaneously the color over many spatial elements. Examples of WCS data are shown in unreduced and reduced form of various water colors. An example of water with and without an oil film is also shown. WISP data are shown in reduced form only. Ref: *P-20 Vol. 24, Part 3, 5 p., 1969.*

3.0 - 34
Bailey, Thomas E. (1966). FLUORESCENT-TRACER STUDIES OF AN ESTUARY
--Proposals embodied in the California Water Plan required that studies be conducted in the Sacramento-San Joaquin Delta and Suisun Bay to determine hydrographic parameters related to operation of water facilities and discharge of wastes into the estuary. Fluorescent tracers Rhodamine B and Pontacyl Pink were used and techniques were developed for making field tests. Observations were made from instrumented boats equipped for collecting discrete and continuous samples of vertical, transverse and horizontal profiles. Results were used to determine diffusion coefficients, mixing and flushing rates, and waste assimilation characteristics. Ref: *J-1 38(12):1986-2001, Dec 1966. 34 refs.*

3.0 - 35
Bailey, Thomas E. (1967). ESTUARINE OXYGEN RESOURCES - PHOTOSYNTHESIS AND REAERATION
--Presents a discussion of the primary sources of oxygen supplied to the Sacramento-San Joaquin Estuary and Suisun Bay system through photosynthesis and reaeration. Field surveys and comparative tests indicated that reaeration and diffusion rates are too complex to be predicted reliably by empirical relationships and that direct field measurements must be made to obtain reliable data. Ref: *P-2 p. 310-330, 1967.*

3.0 - 36
Bailey, Thomas E.; McCullough, Charles A. and Gunnerson, Charles G. (1966). MIXING AND DISPERSION STUDIES IN SAN FRANCISCO BAY
--Studies conducted in the prototype and in the Corps of Engineers' hydraulic model of San Francisco Bay verified the model's ability to simulate natural mixing and dispersion processes as well as stages, velocities, and salinities. The model was accordingly used to predict the effects on the receiving water of discharges of agricultural drainage. Results from model tests supplied data on conservative and nonconservative constituent distribution patterns resulting from variation in inflow, discharging over different time periods, and

discharging at four alternative locations. Ref: *J-3 92(SA5 Paper 4936):23-45, Oct 1966.*

3.0 - 37
Bain, Richard C., Jr. (1967). PREDICTING DIURNAL VARIATIONS IN DISSOLVED OXYGEN CAUSED BY ALGAE IN ESTUARINE WATERS. PART I.
--Photosynthetic oxygenation and respiratory deoxygenation rates of estuarine phytoplankton were measured at various standing crop levels. Variations in algae photosynthetic production rate as related to light adaption, age of cells, nutrition, temperature, and algae type are discussed. DO concentrations were measured over a 24 hour period. DO predictions were compared with field measurements from a tidal reach of the San Joaquin River, California. Ref: *P-2 p. 250-279, 1967. Also as: J-3 94(SA5 Paper 6155):867-881, Oct 1968. 26 refs.*

3.0 - 38
Baker, R. A. (1969). MICROORGANIC MATTER IN WATER
--Papers presented included topics on: nitrogen uptake, pesticide analysis, freeze concentration, thin-layer chromatography to identify phenols, fluorescence techniques, and determination of trace amounts of molybdenum. Ref: *P-23 124 p., 1969. 205 refs.*

3.0 - 39
Ballard, J. A. and Oliff, W. D. (1969). RAPID METHOD FOR MEASURING THE ACUTE TOXICITY OF DISSOLVED MATERIALS TO MARINE FISHES
--To study the effects of industrial and urban wastes discharging into the sea along the Natal Coast, the National Institute for Water Research tested methods of assessing the toxicity of materials to marine fishes. Comparison with others showed that the residual oxygen method was quick and reliable. Animals are held in sealed containers with graded concentrations of test material. The final level of oxygen on the death of the fishes is used as a measure of the toxicity of the material. Ref: *J-12 3(5):313-333, May 1969. 7 refs.*

3.0 - 40
Ballinger, Dwight G. (1968). REVIEW OF CHEMICAL MEASUREMENTS IN WATER POLLUTION CONTROL
--Water quality parameters essential in pollution control efforts are listed. The lists include an analysis of frequency of parameter usage by state authorities, parameters for public supply, metal determinations for public supply, chemical parameters for industrial water, for fish and wildlife pesticides, etc. It is pointed out that waste load analysis must include not only identification of undesirable constituents, but also measurement of impaired desirable constituents such as dissolved oxygen. The constituents to be determined are listed and references to sources of the applicable standards of concentrations of constituents are given. Ref: *J-4 p. R38-R42, Nov 1968. 3 refs.*

3.0 - 41
Ballinger, Dwight G. (1968). AUTOMATED WATER QUALITY MONITORING
--Reports that a variety of automatic samplers has been developed. Telemetry, alarm systems, and the use of monitors, as part of the waste-control

process, are essential parts of the concept. FWPCA performance specifications and lists of producers of monitoring equipment are included. Ref: *J-5 2(8):606-610, Aug 1968. 7 refs.*

3.0 - 42
Baltimore Regional Planning Council. Maryland (1968). A RECONNAISSANCE STUDY OF CHESAPEAKE BAY
--This report synthesizes many older studies. Taken into account are: excessive nutrients, polluted shellfish areas, thermal pollution, plant and animal nuisances. A chapter on water quality contrasts the present condition of streams with their highest protected use as defined by the state's water quality standards. Relative agency responsibilities and studies are listed under various problem areas discussed. Economic indicators are noted. Ref: *Maryland. Baltimore Regional Planning Council. 70 p., Sept 1968. 25 refs.*

3.0 - 43
Bandy, O. L.; Ingle, J.C. and Resig, J.M. (1965). FORAMINIFERAL TRENDS, HYPERION OUTFALL, CALIFORNIA
--The distribution of foraminifera in Santa Monica Bay, California, was studied in relation to the features of Santa Monica Coast and to discharges from the Los Angeles City Hyperion sewage-works outfall system. Planktonic tests were more abundant in the path of the effluent than in other areas. Dominant species were identified. Ref: *J-41 10(3):314-332, July 1965.*

3.0 - 44
Barnes, C. A. and Gross, M. G. (1966). DISTRIBUTION AT SEA OF COLUMBIA RIVER WATER AND ITS LOAD OF RADIONUCLIDES
--Summarizes the results of studies in progress since 1961, on the properties and distribution of the Columbia River 'plume' in the northeast Pacific Ocean. The river water reduces the salinity, and moves along the coast as a surface layer less than 40 m thick. The mixing of nutrients carried by the river with nutrients from the surrounding and underlying sea water results in the production cycle of phytoplankton within the plume differing from that outside. Of the radioactive isotopes studied, chromium-51, dominant in the lower river, tends to remain in solution and is most abundant near the estuary while zinc-65 is apparently associated with filterable particulate matter and is found mainly in the sediments along the continental shelf. Ref: *P-4 p. 291-302, 1966.*

3.0 - 45
Barrett, M. J. and others (1968). RADIOTRACER DISPERSION STUDIES IN THE VICINITY OF A SEA OUTFALL
--The Water Pollution Research Laboratory, (Stevenage, England) made an intensive study in the vicinity of a sea outfall extending some 400 m offshore during two successive summers. This paper reports some physical aspects of the problem of dispersion in the top 2 m in an unstratified coastal water, up to 15 m deep and at a distance up to 1 km offshore. A solution containing a few hundred mCi of bromine-82 was added instantaneously to the sea surface and tracked for several hours. Ref: *P-8 and J-12 p. 124, 1968.*

3.0 - 46
Bartsch, A. F. (1965). STUDY OF PULP AND PAPER

MILL POLLUTION IN PUGET SOUND
--Oceanographic studies were made to determine the dispersion of waste waters in Puget Sound. Results show: penetration of spent sulphite liquor into Possession Sound and Saratoga Passage; the bottom sediments in Everett Harbor and Port Gardner Bay were covered with a layer of black malodorous mud, lacking appreciable populations of macro-organisms, and containing hydrogen sulphide. It was found that juvenile salmonids encounter unfavorable conditions at the Everett waterfront, mortalities varied with tidal stages. Effects on other fauna were noted. Abnormalities were noted in oyster larvae. Ref: *P-10 3,:43-64, 1965.*

3.0 - 47
Basu, A. K. (1965). OBSERVATION ON THE PROBABLE EFFECTS OF POLLUTION ON THE PRIMARY PRODUCTIVITY OF THE HOOGHLY AND MUTLAH ESTUARIES
--By the use of the light and dark bottles technique, a comparative study of the productivity of the Hooghly and the Mutlah Estuaries (India) was made. The Hooghly Estuary is a recipient of various pollutants from industries located on its banks, whereas the Mutlah is free from pollutants. The investigation indicated that whereas the productivity in the Mutlah was between 0.562 mg $C/m^3/$day and 0.375 $C/m^3/day$, the productivity of the Hooghly was negligible. Ref: *J-64 25(1/2): 302-316, March 20, 1965.*

3.0 - 48
Basu, A. K. (1966). STUDIES ON EFFLUENTS FROM PULP-PAPER MILLS AND ITS ROLE IN BRINGING THE PHYSICO-CHEMICAL CHANGES AROUND SEVERAL DISCHARGE POINTS IN THE HOOGHLY RIVER ESTUARY, INDIA
--A study on the effects of effluents from 5 pulp and paper mills on the quality of water in the Hooghly Estuary, India, showed that dissolved-oxygen levels are undesirably low in the vicinity of the outfalls but there are signs of recovery at about 500 yd downstream. Data on the condition of the river water and the volume and composition of the effluents are tabulated, indicating a combined daily discharge of more than 54,000 lb of lignin, 40,000 lb of BOD and 322,000 lb of suspended solids. Possible methods for treating the effluents are reported, including attempts to improve an older electrolytic method. Ref: *J-63 46,:107-116, 1966.*

3.0 - 49
Beasley, Thomas M. (1969). LEAD-210 IN SELECTED MARINE ORGANISMS
--The concentrations of Pb-210 were determined in a variety of marine organisms. The specimens were taken during different times of the year and consequently during different hydrographic regimes which afforded the opportunity to compare Pb-210 concentrations in organisms living in upwelled water further from shore. Less extensive measurements of Po-210 in the same species permitted an estimate of the radiation dose rate to which these organisms may be subject from this internally deposited isotope, in addition to that which results from cosmic rays and the K-40 which is ubiquitous in ocean waters. The radiation dose rate for fishes residing near the surface is shown to increase some 6 fold as a result of internal Po-210 concentrations, yet this figure would be expected to show variation depending upon Po-210 input to

surface waters, and turnover times in the organisms. Benthonic polychetes, which receive high dose rates from Ra-226 incorporated in marine sediments showed an increase in dose rate of some 2 fold, giving possible total dose rates approaching 1.4 rad/year. Ref: *Oregon State University. Thesis, 1969.*

3.0 - 50
Beasley, Thomas M. and Held, E. E.   (1969). NICKEL-63 IN MARINE AND TERRESTRIAL BIOTA, SOIL, AND SEDIMENT
--The radionuclide nickel-63 (half life-92 yrs) produced in the testing of nuclear devices was measured in biological and environmental samples from areas of the Pacific Ocean and the eastern seaboard of the United States. Concentrations are low but this radionuclide may be a useful tracer of oceanic processes because of its long half life and long residence time in lagoons, atolls and the ocean. Ref: *J-6   164(3884):1161-1163, June 6, 1969.   14 refs.*

3.0 - 51
Beckmann, Walter C. (1970). APPLIED OCEANOGRAPHY VITAL TO POLLUTION-CONTROL EFFORTS
--Applied oceanography is described as a primary tool to fight water pollution. The essentials for the control of water pollution are summarized. (1) Define the existing levels of pollution.   (2) Initiate a forceful program that will have as its minimum objective the arrest of further degradation of water quality. (3) Implement a program to clean up waterways by correcting polluting offenders until the pollution level of all waters within the area meets acceptable standards. (4) Establish and maintain a real-time monitoring program to determine water quality in corrected water areas while effecting a long-range program whereby man and the ocean can exist in balance. The experiences of the Alpine Geophysical Associates in this type of activity are reported. Ref: *J-111 11(4):26-29, April 1970.*

3.0 - 52
Bella, David A. and Dobbins, William E. (1968). DIFFERENCE MODELING OF STREAM POLLUTION
--Finite-difference methods are developed for the numerical analysis of BOD and dissolved oxygen profiles confined to cases which may be treated as one-dimensional problems. For estuaries, the methods are applicable to the analysis of the variations of BOD and dissolved oxygen profiles within a tidal cycle. The spreading which results from the tidal velocity variation is shown to have a significant effect on the BOD and dissolved oxygen profiles. The methods should prove useful in studies of estuaries in which the tidal variations are large and the temporal variations in the strengths of the BOD and dissolved oxygen inputs are great. Ref: *J-3   94(SA5 Paper 6192):995-1016, Oct 1968. 4 refs.*

3.0 - 53
Bellamy, D. J.; Clarke, P. H. and others (1967). EFFECTS OF POLLUTION FROM THE TORREY CANYON ON LITTORAL AND SUBLITTORAL ECOSYSTEMS
--An assessment was made of the effects of pollution by crude oil and detergent following the Torrey Canyon disaster in March 1967. A phytosociological survey was made the following August at 29

sites along the coasts of Devon and Cornwall which had been surveyed in September 1966, and the results were compared. The overall effect of pollution by oil and detergent was to alter the balance of ecosystems dominated by attached macrophytes. Ref: *J-7 216(5121):1170-1173, Dec 23, 1967. 11 refs.*

3.0 - 54
Bellamy, D. J.; Jones, D. J. and Whittick, A. (1969).   SOME ECOLOGICAL ASPECTS OF MARINE POLLUTION
--The authors discuss ecological aspects of the pollution of the inshore marine fringe, with particular reference to the kelp-forest ecosystem around the coast of the British Isles, which consists predominantly of *Laminaria hyperborea* with attached plant life and associated animals. The effects of pollution are illustrated by comparative data on kelp-forest ecosystems from the unpolluted waters of north Northumberland and south Berwickshire and from the highly polluted coast of County Durham. The effects of individual pollutants are also considered under the headings toxic substances, sediment, suspended material, and nutrients. Ref: *P-21 8 p., 1969.*

3.0 - 55
Bellan, G. (1965). INFLUENCE OF POLLUTION ON THE ANNELID FAUNA OF MOVABLE SUBSTRATA
--After a review of previous studies and a comparison of the polychaetous annelids in various regions of the sea near Marseilles, the author discusses the species characteristic of water with different degrees of pollution and the role of these organisms as indicators of pollution. Ref: *P-1 p. 123-126, 1965.*

3.0 - 56
Bernhard, M. and Zattera, A. (1969).   COMPARISON BETWEEN THE UPTAKE OF RADIOACTIVE AND STABLE ZINC BY A MARINE UNICELLULAR ALGA
--Batch experiments are reported in natural or artificial sea water with added stable and radioactive zinc, to determine the uptake of each isotope by a marine unicellular alga and by a chelating resin, chelex-100. Results show that alga and resin take up stable and radioactive zinc at different rates and to different extents. When zinc-65 was added to ionic zinc, more radioactive zinc was taken up than stable zinc but when the zinc-65 was added as a complex the stable zinc was taken up initially at a higher rate than was zinc-65. Ref: *P-3 p. 389-398, 1969.*

3.0 - 57
Berridge, S. A.; Dean, R. A.; and others (1968).   PROPERTIES OF PERSISTENT OILS AT SEA
--This paper discusses the physical, chemical, and biological processes which may operate on crude oil after it has been spilled at sea. It is suggested that evaporation is the major process, that biological degradation is insignificant, and that the formation of water-in-oil emulsions will markedly affect the rates of these processes, and extent and ease of removal of pollution. Research into the rates of these processes, particularly biological ones, is urgently needed but the design of the experiments poses many problems. Ref: *J-8 54(539):300-309, Nov 1968. 5 refs.*

3.0 - 58
Berridge, S. A.; Thew, M. T. and Loriston-Clarke, A. G. (1968). FORMATION AND STABILITY OF EMULSIONS OF WATER IN CRUDE PETROLEUM AND SIMILAR STOCKS
--The *Torrey Canyon* oil spillage revealed the importance of 'chocolate mousse' emulsions containing up to 80 per cent water in sea and beach pollution by oil. A simple procedure for preparing such 'mousses' is described. 'Mousses' from typical crudes varied in ease of formation and stability primarily according to chemical composition. Marine organisms and suspended debris are not essential. Bacterial action is not significant. Some 'mousses' are stable for many months on exposure to both the weather and aerated sea water. Other 'mousses' are unstable and are readily broken and dispersed. The stabilization of this type of emulsion appears to be due to complex chemical components present in the non-volatile residues from crude, particularly asphaltenes, and possibly porphyrins, including vanadium complexes. Stable 'mousse' formation can be prevented by the presence of nominal amounts of emulsion-breaking additives. All 'mousses' tested were readily broken into oil and water layers by the addition of nominal amounts of these additives followed by vigorous agitation. Dispersal is achieved by appropriate treatment with commercial detergents followed by vigorous agitation. <u>Ref</u>: *J-8 54(539):333-357, Nov 1968. 21 refs.*

3.0 - 59
Bevan, Donald E. and Salo, Ernest O. (1969). STUDIES OF JUVENILE SALMON IN THE NOOKSACK RIVER SYSTEM AND BELLINGHAM BAY
--Reports studies made since 1963 by the Fisheries Research Institute in the Nooksack River system and Bellingham Bay. The object of the studies was to describe early life history with emphasis on seasonal abundance and natural mortality and growth rates. Coho salmon were studied most extensively. They were concerned with movement and behavior of juvenile salmon during migration and their distribution in relation to concentration of sulfite waste liquor, dissolved oxygen, salinity, and temperature. Pulp mill wastes and their effects upon fish are a major concern. <u>Ref</u>: *Washington Water Research Center. Final Rept. OWRR Project B-003-Wash. 53 p., Jan 1969. 25 refs.*

3.0 - 60
Bianchi, A. and Marquet, R. (1965). STUDY OF POLLUTION IN THE GULF OF MARSEILLES. I. PRELIMINARY NOTE: STUDY OF THE DIFFUSION OF POLLUTED WATERS IN TERMS OF THE DISTRIBUTION OF CERTAIN INTESTINAL BACTERIA
--Results show that, whatever the wind, the waters along the shore at Marseilles always contain high counts of intestinal bacteria, the coliform count frequently exceeding 20,000 per litre; and the Huveaune River still remains the principal source of pollution, containing more than 200,000 coliform organisms per litre when it discharges into the Gulf at Prado; high counts of intestinal bacteria are found 3 km from the mouth and enterobacteria still occur more than 6 km from the shore. In calm weather the plume of polluted water from the Huveaune moves out to sea; with easterly winds it moves still more rapidly towards the Pomègues and Ratonneau Islands; but with north-

westerly (Mistral) winds it is brought towards the shore. Waste waters discharged into Cortiou Cove do not appear to reach the Gulf of Marseilles even when the wind is easterly. Bacterial pollution seems to be limited to the surface layers.
<u>Ref</u>: *P-1 p. 59-66, 1965.*

3.0 - 61
Biggs, Robert B. (1968). ENVIRONMENTAL EFFECTS OF OVERBOARD SPOIL DISPOSAL
--Navigation channel improvements in upper Chesapeake Bay required that silt and clay be dredged, and the spoil be deposited in shallow water 1000 m west of the dredging site. During the actual spoil disposal, continuous determinations of the distribution of suspended sediment were made and compared with 'background' levels. Results indicate that measurable quantities of suspended sediment extended as far as 4 km from the disposal site, that the spoil on the bottom did not remain within limits of the disposal area, and that dissolved nutrients contained in the spoil sediment porewater were probably released to the environment.
<u>Ref</u>: *J-3 94(SA3 Paper 5979):477-487, June 1968. 1 ref.*

3.0 - 62
Blum, A. (1968). TECHNICAL CONSIDERATIONS FOR THE CONSTRUCTION OF COASTAL OUTFALL SEWERS
--Design of a coastal outfall sewer requires a knowledge of the preliminary treatment received by the waste water and of the hydrological and meteorological conditions and nature of the sea bed in the discharge area. These factors influence the location, length, choice of material, and installation of the pipeline. The advantages of polyethylene pipes and a method for burying these in the sea bed were indicated. <u>Ref</u>: *P-19 and J-59 9,:123-126, 1968.*

3.0 - 63
Blumer, Max (1969). OIL POLLUTION OF THE OCEAN
--Oil influx to the ocean from shipping losses only, is about 10^{12} g/year. Oil composition and biological effects, and the long term effects are briefly reviewed. The use of detergents or dispersants are not considered a solution to this problem. Burning of the oil where possible or containment and rapid recovery are the only acceptable solutions. <u>Ref</u>: *P-14 p. 5-13, 1969. 10 refs. Also as: WHOI (Woods Hole Oceanographic Institute) Contribution # 2336.*

3.0 - 64
Board of Trade. London. (1967). MANUAL ON THE AVOIDANCE OF POLLUTION OF THE SEA BY OIL
--This manual describes procedure for preventing spillage, leaks, and accidental discharges of oil from ships, and methods for the disposal of oil-contaminated water and oil residues. In appendices the legal prohibitions and requirements are summarized and the prohibited sea areas are delineated and illustrated in charts. <u>Ref</u>: *London. Board of Trade. H.M. Stationery Office 26 p.,1967.*

3.0 - 65
Bobalek, Edward G. (1967). CHEMICAL REACTOR THEORY APPLIED TO MODELING THE DYNAMICS OF A CONTROL SYSTEM FOR WATER QUALITY OF A RIVER. PHASE I. A FEASIBILITY STUDY
--The Penobscot River Estuary was selected as rep-

resentative of conditions existing in the state with respect to water pollution. The key problem requires prediction of the velocity profile in response to intermixing of tidal and fresh waters. Appraisal of such intermixing correlations is of importance in determining residence times for pollutants which are nullified by available oxidation and dilution mechanisms. The determination of mixing effects is projected as a primary goal of Phase II which continues this study through acquisition and analysis of data which can permit more precise development of the models proposed. Ref: *University of Maine. Rept. 39 p., July 1967. 33 refs.*

3.0 - 66
Bonde, G. J. (1965). BACTERIOLOGICAL EXAMINATION OF SURFACE WATER AND BOTTOM DEPOSITS OF A MARINE ENVIRONMENT
--A preliminary report is given on the bacteriological aspects of pollution in The Sound, which separates the island of Sjaelland and the Scandinavian peninsula. *Escherichia coli* and *Pseudomonas aeruginosa* indicate fresh pollution in the surface layers, but these organisms do not penetrate the thermocline. Faecal pollution from sewage outfalls disappears rapidly and both organisms were found only near the most polluted regions. *Clostridium perfringens* was found the most reliable indicator of pollution. The numbers of fluorescent pseudomonads and coliform organisms in The Sound were found to depend, not specifically on faecal pollution, but on the admixture of fresh water from outlets in the Baltic Sea. Ref: *P-1 p. 195-204, 1965.*

3.0 - 67
Bonde, G. J. (1966). BACTERIOLOGICAL METHODS FOR ESTIMATION OF WATER POLLUTION
--The author lists ideal requirements for an indicator bacterium doubting whether coliform bacteria are satisfactory as indicators. Coliform is vaguely defined, does not represent any homogeneous group. Sulphate - reducing bacteria and green fluorescent pseudomonads are the better pollution indicators. Ref: *J-65 3,:124-128, 1966.*

3.0 - 68
Bonde, G. J. (1967). HETEROTROPHIC BACTERIA IN A POLLUTED MARINE ENVIRONMENT
--In bacteriological studies of the Sound between Denmark and Sweden, which receives discharges of sewage and polluted surface water, the numbers of heterotrophic bacteria and the autotrophic *Thiobacillus* were determined in the water and bottom deposits. The dominant organisms found were typical of pollution or were of freshwater or soil origin; compared with the North Sea, more strains of *Bacillus* and more coliform organisms were found, and about the same numbers of *Micrococcus, Pseudomonas,* and *Vibrio*. In general, bacteria in the water were found mainly above the thermocline. Results indicate that the extent of pollution can be estimated by frequent counts of *Esch.coli* in the surface waters and of *Clostridium perfringens* in the sediments. Ref: *P-9 3,:87-103, 1967.*

3.0 - 69
Bonde, G. J. (1967). POLLUTION OF MARINE ENVIRONMENT
--The program carried out by a Swedish-Danish committee in the Sound showed the existence of pronounced stratification, and patterns of wind and current. The chemical tests showed less influence of wastewater than expected yet pollution of the sediments resulted in lack of oxygen and the presence of bacterial and animal communities. Only the herring showed possible influences of pollution. Ref: *J-1 39(10 Pt 2):R44-R63, Oct 1967. 27 refs.*

3.0 - 70
Bonde, G. J. (1968). STUDIES ON THE DISPERSION AND DISAPPEARANCE PHENOMENA OF ENTERIC BACTERIA IN THE MARINE ENVIRONMENT
--In bacteriological studies on water and sediments of the Sound, Denmark-Sweden, and the Gulf of Gothenburg, Sweden, it was found that the same species predominated, and numbers of *Esch. coli* declined sharply with depth and distance from the source of pollution. Quite different species (principally *Comamonas,* Coryneiforms, and *Cytophaga)* were dominant in samples, rich in organic matter, taken off the coast of Peru, while in the Sargasso Sea, which contains little organic matter, few species other than *Acinetobacter* were found. *Clostridium perfringens,* which was found in all polluted waters, suffered a reduction in numbers similar to that for *Esch. coli,* but a small proportion could be found 20-30 km from the source. Radioactive-tracer studies of sewage dilution in the Sound, in conjunction with *Esch. coli* counts, showed that other factors (presumably sedimentation and death) as well as dilution are responsible for the decline in numbers of *Esch. coli.* It was demonstrated that bacilli which produce antibiotics inhibitory to *Esch. coli* occur in the Sound; both the antibiotics and the·bacilli were classified. Ref: *P-19 and J-59 9,:17-44, 1968. 58 refs.*

3.0 - 71
Booth, G. H.; Cooper, A. W. and Tiller, A. K. (1965). CORROSION OF MILD STEEL IN THE TIDAL WATERS OF THE THAMES ESTUARY. II. RESULTS OF TWO YEARS' IMMERSION
--The investigation of corrosion of steel plates in the Thames Estuary has been continued and the results of immersion for 2 years are compared with those previously reported after exposure for one year to the same conditions. The rate of corrosion and degree of pitting were slightly less after the longer period, possibly due to protection afforded by the corrosion products. The findings, which are discussed in relation to the condition of the estuary water, indicate that aerobic corrosion by the saline water is more important than anaerobic microbial attack. Ref: *J-9 15,:250-256, June 1965.*

3.0 - 72
Bosley, Joseph R.; Cibulka, John J. and Krutchkoff (1969). TEMPERATURE AND TURBULENCE EFFECTS ON THE PARAMETER DELTA IN THE STOCHASTIC MODEL FOR BOD AND DO IN STREAMS
--A literature review and laboratory study were made on the effects of water temperature and turbulence on dissolved oxygen and BOD in streams. Methods used to calculate the effects of pollution upon the assimilative capacity of a stream are re-

viewed. It is concluded that intelligent pollution control decisions can be made on the basis of the probability function. Ref: *Virginia Polytechnic Institute. Water Resources Research Center Bulletin 33 38 p., Nov 1969.*

3.0 - 73
Boury, M. and Borde, J. (1965). CHANGES IN THE BACTERIAL FLORA OF SHELLFISH KEPT OUT OF WATER
--Tabulated data are given showing the changes in counts of *Escherichia coli*, coliform bacteria, and aerobic bacteria in shellfish during transport and storage at various temperatures. The absence of proliferation of enteric bacteria is attributed to the properties of the sea water which fills the shell and penetrates into the body. Ref: *P-1 p. 285-292, 1965.*

3.0 - 74
Boury, M. and Borde, J. (1965). BACTERIAL CONTAMINATION OF SHELLFISH
--Using *Escherichia coli* as the index of contamination, various shellfish were examined to investigate the distribution of bacteria between the body of the shellfish and the intervalvular water, the content of bacteria in different parts of the body, and the processes of contamination and self-purification. Results show that the degree of contamination can be assessed best by examining the body of the shellfish after separation of the liquid, but examination of the liquid is useful to detect contamination after harvesting. There is a marked concentration of bacteria in the visceral mass, and in less-contaminated samples a significant number of bacteria is found only in this organ. Bivalves from polluted areas can be cleaned by a process using their self-purifying capacity provided favorable conditions are maintained and the quality of the product is controlled by bacteriological examination. Ref: *P-1 p. 277-284, 1965.*

3.0 - 75
Brehmer, M. L. (1965). TURBIDITY AND SILTATION AS FORMS OF POLLUTION
--Outlines some of the polluting effects caused by suspended and sedimenting solids in estuaries, including the increased turbidity, the inhibition of feeding in shellfish caused by high concentrations of inorganic solids, and the covering of benthic forms by silt. The transition zone between fresh and salt water is used as a nursery area by many species of fish; this zone also has the highest load of suspended inorganic solids and variations in this loading may be the cause of seasonal fluctuations in populations of estuarine fish.
Ref: *J-11 20,:132-133, 1965.*

3.0 - 76
Brezenski, Francis T. and Russomanno, Rocco (1969). DETECTION AND USE OF SALMONELLAE IN STUDYING POLLUTED TIDAL ESTUARIES
--Bacteriological analyses were made of water and shellfish from the Raritan Bay area, N. J., including part of the Narrows, Lower Bay, Sandy Hook Bay, tidal portions of the Raritan River, Arthur Kill, and other small tributaries. The analyses showed that the percentage recovery of salmonellae increased proportionally as the faecal coliform density increased and the faecal coliform density was generally more than 3000 per 100 ml when sal-

monellae were detected; the relatively low percentage recovery of salmonellae with coliform densities of 1-200 per 100 ml supports the proposed use of a faecal coliform standard for contact recreational waters. It was noted, however, that at very high coliform densities, above 20,000 per 100 ml, in salt water, the isolation of salmonellae was inhibited. *Salmonella derby* was the predominate serotype isolated from both polluted water and clams. In most cases shellfish containing at least 1000 faecal coliform bacteria per 100 g also contained salmonellae; but when the temperature of the water was less than 5°C and the clams were inactive, some samples contained salmonellae even when the coliform density was less than 20 per 100 g, thus suggesting greater survival of the salmonellae in the clams. In general, the average faecal coliform density in shellfish meats was about 6 times greater than that in the overlying water, but at temperatures below 10°C the indicator densities were less than those in the overlying water. Ref: *J-1 41(5 Pt 1):725-737, May 1969. 16 refs.*

3.0 - 77
Bridie, A. L. A. M. (1969). DETERMINATION OF BIOCHEMICAL OXYGEN DEMAND WITH CONTINUOUS RECORDING OF OXYGEN UPTAKE
--An electrolytic respirometer was used in testing degradability. It consists of six measuring units mounted in a thermostatic bath and works independent of changes in barometric pressure. Ref: *J-12 3(2):157-165, Feb 1969. 7 refs.*

3.0 - 78
Briggs, R. and Melbourne, K. V. (1968). RECENT ADVANCES IN WATER QUALITY MONITORING
--Provides a review of water quality monitoring systems and the equipment involved. Includes descriptions of submersible temperature and oxygen recording equipment, and nitrate, fluoride and enzyme electrode measuring systems as well as continuous recording of ammonia. Ref: *J-13 17(Part 2): 107-120, 1968. 20 refs.*

3.0 - 79
Brinkhurst, R. O. and Simmons, N. L. (1968). AQUATIC OLIGOCHAETA OF THE SAN FRANCISCO BAY SYSTEM
--In a continuing study of the oligochaeta, it was found that organic pollution reduced the numbers and diversity of the fauna so that in a heavily polluted area oligochaetes represented 100 percent of the fauna. Ref: *J-14 54,:180-194, 1968.*

3.0 - 80
Brisby, William L. (1969). OIL SLICK EFFECTS ON RINCON ISLAND
--Oil leakage occured in the vicinity of the Atlantic Richfield Oil Company's offshore drilling island 0.5 miles off Point Gordo, Mussel Shoals, Ventura County. When the oil slick reached Rincon Island there was some destruction to the biota, but it was said to be minimal. The writer's opinion is that while the oil seepage did kill some of the intertidal organisms on Rincon Island, the destruction was not as great as anticipated. The greatest damage to life was found to be the result of silting and pollution from recent storms.
Ref: *P-24 p. 147-150, May 1969. 1 ref.*

3.0 - 81
Brisou, Jean (1968).   REACTION OF THE BACTERIA IN
THE PRESENCE OF PRODUCTS ELABORATED BY MARINE
PHYTOPLANKTON
--It was found that in the antibiotic activity of
rare samples of plankton, in all cases, aldehydes
were present and the activity had no specificity.
The hypothesis attributing antibacterial action
to iodine and iodine by-products cannot be sus-
tained. Chlorophyll and its by-products have no
antimicrobic action. None of the products examined
was capable of preventing the growth of pathogenic or autochthonous bacteria. Some algae can
show a non-specific antiseptic activity. Ref:
P-8 and J-12   p. 111, 1968.

3.0 - 82
Brisou, Jean (1968).   MICROBIAL, VIRAL AND
PARASITIC POLLUTION OF THE LITTORAL WATERS AND ITS
CONSEQUENCES FOR THE PUBLIC HEALTH
--The most important pathogenic organisms occurring in sea water are identified: Gram-negative
bacteria are the most common in coastal waters;
Streptococcus faecalis and other coliform organisms occur, but *Salmonella spp.* are more dangerous though less common; *Shigella* has low resistance to saline water; *poliomyelitis, coxsackie,*
and other enteroviruses are well known in sewage
and may persist when effluent is discharged into
coastal waters. *Candida albicans,* C. *tropicalis,*
C. *parapsilosis,* and *Trichophyton cutaneum* are the
most frequent vegetable parasites; animal parasites such as ascaris eggs and amoebic cysts are
less common. The maximal acceptable counts, above
which there are risks of infection are about
10,000 per liter, water for coliform organisms and
200 per liter for *S. faecalis.* Ref: *J-15   38,:
79-118, 1968.*

3.0 - 83
British Petroleum Co. Ltd.   BOOM FOR RETENTION OF
OIL SPILLAGES ON WATER
--A boom for retaining oil spilled on water, to
prevent pollution of harbors and beaches, is constructed from polyurethane foam material with one
or more buoyancy chambers along its length, these
being lined or coated with material impermeable to
air or liquids. Ref: *British Patents 1,028,470
(no date shown)*

3.0 - 84
Brocks, Graham J. (1967).   PREVENTING OIL
POLLUTION OF THE SEA
--Presents an account of the load-on top procedure
designed to prevent oil pollution by tankers.
Ref: *J-106   16(4):296-305, Dec 1967. 2 refs.*

3.0 - 85
Brown, Charles L. and Clark, Robert   (1968).
OBSERVATIONS ON DREDGING AND DISSOLVED OXYGEN IN
A TIDAL WATERWAY
--It was found that resuspension of oxidizable
bottom sediments in a tidal waterway caused re-
ductions in the DO concentration. During dredging
DO was reduced between 16-83% below normal.
Ref: *J-16   4(6):1381-1384, Dec 1968. 4 refs.*

3.0 - 86
Brown, Lewis R. and Tischer, Robert G.   (1969).
DECOMPOSITION OF PETROLEUM PRODUCTS IN OUR NATURAL
WATERS

--Experimental data suggest that water-soluble
products formed during microbial decomposition of
petroleum products are harmful to fish. Microflora
caused marked physical changes in the oil under
both aerobic and anaerobic conditions. The disappearance of oil was more rapid under aerobic
conditions. A thin layer chromatographic technique
was developed and used to demonstrate chemical
changes that occurred in the oil during microbial
decomposition. Addition of a nitrogen source and
supplemental inorganic phosphate enhanced microbial
activity. The waters were toxic for fish even
after separation and removal of bacteria and oil.
Ref: *Mississippi State Univ. Water Resources
Research Institute. Completion Rept. 41 p.,
July 1969. 5 refs.*

3.0 - 87
Brunnock, J. V.; Duckworth, D. F. and Stephens,
G. G. (1968).   ANALYSIS OF BEACH POLLUTANTS
--This paper is concerned with beach pollution
arising from material of petroleum origin. It describes the nature of coastal deposits and suggests
methods of analysis for identifying the type and
origin of discharges likely to occur along the
main European supply routes. Reference is made to
samples from the Torrey Canyon disaster. Ref:
J-8   54(539):310-323, Nov 1968. 8 refs.

3.0 - 88
Bruun, Per   (1965).   USE OF TRACERS IN COASTAL
ENGINEERING
--Describes examples of the use of radioactive
tracers for investigating various aspects of sediment transport and for other purposes such as
selecting the best site for a cooling-water intake
and the spread of pollution from an outfall.
Ref: *J-67 34,:13-17, 1965.*

3.0 - 89
Bruun, Per and others (1966). COASTAL ENGINEERING
MODEL STUDIES OF THREE FLORIDA COASTAL INLETS
--This publication includes sections on the factors involved in the stability of tidal inlets,
the rules governing the use of hydraulic models especially in coastal engineering research,
and model studies carried out on the Sebastian,
Hillsboro, and South Lake Worth inlets. Recommendations for improving the navigation and maintenance conditions in the inlets and overcoming the
problem of stagnation in the south of Lake Worth
are included. Ref: *University of Florida.
Engineering Progress. Bulletin Series No. 122
20(6) 72 p., 1966.*

3.0 - 90
Bruun, Per (1970).   USE OF TRACERS IN HARBOR,
COASTAL AND OCEAN ENGINEERING
--Describes the use of tracers in various engineering fields including ocean, harbor, coastal and
river engineering and some special applications of
tracers, e.g., in pollution control. A list of
references and a special bibliography is included,
the latter giving examples of literature on actual
tracer projects in various fields of science and
technology. Ref: *J-17   4(1):73-78, Jan 1970.*

3.0 - 91
Bryan, G. W. (·1965).   IONIC REGULATION IN THE
SQUAT LOBSTER *GALATHEA SQUAMIFERA,* WITH SPECIAL
REFERENCE TO THE RELATIONSHIP BETWEEN POTASSIUM

METABOLISM AND THE ACCUMULATION OF RADIOACTIVE CAESIUM
--Studies on the ability of decapod crustacea to accumulate radioactive caesium have continued with the squat lobster *Galathea squamifera*. The concentration in the tissues is the limiting factor for the uptake of isotopes. Accumulation of radioactive caesium is unaffected by the concentration of inactive caesium in the sea water, but a low potassium content increases the concentration factor for both caesium and potassium. Absorption and loss of potassium and caesium take place mainly across the body surface; urinary excretion of both isotopes was found to be negligible. Ref: *J-2 45(1):97-113, April 1965.*

3.0 - 92
Buck, J. D. and Meyers, S. P. (1965). ANTI-YEAST ACTIVITY IN THE MARINE ENVIRONMENT. I. ECOLOGICAL CONSIDERATIONS
--In studies on the inhibition of yeasts by bacteria in the marine environment, 60 extracts from a number of substrates were examined and 3 were found to possess this property. In an amphipod community the numbers of bacteria and yeasts were reasonably constant throughout an 11-month test period. Approximately 8 per cent of the bacteria isolated from this community were inhibitory to certain test yeasts. The comparative inhibitory powers of pseudomonads originating from clinical cultures, soil, and fresh water are listed; 2 marine strains tested with this group proved noninhibitory. It is suggested that such inhibition may provide a natural control for pathogenic yeasts discharged from sewage outfalls. Ref: *J-41 10(3):385-391, July 1965.*

3.0 - 93
Budd, William E. and Powers, Thomas J. (1969). TREATMENT OF POLLUTED STREAMS IN PLACE
--This invention relates to a system and a method for combating pollution by treating the polluted water collectively in the flowing stream itself, instead of separately treating the individual contributing sources of pollution in order that the construction of numerous shore-located individual expensive sewage treatment plants may be avoided. This system provides for applying aeration- and flocculation treatment to a predetermined length of the stream, so that the resulting floc structures weighted by entrapped inert solids, will settle in a downstream adjoining sedimentation zone as sludge which may be removed or pumped away periodically. Ref: *U.S. Patent No. 3,470,091. Assigned to Dorr-Oliver Inc. and Dow Chemical Co. 1969.*

3.0 - 94
Buelow, Ralph W. (1968). OCEAN DISPOSAL OF WASTE MATERIAL
--Presents findings of studies made by the Northeast Marine Health Sciences Laboratory of two sewage sludge dump areas, the New York Bight, and a site off Delaware Bay. Consideration was given to the spread of bacterial contamination caused by the discharge of sewage sludge. Possible contamination of surf clams that may be harvested for human consumption is assessed. No approval of the present disposal areas or decision for relocation can be recommended. Ref: *P-25 p. 311-337, 1968. 17 refs. Also as: Contribution No. 28. Northeast Marine Health Sciences Laboratory. D.H.E.W. Narragansett, R. I.*

3.0 - 95
Bumpus, Dean F.; Wright, W. R. and Vaccaro, R. F. (1969). CONSIDERATIONS ON A SEWER OUTFALL OFF NOBSKA POINT
--Considers the effect of prospective secondary treatment of domestic sewage effluent of about 14 thousand cu m per day on Martha's Vineyard and Nantucket Sound. A steady state condition would be reached in 75 days. The concentration of nutrients added to the Sound and the ecological effects would be less than is experienced in the normal annual cycle. Ref: *Woods Hole Oceanographic Institute. Ref 69-87 42 p., 1969.*

3.0 - 96
Burd, Robert S. (1969). WATER-QUALITY STANDARDS FOR TEMPERATURE
--Discusses the development of temperature standards, the Department of the Interior's reaction to temperature standards and the administration of temperature standards. In the discussion which follows, MILO A. CHURCHILL discusses the philosophy of standard-setting. Ref: *P-30b Chap. 3 p. 72-109, 1969.*

3.0 - 97
Burdick, G. E. (1967). USE OF BIOASSAYS IN DETERMINING LEVELS OF TOXIC WASTES HARMFUL TO AQUATIC ORGANISMS
--A brief explanation of intent and procedure of bioassay methods is given. Application factors to derive a safe concentration are discussed and the inapplicability of a uniform factor is pointed out in terms of specific data. Results of bioassay are specific to water and assay conditions and may not be considered applicable to others. Problems in long-term assay are discussed in reference to the water, maintenance of fish supply, desirable oxygen concentration, choice of test organism and simulation of natural conditions. Bioassays with continuous flow and constant concentration are compared with bioassays with static solutions in terms of the situations to which they are applicable. Although emphasis should be on the ecological approach, bioassay will still be required under controlled laboratory conditions to interpret the interaction between factors. The attack on long-term toxic effects must be evaluated in terms of the entire ecosystem in addition to the direct toxicological effect on the individual species. Ref: *P-32 and J-23 96(1):7-12 Suppl., 1967. Spec. Pub. No. 4. 16 refs.*

3.0 - 98
Butler, Philip A. (1966). PROBLEM OF PESTICIDES IN ESTUARIES
--Laboratory studies of their acute and chronic toxicity indicate that pesticides may be the cause of ill-defined but significant mortality, loss of production and, perhaps, changes in the direction of natural selection in estuarine fauna. There is a need for a continuing surveillance program to identify the seasonal and geographical distribution of pesticide pollution in estuaries. Ref: *P-5 and J-23 95(4):110-115, 1966. Special Publication No. 3.*

3.0 - 99

Buttiaux, R. and Ferrand, R. (1965). SELF-PURIFICATION IN MUSSELS FROM THE MEDITERRANEAN. ITS USEFULNESS. ITS ACCOMPLISHMENTS. RESULTS OBTAINED
--Reports that a plant was set up at Toulon, France, (Lazaret Bay) for the self-purification of shellfish (particularly mussels) in clean sea water. This was done becuase heavy pollution caused serious typhoid epidemics in the past. Good results were obtained on the basis of standards for the content of *Escherichia coli* and *Streptococcus d*. Ref: *P-1 p. 299-306, 1965*.

3.0 - 100
Cabinet Office. London. (1967). "THE TORREY CANYON". REPORT OF THE COMMITTEE OF SCIENTISTS ON THE SCIENTIFIC AND TECHNOLOGICAL ASPECTS OF THE TORREY CANYON DISASTER
--The course of events following the grounding of the Torrey Canyon off the coast of Cornwall is reviewed, with an account of measures taken to reduce and remove contamination of the beaches and harbors by the spilled oil, and the effects of the oil, and the detergents used to remove it, on fish, shellfish, intertidal plants and animals, and sea birds. Based on the experience gained, recommendations are made for dealing with similar disasters in future to minimize pollution effects. Ref: *London, Cabinet Office. H.M. Stationery Office 56 p., 1967*.

3.0 - 101
Cabiöch, Louis and Lacassagne, Michel (1969). HOW ROSCOFF WON THE TORREY CANYON BATTLE
--Describes the booms which successfully kept the port and the marine biological laboratory foreshore at Roscoff, North Brittany, clear of oil spillage from the Torrey Canyon disaster in April 1967. Straw was used extensively in the construction of the booms because of its surface properties. On contact, the oil film becomes concentrated and the accumulated oil becomes trapped in the straw. The polluted straw produces an oily mass which can be collected with a pitchfork. Ref: *J-84 Reprint L(583) 3 p., May 1969*.

3.0 - 102
Cable, Carl C. (1969). OPTIMUM DREDGING AND DISPOSAL PRACTICES IN ESTUARIES
--Various types of dredging plants are described; their capabilities and limitations are listed. The importance of selecting the most suitable disposal method for the job at hand is stressed. Present day emphasis on clean waters dictates that planning be redirected to studying alternate disposal methods to reduce pollutional aspect of some dredging projects. The trend is towards more positive containment of dredged materials to reduce repetitive redredging of material in the ship channels. Ref: *J-18 95(HY 1 Paper 6343):103-114, Jan 1969*.

3.0 - 103
Call, P. David; Terry, S. A.; and Pressman, A. E. (1969). AIRBORNE INFRARED MEASUREMENTS APPLIED TO OCEANOGRAPHIC HYDROLOGIC AND WATER POLLUTION PROBLEMS
--Results of several airborne infrared data collection and processing experiments for remote thermal measurements are discussed. Sensor equipment used includes an infrared mapping system modified to produce quantitative radiometric data

simultaneously with imagery, a Forward Looking Infrared System for tracking currents and thermal effluents in real-time and cartographic and spectral aerial cameras. Computer programs were used to produce rectified isothermal maps of water surfaces with 1°F contour intervals. Ref: *P-26 p. 227-252, June 1969. 5 refs*.

3.0 - 104
Canevari, Gerard P. (1969). ROLE OF CHEMICAL DISPERSANTS IN OIL CLEANUP
--This paper discusses the role of oil dispersants and deals with the behavior of an oil spill on water, the detrimental effects of the spill and basis for dispersing, the mechanism and results of dispersing, toxicity study of dispersants, practical aspects of field application. It is suggested that the dispersant should not be any more toxic than the oil. Development work is underway on gelling compounds to solidify the oil cargo in situ and thereby prevent its release where danger of break up of a tanker may exist. Where possible the use of polyurethane foam to absorb spilled oil is recommended. Ref: *P-14 p. 29-51, 1969. 8 refs*.

3.0 - 105
Carey, A. G. (1969). ZINC-65 IN ECHINODERMS AND SEDIMENTS IN THE MARINE ENVIRONMENT OFF OREGON
--Studies are reported on the fate of the artificial radionuclides discharged in waste waters from the Hanford reactors and entering the Pacific Ocean via the Columbia River. Using gamma-ray spectrometry, zinc-65 was determined in sediments and benthic organisms. The amount of zinc-65 in both sediments and benthic animals decreased with increasing distance from the mouth of the river and with increasing depth of water. The specific activity of zinc-65 varied less than the concentration of zinc-65 alone. Differences in the specific activity of the benthic organisms appeared to be related to the flow of the Columbia River plume and also to the feeding habits of the different species. Although zinc-65 could not be detected in sediments 181 km south of the Columbia River, benthic invertebrates at this point concentrated the isotope to readily-detectable levels. Deposit-feeding organisms seem to pass zinc-65 on to their predators. Ref: *P-3 p. 380-388, 1969*.

3.0 - 106
Carey, A. G.; Pearcy, W.G. and Osterberg, C. L. (1966). ARTIFICIAL RADIONUCLIDES IN MARINE ORGANISMS IN THE NORTHEAST PACIFIC OCEAN OFF OREGON
--The authors summarize results of a 4-year study of the radioactivity of marine organisms in the Pacific Ocean off Oregon, which showed the presence of induced nuclides, such as zinc-65, originating from cooling water from the Hanford reactors, as well as fission products, in organisms as far as 490 km from the coast and at depths down to 2860 m. The concentrations of zinc-65 in marine organisms showed seasonal maxima, associated with seasonal movements in the position of the Columbia River plume. Before the end of atmospheric testing of nuclear devices, zirconium-95-niobium-95 were found in the fauna at all depths, and the amounts of these short-lived isotopes in the benthic fauna from the deepest stations were greater than expected. Ref: *P-4 p. 303-319, 1966*.

3.0 - 107
Carlisle, John G., Jr. (1969).   RESULTS OF A
SIX-YEAR TRAWL STUDY IN AN AREA OF HEAVY   WASTE
DISCHARGE: SANTA MONICA BAY, CALIFORNIA
--A trawl study was conducted in Santa Monica Bay,
an area of large-scale waste disposal, during the
years 1958-1963. Five species made up the bulk of
the catch. There was a moderately high yield of
fish per tow in 1958, an extreme low in 1959, a
buildup in 1960, a high in 1961, and a moderate
drop in 1962 and 1963. It was impossible to show
that fluctuations in abundance were the result of
waste discharge in the study area. The sport
catch for the years 1958 through 1963 showed only
small fluctuations. Artificial reefs offered
evidence that giant kelp was unable to survive in
areas affected by the 'fallout' of particulate matter from waste discharges, and possibly from turbidity from the same source. Ref: *J-14 55(1):
26-46, Jan 1969.*

3.0 - 108
Carpenter, J. H. and Grant, V. E.   (1967).
CONCENTRATION AND STATE OF CERIUM IN COASTAL
WATERS
--The cerium content of coastal sea-water samples
was determined and amounts ranging from 0.1-0.6
μg per litre were found except in samples taken
off Bermuda which contained only 0.004 and 0.014
μg per litre. The edible portions of marine organisms were tested for concentration factors which
were found to be less than 20 for striped bass,
less than 100 for oysters, and 1000 for soft clams.
Studies on the oxidation of cerium indicated that
it is pH-dependent and inhibited by an increase
in phosphate concentration. When radioactive cerium was added to sea water a high proportion became associated with particles of 0.01-0.1μ in
size. Ref: *J-20 25(3):228-238, Sept 15, 1967.
Also as: Chesapeake Bay Inst. Contribution 105.*

3.0 - 109
Carter, H. H. (1968).   DISTRIBUTION OF EXCESS
TEMPERATURE FROM A HEATED DISCHARGE IN AN   ESTUARY
--Reports on a dye tracer and temperature distribution study in the Patuxent Estuary, Maryland, to
determine the effect of powerplant heat discharges
on water temperatures. The theoretical temperature
distribution in time and space is discussed, and
the measured results compare reasonably well with
predictions. The tracer study was faulty because
of high chlorine residuals in the condenser discharge water. Ref: *Johns Hopkins University,
Chesapeake Bay Inst. Ref. No. 68-14 (Tech Note 44)
45 p., Oct 1968. 4 refs.*

3.0 - 110
Carter, H. H. (1969). PRELIMINARY REPORT ON THE
CHARACTERISTICS OF A HEATED JET   DISCHARGED
HORIZONTALLY INTO A TRANSVERSE CURRENT. PART I.
CONSTANT DEPTH
--Reports an investigation of the behavior of a
heated discharge of water jetted at right angles
into a moving stream of water. The discharge ori-
fice is rectangular to simulate a discharge canal
and both the jet stream and receiving waters are
confined vertically between a free surface, the
sea surface, and a solid level boundary, the sea
bottom. Details are given on the experimental set-
up and tests. The nonconservative processes of
heat loss (cooling) at the sea surface are dis-

cussed. Ref: *Johns Hopkins University, Chesapeake Bay Inst. Ref. No. 69-14 (Tech Rept. 61)
38 p., Nov 1969. 14 refs.*

3.0 - 111
Carter, H. H.; Carpenter, J. H.; and Whaley, R. C.
(1967). BACTERICIDAL EFFECT OF SEA WATER UNDER
NATURAL CONDITIONS
--An experiment was carried out at the Seaside
Heights, N.J. sewage works, in which a large volume, or slug, of the primary effluent, labeled
with a fluorescent tracer (Rhodamine WT), and with
a high coliform index and containing no residual
chlorine, was discharged into the sea; it was immediately preceded and followed by effluent with a
low coliform index and with a high concentration
of residual chlorine. The point of discharge was
within 1000 ft of the beach, in water less than 24
ft deep, with uniform temperature and salinity
from surface to bottom. The results showed a marked
decrease in bacterial numbers, with a kill of over
99.9 per cent in slightly over 3 hours. In designing submarine outfalls, therefore, the minimal period of travel between the point of discharge and
the closest controlled shore area should be about
2.5 hours, considering only mortality and not allowing for dilution. Ref: *J-1 39(7):1184-1189,
July 1967.*

3.0 - 112
Cedarwall, K. (1966).   SYSTEMATIC EVALUATION OF
DISCHARGING POLLUTED WATER INTO THE SEA
--Sewage is frequently discharged into the sea, but
the coastal waters around Sweden are hydrographi-
cally unique, since the interchange of water between the North Sea and the Baltic Sea causes vertical stratification of salt concentration, and
hence a density stratification. Sewage discharged
through a submarine diffuser can be stored as a
submerged sewage field, but the stability of this
stored field depends on various conditions. A method for determining horizontal jet diffusion in a
density-stratified receiver was developed for use
in planning sewage outfalls, and a theory of initial mixing is outlined. Results of laboratory experiments were found to be in good agreement with
the theory. Ref: *J-68 22,:45-54, 1966.*

3.0 - 113
Cerame-Vivas, M. J. (1968).   OCEAN EAGLE OIL
SPILL
--Presents results of detergent and adsorbant tox-
icity studies, by bioassay, and adsorbancy tests.
The activities of the Department of Marine Scien-
ces U.P.R., Mayaguez, during and following the
Ocean Eagle Oil spill. Ref: *Puerto Rico. Univ.,
Mayaguez, Dept. of Marine Sciences. 26 p., Dec
1968.*

3.0 - 114
Chandler, Philip B. (1969).   OIL POLLUTION
DETECTION WITHIN THE 8-14 MICRON INFRARED REGION
--Oil slicks in harbors and open sea environments
along the Southern California Coast have been observed by the North American Rockwell (NR) remote
sensing aircraft on several occasions. At the time
of detection, an 8-14μ infrared mapper, 19.35 Ghz
microwave radiometer, aerial cameras, and multiband video system were utilized. However, best definition of slicks was within the 8-14μ thermal
infrared region; although the microwave radiometer

also exhibited strong anomalies over the oil. The radiometric cold response of oil covered water in the $8-14\mu$ appears to be due to the large difference between the thermal conductivities of water and petroleum. Thermal gradients with a slick appear to result from a dependence of emissivity on thickness which pertains to semi-transparent bodies such as oil. Hence it is felt that oil slick volume may be easier to estimate using the $8-14\mu$ thermal region than with conventional aerial photography. However, before such a technique can be considered operational, detailed investigations into the nature and interaction of numerous environmental and physical parameters of an oil/sea system are needed. Ref: *J-107 50(11):629, Nov 1969. (abstract only)*

3.0 - 115

Chasse, C.; Halos, M.T.H. and Perrot, Y. (1967). OUTLINE OF A BALANCE OF BIOLOGICAL LOSSES CAUSED BY THE FUEL OIL FROM THE TORREY CANYON ON THE TREGOR SEABOARD
--The effect of oil pollution from the Torrey Canyon on fisheries along the coast of Brittany was estimated. For a 50-km stretch of coast, and a depth down to 15 m, it was estimated that 100,000 tons of algae and 35,000 tons of fish were destroyed, representing a loss of 10 mil. kcal with a potential value of 5.4 mil. francs. Ref: *J-60 6(50):107-112, 1967.*

3.0 - 116

Chesapeake Biological Laboratory (1967). INTERIM REPORT ON GROSS PHYSICAL AND BIOLOGICAL EFFECTS OF OVERBOARD SPOIL DISPOSAL
--Describes the effects associated with 1966 channel dredging in Chesapeake Bay: (1) Fine sediments from the channel were released in shoal water, over similar sediments, as a semi-liquid mixture. (2) Sediments were spread over five times as large as the designated disposal area. (3) There was a highly localized release of nutrient chemicals. (4) No gross effect was observed on the microscopic plants and animals in the water, nor on the eggs and larvae of fish, nor on adult fish held in cages near the outfall or caught near the area. (5) Some bottom animals were smothered over a wide area, so that a significant loss occurred. Some species survived deposition, and certain species began repopulation soon after deposition. Ref: *Chesapeake Biological Laboratory. Natural Resources Institute. University of Maryland. Ref. No. 67-34, May 1967.*

3.0 - 117

Chesselet R.; Lalou, C. et al. (1965). RECENT STUDIES ON THE RADIOACTIVITY OF PLANKTON AND OF ORGANIC REFUSE
--A study of the coastal waters of the Mediterranean near Nice in 1963, showed the importance of plankton and organic debris in concentrating radioactive fallout isotopes such as zirconium-95, niobium-95, ruthenium-103 and -106, and cerium-141 and -144. From observations on the effects of rate of fallout on the activity of the water and the activity of the plankton it is concluded that, at least for the isotopes studied, the contamination of zooplankton is related mainly to the injection conditions of the particles rather than to the specific activity of the sea water. Ref: *J-108 17,:67-97, 1965.*

3.0 - 118

Chester, R. (1965). ADSORPTION OF ZINC AND COBALT ON ILLITE IN SEA WATER
--The removal of radionuclides from ocean waters by adsorption on sedimentary minerals has been investigated. The results showed that the amounts of zinc and cobalt adsorbed are proportional to the amounts in solution until the adsorbent surface becomes saturated; the proportion of cobalt adsorbed increases with temperature, but adsorption of zinc is slightly less at higher temperatures. The effect of chemical association and ionic state on the reaction is discussed. Ref: *J-7 206(4987):884-886, May 29, 1965.*

3.0 - 119

Chipperfield, P.N.J. (1967). POLLUTION OF ESTUARIES - INDUSTRIAL VIEW
--Information on gross composition of effluent, temperature, pH, suspended solids, COD, BOD, and any specific substances likely to be toxic to fish, together with volumes and rates of discharge, is not difficult or costly to obtain. It is, however, important that actual weight of substances discharged or their oxygen equivalents should be considered, rather than concentrations; fish bioassays and hydrographic surveys to determine dilution and dispersion should also be made. Ref: *J-21 (29):1245-1247, July 22, 1967.*

3.0 - 120

Chow, M. P. (1965). POLLUTION OF A HARBOUR IN A SUB-TROPICAL AREA
--Reports an investigation of conditions of pollution of the Kaohsiung Harbor, Taiwan. Seasonal changes in temperature have a significant effect on the BOD. Pollution was greatest at the surface. The highest BOD values were found in the confined inlets and anchorages near the sources of pollution. Ref: *P-10 3,:65-83, 1965.*

3.0 - 121

Chow, Tsaihwa J. and Patterson, C. C. (1966). CONCENTRATION PROFILES OF BARIUM AND LEAD IN ATLANTIC WATERS OFF BERMUDA
--This study demonstrates that significant amounts of industrial lead aerosols are washed out of the atmosphere directly onto the surface of the oceans, and that barium is depleted from the upper layers by incorporation into biological matter which settles toward the bottom. Lead is subsequently removed and becomes a pollutant in the same manner. Ref: *J-112 1(6):395-400, Nov 1966. 17 refs.*

3.0 - 122

Chow, Tsaihwa J. (1968). ISOTOPE ANALYSIS OF SEAWATER BY MASS SPECTROMETRY
--Mass spectrometry and the isotope dilution method can be used to determine the concentration of any chemical element which consists of at least two stable isotopes. The isotope dilution technique is specific and is capable of detecting quantities of elements to 10^{-9}. One of the advantages of this method is that after the sample is equilibrated with the tracers, quantitative or known recoveries of the elements in question are no longer necessary. Laboratory contamination, and interference problems can be overcome. The distribution of lead in the oceans shows man's influence on his aquatic environment. The lead isotopes

can serve as indices to identify and to trace pollutants from their originating sources to the final deposition in the oceans. Ref: *J-1 40(3): 399-411, March 1968. 67 refs.*

3.0 - 123
Christianson, Alden G. and Tichenor, Bruce A. (1968).   INDUSTRIAL WASTE GUIDE ON THERMAL POLLUTION
--This is a guide to the sources, effects, and methods of control of thermal water pollution. An important bibliography is included. The general topics covered are heat loads from general industry, electric power, and manufacturing; physical, chemical, and biological effects; and methods of control and utilization of excess heat. Ref: *Federal Water Pollution Control Administration. Rept. 112, Sept. 1968. 91 refs.*

3.0 - 124
Cioglia, L. and Scarpa, B.   (1965).   PROCESS OF SELF-PURIFICATION IN A MARINE ENVIRONMENT
--Reports experiments to determine whether there was any significant difference in the self-purifying properties of sewage-polluted sea water and river water. The contamination and self-purification of both the common mussel and the carpet shell were examined. Maximal infection of the molluscs occurred within 30 min. of immersion in sea water containing 25 per cent sewage. Transferred to fresh water, the rate of self-cleansing was found to be independent of the initial amount of pollution in the sea water, although this did affect the required cleansing time. It appeared that the presence of shellfish increased the rates of purification of polluted sea water. Ref: *J-69 16,:267-290, 1965.*

3.0 - 125
Clark, J. (1967).   FISH AND MAN, CONFLICT IN ATLANTIC ESTUARIES
--Presents a review of the activities of each of the Atlantic coastal states in relation to conservation of their estuaries: Conflicts of interest between the need for conservation of estuarine resources and the need for land fill, navigation, gravel and sand mining, mosquito control and marsh impoundment, highway construction, and water control. Even small amounts of damage to estuarine areas can cause widespread losses to estuarine resources. Ref: *American Littoral Society. Special Publication No. 5, 1967.*

3.0 - 126
Clark, John R.   (1969).   THERMAL POLLUTION AND AQUATIC LIFE
--Intended for the general reader, this article provides an overall view of the effects of thermal pollution on aquatic life. The author indicates that while the effects of a single factor may be tolerable, the cumulative and synergistic action of all of them seems likely to be drastic. Ref: *J-22 220(3):19-27, March 1969.*

3.0 - 127
Cole, H. A.   (1969).   MARINE POLLUTION
--With a bibliography of 29 references, the various aspects of marine pollution are discussed including the effects on the marine environment of sewage disposal, trade waste waters, heavy metals, inert waste materials, pesticides, oil, radio-

active wastes (solid and liquid), and gravel extraction, and the need for control is emphasized. Ref: *P-21 9 p., 1969. 29 refs.*

3.0 - 128
Collett, W. F.   (1967).   CONTROL OF ESTUARINE POLLUTION
--It is proposed to divide an estuary into a number of zones, in each of which all discharges will be subject to similar limitations. Since discharges may vary widely in nature and original strength, there would be differing degrees of difficulty in treatments to produce the same effluent standard. In practice, equality of effort, rather than result, may be more attractive, i.e., to require each discharger to reduce the strength of effluents by the same proportion; certain very small discharges of domestic sewage and probably certain intractable industrial wastes will require to be excepted from the general rule of reduction of effluent strength. Ref: *J-21 (1):25-29, Jan 7, 1967.*

3.0 - 129
Commission Internationale Pour l'Exploration Scientifique De La Mer Méditerranée. Paris (1965). MARINE POLLUTION BY MICRO-ORGANISMS AND PETROLEUM PRODUCTS
--This publication contains the full text of 40 papers presented at a symposium on marine pollution held in Monaco, April 1964. The symposium was divided into 3 separate working groups, dealing respectively with the occurrence of bacterial pollution in marine environments; causes of bacterial pollution and the hygienic problem of shellfish; and pollution by hydrocarbons and petroleum products. The recommendations of each working group are appended, together with summaries of roundtable discussions on the self-purifying capacity of marine environments and on pollution by hydrocarbons. (Abstracted and filed under individual authors' names in this bibliography) Ref: *P-1 384 p., 1965.*

3.0 - 130
Conomas, T. John and Gross, M. G. (1968). MIXING OF COLUMBIA RIVER AND OCEAN WATERS
--Mixing between Columbia River water and the adjacent ocean water is a two-stage process controlled primarily by high river discharge. The first-stage mixing, of fresh water of the river and upwelled deeper ocean water, occurs within the estuary and yields low-salinity water. The second-stage mixing, of seaward-flowing low-saline water and deeper ocean water, occurs primarily in the transition area within 20 km of the river, and adds additional nitrate and phosphate. During summer the river is the dominant contributor of dissolved silicate. Because of summer photosynthetic depletion, the river contributes virtually no nitrate; the deep ocean water contributes most of the phosphate and nearly all the nitrate. In the oceanic area, the low-salinity surface water lies above the surface ocean water which inhibits further upward nutrient transfer by mixing. Nitrate is depleted within 30 km of the river. The lack of nitrate therefore limits photosynthetic activity in the surface ocean layers. Ref: *J-3 94 (SA5 Paper 6187):979-994, Oct 1968.*

3.0 - 131

Cooper, Edwin L. (Editor) (1967). SYMPOSIUM ON WATER QUALITY CRITERIA TO PROTECT AQUATIC LIFE --Published as: American Fisheries Society Transactions. Special Publication No. 4. 1967. J-23. Ref: P-23, 1967.

3.0 - 132
Copeland, B. J. (1966). EFFECTS OF INDUSTRIAL WASTE ON THE MARINE ENVIRONMENT
--Phosphate-phosphorus, Ohle anomalies, redox potential, species diversity, salinity, alkalinity, and chlorophyll were measured in St. Joseph's Bay, Fla. Toxicity bioassays of several Texas industrial wastes were conducted, and community metabolism of three industrial effluents was measured. Effects of long periods of effluent retention were evaluated. High phosphorus concentrations, reducing Ohle anomalies and redox potential, and low species diversity in St. Joseph's Bay indicated some degree of organic pollution. Although some industrial effleunts did not kill 50 percent of the fish, they caused a decided increase of the fish's metabolic rates. Long periods of retention allowed biological communities in industrial effluents to stabilize to the point of balance. Ref: J-1 38(6):1000-1010, June 1966. 20 refs.

3.0 - 133
Copeland, B. J. (1966). EFFECTS OF DECREASED RIVER FLOW ON ESTUARINE ECOLOGY
--A survey of the literature shows that high salinity, which results from low input of fresh water, can cause far-reaching changes in the ecology and productivity of an estuary. High salinities may cause the multiplication of parasites and species competing with oysters, damage to the nutritional requirements of shrimp, lessening of reproduction of the blue crab, lowering of primary productivity, and upset of the life cycles of fish. The effects of regulating river flow by dams on the ecology of estuaries should be considered carefully. Ref: J-1 38(11):1831-1839, Nov 1966. 59 refs.

3.0 - 134
Copeland, B. J. and Jones, Robert S. (1965). COMMUNITY METABOLISM IN SOME HYPERSALINE WATERS
--The Laguna Madre of Mexico is the only remaining coastal bay area resembling the primeval conditions which existed prior to the intensive industrialization of the Texas coast. Some physical characteristics of the hypersaline Laguna Madre, salt evaporating ponds of Puerto Rico, and tidal pools of the Texas coast are discussed. It was indicated that the metabolic characteristics of hypersaline communities resembled those of polluted environments. Ref: J-53 17(2):188-205, June 1965. 25 refs.

3.0 - 135
Corner, E. D. S.; Southward, A. J. and Southward, E. C. (1968). TOXICITY OF OIL-SPILL REMOVERS ('DETERGENTS') TO MARINE LIFE: AN ASSESSMENT USING THE INTERTIDAL BARNACLE ELMINIUS MODESTUS
--Experiments were made to find the effect of the oil-spill removers BP 1002, Gamlen, Slipclean, and Dasic on the barnacle Elminius modestus. Samples of Kuwait crude oil, 'Torrey Canyon' oil and Teepol L were tested. The oil-spill removers 'detergents' used were generally more toxic to nauplii than either 'pure' Kuwait or 'Torrey Canyon' oil. BP

1002 was most toxic and Dasic the least toxic of the 'detergents' examined. The solvent fraction of BP 1002 had a toxicity almost equal to that of the mixture; the stabilizer was less toxic and the surface-active component much less toxic. Toxicity of all 'detergent' mixtures was greatly reduced after the volatile components had evaporated. The mode of action of the toxic agents and their general effect on the environment through the food chain is discussed. Ref: J-2 48(1):29-47, Feb 1968.

3.0 - 136
Cory, Robert L. and Nauman, Jon W. (1968). TEMPERATURE AND WATER-QUALITY CONDITIONS OF THE PATUXENT RIVER ESTUARY, MARYLAND. JANUARY 1966 THROUGH DECEMBER 1967
--The effects of a coal-fueled power plant condenser-water discharge on the temperature of water in the Patuxent River Estuary from Jan 1966 to Dec 1967 were studied. Surface temperatures 1000 ft downstream from discharge averaged 4°C higher than normal and at times were 8° higher. Infrared imagery showed elevated surface temps as far as 3 miles upstream at flood tide. Ref: U.S. Geological Survey Open-File Rept. 70 p., 1968. 9 refs.

3.0 - 137
Cory, R. L. and Davis, H. F. (1964). AUTOMATIC DATA SYSTEM AIDS THERMAL POLLUTION STUDY OF PATUXENT RIVER
--A study was conducted to determine the effects of thermal pollution on natural water quality parameters and on life cycles of indigenous biota. An eight-parameter water quality data collection system was installed at the center pier of the bridge. The system continuously and automatically records surface and bottom water temperature, surface conductivity, dissolved oxygen content, turbidity, wind velocity, wind direction and tide stage. Ref: J-4 112(4):129-134, April 1964.

3.0 - 138
Coulter, James B. (1968). MARINE SHIPPING INDUSTRY-EFFECTS AND IMPACTS ON THE CHESAPEAKE BAY
--Outlines the actions to be taken by state and federal government regarding water pollution and shipping channel and harbor improvements in the Chesapeake Bay area. Ref: Governor's Conference on Chesapeake Bay. Wye Institute, Queen Anne's County, Maryland, Sept 12-13, 1968.

3.0 - 139
Craig, R. E. and Adams, J. A. (1967). CROMARTY FIRTH
--The Cromarty Firth, a deep-water harbor between the Tay and the Orkneys, was surveyed to determine the degree of pollution and circulation of fresh and tidal waters within the estuary. A large grain distillery and an oil depot are the main sources of pollution. Salinity, oxygen and BOD were determined and water movement was measured with a direct-reading current meter and with a fluorimeter after discharge of Rhodamine B dye. Biological samples were collected and lists of organisms found are presented in appendices. The present degree of pollution, although causing some nuisance from smell and discoloration, is not a hazard to fish. Ref: Scotland. Marine Laboratory, Aberdeen. 20 p., 1967.

3.0 - 140
Crew, H. and Worrall, C. G. (1965). DIFFUSION STUDIES IN THE POINT ARGUELLO REGION, JULY 1964
--Reports diffusion studies performed in the Point Arguello region in July 1964. Rhodamine dye was released on the surface as an instantaneous point source at a nearshore location and at an offshore location the following day. On the next day dye was released continuously from a source on the bottom (nearshore), and mimeograph paper was released on the surface. Horizontal distributions from the instantaneous releases agree with the Joseph and Sendner theory. The distribution from the continuous source could not be compared with theory. Ref: *California University. Institute of Marine Resources, IMR Ref. No. 65-2 15 p., Jan 1965. 9 refs.*

3.0 - 141
Croker, R. A. and Wilson, A. J. (1965). KINETICS AND EFFECTS OF DDT IN A TIDAL MARSH DITCH
--DDT was applied at a rate of 0.2 lb per acre throughout the length of a tidal marsh ditch on Santa Rosa Island, Fla. and its persistence, distribution and toxicity to fish were studied during the 4 following months. During the first month fish representing 8 of the local species were held at two test sites, one in the upper and the other in the lower reach of the ditch. At the lower site, 50 per cent of the fish, excepting large mullet, died within 3 days of treatment and the final mortality was 91.3 per cent. Ref: *J-23 94(2):152-159, April 1965.*

3.0 - 142
Cushing, C. E. and Porter, N. S. (1969). RADIONUCLIDE CYCLING BY PERIPHYTON: AN APPARATUS FOR CONTINUOUS IN-SITU MEASUREMENTS AND INITIAL DATA ON ZINC-65 CYCLING
--A system was developed which has the advantages of laboratory controlled experiments, while maintaining some semblance of natural conditions, and permits continuous measurement of the uptake and cycling of radionuclides between stream periphyton and a controlled aqueous environment, without the need for destructive sampling of the community for sequential analyses. Tests made in the Columbia River are reported. Ref: *P-3 p. 285-290, 1969.*

3.0 - 143
Custer, Stephen W. and Krutchkoff, Richard G. (1969). STOCHASTIC MODEL FOR BOD AND DO IN ESTUARIES
--Water quality standards are usually set in terms of the mean BOD and DO levels. Streams and estuaries represent a dynamic environment so observed pollution and oxygen concentration vary markedly. Maintenance of satisfactory mean concentrations may not lead to the anticipated water quality. If oxygen concentrations fall below certain critical levels for extended lengths of time irreversible damage may result, even though the mean concentration is within acceptable limits. More effective standards can be developed utilizing the entire DO probability distributions, i.e., there is a probability of occurrence associated with each DO concentration level. Knowledge of the DO probability distribution implies knowledge of the average DO level, but conversely. Ref: *J-3 95 (SA-5):865-885, Oct 1969. 11 refs.*

3.0 - 144
Czapke, K. (1966). SEAWEEDS AS RADIOACTIVITY INDICATORS OF MARINE ENVIRONMENT
--Investigations carried out under natural conditions, using 3 species of seaweed (*Enteromorpha intestinalis, Cladophora rupestris* and *Fucus vesiculosus*), showed that all these species have a high ability to accumulate radioactive substances. A slight increase in the activity of the surrounding water can be detected by a strong increase in the activity of the seaweeds, and since the seaweeds grow at a fixed point under the water they are therefore considered to be valuable indicators of the presence and extent of radioactive contamination in the sea. The range of error due to the biological selectivity shown by individual species of seaweed is comparatively small. Ref: *P-6 5,:371-373, 1965. 1966.*

3.0 - 145
D'Arca, S. U.; Graziano, F. and Bellante, E. (1966). POLLUTION IN THE RIVER TIBER. V. THE BEACH AND HARBOUR AREA OF FIUMICINO
--Studies of the beach and harbor area of Fiumicino (Italy) showed pronounced pollution caused by the right branch of the Tiber River (coliform counts) and of the shore near Ostia which was polluted by the other branch of the river. Ref: *J-69 17,:574-590, 1966.*

3.0 - 146
Davidson, Burton and Bradshaw, Robert W. (1967). THERMAL POLLUTION OF WATER SYSTEMS
--Literature of thermal pollution is reviewed and related to a mathematical simulation model of BOD and DO content. The DO factor is used to derive an optimal temperature in a polluted stream through a series of pollution-purification balance equations. Ref: *J-5 1(8):618-630, Aug 1967. 14 refs.*

3.0 - 147
Davis, Donald R. (1968). MEASUREMENT AND EVALUATION OF CERTAIN TRACE METAL CONCENTRATIONS IN THE NEARSHORE ENVIRONMENT OF THE NORTHWEST GULF OF MEXICO AND GALVESTON BAY
--Research was directed towards the determination of manganese, nickel, copper, zinc, and lead in the nearshore environment. A method utilizing filtration, ion exchange, persulfate oxidation, and hydrofluoric acid digestion in conjunction with atomic absorption spectroscopy was developed. A total of 66 water and 20 sediment samples from Galveston Bay, the Gulf of Mexico, and the Mississippi River were analyzed. It was concluded that the particulate form predominates over the ionic form for all the metals with a significant portion of nickel and copper existing as soluble-nonreactive complexes. This has been attributed to solubilization by organic complex formation (e.g., chelation). Attempts to correlate the forms of the metals with parameters such as pH, salinity, temperature, and organic carbon content were inconclusive and not reported. Ref: *Texas A & M University. Thesis, 1968.*

3.0 148
Desty, Denis Henry; Bretherick, Leslie and Webb, Michael Guthrie (1970). BARRIER FOR OIL SPILT ON WATER
--A floatable barrier for skimming spilt oil off water. A flexible flap whose density is between

that of oil and water is connected below the skimming inlets. During use the flap finds the oil/water interface to encourage preferential skimming of oil. Ref: *U.S. Patent No. 3,503,508. Assigned to: The British Petroleum Co., Ltd. & Gordon Low (Plastics) Ltd., England. 1970.*

3.0 - 149
Desty, Denis Henry; and Bretherick, Leslie (1970). BARRIER FOR OIL SPILT ON WATER
--An inflatable barrier having water and air chambers which, when suitably inflated with air and water, floats with part below and part above the water surface to impede the passage of floating oil, e.g. a figure-of-eight cross-section which floats with its waist at the water-level. The barrier may also have a skimming chamber which connects to water level. Ref: *U.S. Patent No. 3,503,512. Assigned to: The British Petroleum Co., Ltd., England. 1970.*

3.0 - 150
Desty, Denis Henry; Bretherick, Leslis and Webb, Michael Guthrie (1970). BARRIER FOR OIL SPILT ON WATER
--An inflatable barrier which comprises a plurality of air hoses positioned side by side to form, when inflated, a raft which has one or more water ballast chambers attached below. The barrier floats with part below and part above the water surface to impede the passage of floating oil. Preferably the air hoses are graded to give a wedge-shaped raft. Ref: *U.S. Patent No. 3,503,214. Assigned to: The British Petroleum Co., Ltd. and Gordon Low (Plastics) Ltd., England. 1970.*

3.0 - 151
de Sylva, Donald P. (1969). THEORETICAL CONSIDERATIONS ON THE EFFECTS OF HEATED EFFLUENTS ON MARINE FISHES
--This discussion revolves about the theoretical effect of high temperatures on marine fishes at all stages of their life histories, including reproduction, development and growth, food and feeding, physiology, behavior, and ecology. Emphasis is placed upon the effects that effluent high temperatures both alone and in combination with other substances, may have upon the physico-chemical environment. The need is stressed for careful surveys and a reasonably detailed knowledge of the environment prior to the selection of sites where thermal pollution may occur. Includes a review of the literature based on 245 references. Ref: *P-30 p. 229-293, 1969. 245 refs.*

3.0 - 152
de Sylva, Donald P. (1969). UNSEEN PROBLEM OF THERMAL POLLUTION
--Points out that heat is a relative pollutant and, when discharged uncontrolled into the aquatic environment, can cause direct and indirect harm, both to a particular organism and to the environment in which it lives. Conventional power plants raise the water temperature by about 10° to 30° F. Nuclear power stations use much more water for cooling and return the water to the environment at even higher temperatures. Ref: *J-113 1(1):38-41, Jan 1969.*

3.0 - 153

Di Luzio, Frank C. (1968). FEDERAL GOVERNMENT AND ESTUARINE POLLUTION ABATEMENT
--Estuaries are a valuable and vulnerable natural resource of national importance, the history of which has been steady and accelerating destruction from physical, chemical, and biological pollution. Coordinated national action is urgently needed to protect and restore the estuaries. The Federal role today is twofold: (1) Pollution control actions to the fullest extent of our present knowledge and legal authority to limit and prevent damage now being done to the estuaries and to restore the damaged environment; and (2) simultaneously, studies by several federal agencies in various aspects of estuarine pollution and its control in order to fill the large gaps in our knowledge and recommend stronger estuarine pollution control programs. Ref: *J-3 94 (SA 2 Paper 5884):201-211, April 1968.*

3.0 - 154
Di Toro, Dominic M. and O'Connor, Donald J. (1968). DISTRIBUTION OF DISSOLVED OXYGEN IN A STREAM WITH TIME VARYING VELOCITY
--By introducing the concept of the release time, that is, the time at which the particle of water being observed at point x at time t was released at point x = 0, the solution for the time varying flow and velocity follows. The formal solution can also be obtained by using the La Place transform with respect to the space variable x. The effect of random component of velocity on the BOD and DOD distributions are approximately equal to the coefficient of variation of the velocity times the BOD and DOD distributions calculated using the mean velocity. Ref: *J-16 4(3):639-646, June 1968. 5 refs.*

3.0 - 155
Ditsworth, George R. (1968). ENVIRONMENTAL FACTORS IN COASTAL AND ESTUARINE WATERS: BIBLIOGRAPHIC SERIES. VOL II. COAST OF WASHINGTON
--Provides an index to literature pertaining to the marine waters of the State of Washington. Most of these references were published after 1955. Ref: *Federal Water Pollution Control Assoc. Northwest Region. Pacific Northwest Water Lab. Corvallis, Oregon, Aug 1968.*

3.0 - 156
Dobbins, W. E. (1965). DIFFUSION AND MIXING
--Based on Fick's laws of diffusion, and convection, and movement of nonconservative substances an analysis is made on transport of sediment in river, and river and estuary pollution. Diagrams are plotted for variation of eddy diffusivity with scale, rate of absorption of oxygen at fixed point on surface, and oxygen absorption coefficients. Ref: *J-24 52(2):108-128, April 1965. 20 refs.*

3.0 - 157
Domenowske, Ralph S. and Matsuda, Robert I. (1969). SLUDGE DISPOSAL AND THE MARINE ENVIRONMENT
--Reports that the Municipality of Metropolitan Seattle diverted the North Trunk outfall raw waste water to the new West Point treatment plant and for two years has disposed of the effluent and digested sludge through the outfall diffuser system. To assess the effect of this primary treated discharge into Puget Sound, sediments, water, and benthic fauna, were sampled using a multiple tube

corer, Van Doren water samplers, and a Van Veen grab, respectively. It was found that bacteriological counts (MPN) declined, but seasonal variations far exceeded annual changes. Slight increases in bottom chemical oxygen demand values from the deep-water stations could not be attributed directly to natural sediment, dredge spoils, or sludge disposal. Scattered fluctuations in the benthic population observed suggest natural variations. Ref: J-1 41(9):1613-1624, Sept. 1969. 17 refs.

3.0 - 158
Dornhelm, Richard B. and Woolhiser, David A. (1968). DIGITAL SIMULATION OF ESTUARINE WATER QUALITY
--Partial differential equations describing the unsteady, one-dimensional mixing process in an idealized homogeneous, linearly expanding estuary are presented and solved numerically, using an implicit finite-difference scheme. These solutions portray the change in concentration of conservative substances with time and distance as a result of tidal fluctuations and variable inflows. Although the model is highly simplified in terms of estuarine geometry, experiments with varying boundary conditions can provide insight into adequacy of the more commonly used quasi-steady-state models. Ref: J-16 4(6):1317-1328, Dec 1968. 10 refs.

3.0 - 159
Doudoroff, Peter and Shumway, Dean L. (1967). DISSOLVED OXYGEN CRITERIA FOR THE PROTECTION OF FISH
--Fishery biologists should decline to specify any particular dissolved oxygen level as a minimal requirement of any fish population or as a proper standard of water quality until the necessary clear guidelines or explicit definitions of terms are provided by pollution-control agencies desiring such simple criteria. No reduction of dissolved oxygen below natural levels probably is the only 'standard' that would afford complete protection for fishery resources. The choice of suitable criteria or standards probably should be based in part on bioenergetic considerations relating to fish growth and production rates, many considerations other than biological being pertinent. Ref: P-32 and J-23 96(1):13-19, Spec. Pub. 4, 1967.

3.0 - 160
Duke, T. W. (1967). POSSIBLE ROUTES OF ZINC-65 FROM AN EXPERIMENTAL ESTUARINE ENVIRONMENT TO MAN
--Results are given on the distribution of zinc-65 introduced into an experimental pond connected to an adjoining estuary in North Carolina. It was found that shellfish accumulated zinc-65 rapidly and to higher levels than did other organisms, and the zinc-65 accumulated in the edible portions of these animals could easily have been transferred to humans. If man were to use the organisms from the pond periodically as a source of food, the clams, which had the highest specific activity, would be the greatest potential source of zinc-65; if, however, seafood from the pond was eaten only once, more radioactivity would be received from the oysters since the meat of these animals contained the largest amount of radioactivity. Under the conditions in the experiment-

al pond scallops were found to be good indicators of the presence of zinc-65 if samples were collected one day after the isotope was added to the water; oysters, however, retained zinc-65 longer than did the scallops and after 100 days contained more of the isotope on a whole-animal basis. The results of these experiments cannot be applied directly to other estuaries with different conditions of pH value, temperature, salinity, and rates of water exchange, since all these factors affect the movement of zinc-65 in the environment. Ref: J-1 39(4):536-542, April 1967. 13 refs.

3.0 - 161
Duke, T. W.; Willis, J.N. and Price, T.J. (1966). CYCLING OF TRACE ELEMENTS IN THE ESTUARINE ENVIRONMENT. I. MOVEMENT AND DISTRIBUTION OF ZINC-65 AND STABLE ZINC IN EXPERIMENTAL PONDS
--Observations were made on the movement and distribution of zinc-65 and the distribution of stable zinc in water, sediments, and biota of 2 estuarine ponds, one of which was essentially a closed system and the other was connected to an adjoining estuary. In the closed pond zinc-65 was taken up rapidly by the sediments and biota, and after one day only 66 per cent of the zinc-65 remained in the water. In the other pond about 82 per cent of the zinc-65 was flushed out by tidal action in the first day, and of the remainder 36 per cent was in the bottom deposits, 59 per cent in the water and suspended solids, and 5 per cent in the biota. After 100 days, in both ponds, most of the zinc-65 was associated with the bottom deposits. Ref: J-25 7(1):1-10, 1966.

3.0 - 162
Duke, T. W.; Willis, J.; Price T. and Fischler, K. (1969). INFLUENCE OF ENVIRONMENTAL FACTORS ON THE CONCENTRATIONS OF ZINC-65 BY AN EXPERIMENTAL COMMUNITY
--In laboratory experiments on the effects of salinity, temperature, pH value, and total concentration of zinc on the accumulation of zinc-65 from sea water by benthic estuarine organisms (oysters, clams, scallops and mud crabs) and their sediment substrates, each factor was studied at 2 levels and a polyfactorial approach was used to indicate the interaction between the environmental factors. Tabulated and diagrammatical results show that each of the 4 factors affected the concentration of zinc-65 in animals and sediments, but there was no significant effect attributable to interaction between the factors and no one factor affected all the components of the community. Concentration factors for zinc-65 varied inversely with salinity and total zinc concentration and directly with temperature and pH value. The implications of these results are considered. As shown graphically, there were significant temporal variations in the concentration factors for control animals and sediments, possibly owing to the different biochemical composition of the animals and different physico-chemical composition of the sediments at different times of the year; and it is therefore emphasized that the exact conditions of the experiment must be specified when reporting concentration factors for estuarine organisms. Ref: P-3 p. 355-362. 1969.

3.0 - 163

Dunster, H. J. (1969). RADIOACTIVE WASTE IN THE SEA
--After outlining the sources and significance of radioactive waste waters discharged to the sea, the author discusses the scientific and administrative basis of the control of such discharges, the possible pathways of movement of radioactivity through the marine environment, and methods for evaluating the effects of a proposed discharge. Ref: P-21 6 p., 1969.

3.0 - 164
Duursma, E. K. (1966). MOLECULAR DIFFUSION OF RADIO-ISOTOPES IN INTERSTITIAL WATER OF SEDIMENTS
--Radio-active isotopes in sea water can penetrate into the bottom deposits and considerable amounts may be accumulated by the sediment. This is important for bottom feeding animals and in coastal areas where tides and wave action may bring the surface layer of the sediment into suspension and transport it to other areas. To determine the extent to which isotopes migrate into sediments, the author considers that migration should be regarded simply as a diffusion process, defined by the basic diffusion law. The coefficient of diffusion may differ from sediment to sediment and may depend on the chemical properties of the isotope, but when the coefficient is known it is possible to calculate the course of concentration in the sediment with depth and time. Preliminary experimental work indicates that in fine and coarse marine sediments the penetration of non-reactive ions such as chloride is a process of about half the order of magnitude of the free molecular diffusion of ions in sea water, calculated for the diffusion coefficient, and that many important radio-active isotopes have a great affinity for clay and calcareous sediments, with the result that their diffusion coefficients are depressed by factors up to 10^6 in relation to the value in free solution, so that it may take years before they penetrate even a few cm. Ref: P-4 p. 355-371, 1966.

3.0 - 165
Eden, G. E. (1966). SYNTHETIC DETERGENTS AND THEIR POLLUTION PROBLEMS
--A brief review of pollution problems caused by the use of synthetic detergents and of some associated research, is given. A reduction in residual surface-active material after treatment of more biodegradable material has been noted at Luton and other sewage works. Inhibition of sludge digestion due to the presence of ABS-type detergents has been shown to begin at concentrations of about 700 mg per litre, although acclimatization may occur, to raise the tolerable concentration to 1000 mg per litre. Regarding foaming problems, the synergistic effect, causing foam stabilization, when non-ionic detergents are added to ABS, which persists at very low concentrations, would make it necessary to reduce concentrations of detergent residues in river waters to about 0.2 mg per litre if foaming is to be abolished. Ref: J-71 143,:458-459, 1966.

3.0 - 166
Eden, G. E. and Briggs, R. (1967). RADIO-ISOTOPE TECHNIQUES DEVELOPED IN WATER-POLLUTION STUDIES
--The authors discussed the application of radio-active isotopes in studies on the dispersal of sewage at sea and on the segregation of solid and liquid phases during the treatment of waste waters. A typical series of results is shown in the form of dilution patterns for 3 different depths. Plotted on logarithmic probability paper, the results show that the retention periods for the liquid phase follow a log-normal distribution, but for suspended matter, the retention periods deviate considerably from a log-normal distribution. The double-tracer technique used to study the relative adsorption of various radioactive isotopes on the walls of a sewer and a similar procedure, with bromine-82 as standard, could also be used to assess the degree of retention of any proposed tracer. Preliminary results obtained with lithium suggest that, as in the case of the radioactive isotopes, the passage of lithium through a channel may be delayed with respect to radioactive bromide owing to adsorption processes. Ref: International Atomic Energy Agency Proc. Ser. STI/PUB/141, 1967-191-206. Paper No. SM 83-13.

3.0 - 167
Edinger, John Eric and Geyer, John C. (1968). ANALYZING STEAM ELECTRIC POWER PLANT DISCHARGES
--Temperature distribution resulting from the advection, dispersion, and cooling of water from a steam electric power plant condenser is analyzed for a station located on a peninsula and discharging waste heat near the midpoint of a small narrow estuary. A case study indicates that temperature gradients are steep enough near a large heat discharge to allow the use of simplified, receiving waterbody characteristics to derive boundary value solutions. Ref: J-3 94(SA4 Paper 6064): 611-623, Aug 1968. 4 refs.

3.0 - 168
Eieland, E. (1966). INVESTIGATION INTO THE POLLUTION OF BATHING PLACES NEAR TRONDHEIM BY SEWAGE
--Reviews the causes and effects of pollution of bathing beaches in Trondheim, Norway, and gives details of the extension and construction of the Trondheim Harbor. Tabulated data includes details of investigations which were carried out using Serratia indica to follow the path of sewage discharged into the sea. Results showed that the direction of travel of sewage depended on winds and was controlled by tidal currents; the highest concentration occurred on the surface of the sea since river water is less dense than sea water. Ref: J-72 199,:216-225, 1966.

3.0 - 169
Eisler, Ronald (1969). ACUTE TOXICITIES OF INSECTICIDES TO MARINE DECAPOD CRUSTACEANS
--This is part of a program to evaluate the impact of pesticides on marine and estuarine fauna. This study reports on the concentration of seven organochloride and five organophosphorous insecticides that killed 50 percent of three species of decapod crustaceans during a 96-hour period. The influence of temperature and salinity of the medium on pesticide-induced mortality is also reported. Ref: J-44 16(3):302-310, May 1969.

3.0 - 170
Eisler, R. and Deuel, D. G. (1965). ACUTE TOXICITY OF SOAPS TO ESTUARINE FISHES

--Experiments were carried out on the toxicity of representative household soaps to estuarine fish at a salinity of 23 per thousand and on the effect of different salinities on toxicity. The test fish were juvenile and adult mummichogs, juvenile striped mullet, and juvenile Atlantic silversides. It was found that the soaps were most soluble at salinities approaching fresh water, but formed precipitates and insoluble complexes with increasing salinity. Heavy mortalities occurred among mummichogs exposed to high concentrations of each soap at salinities of 21 per thousand or less, but at higher salinities few or no deaths were observed. Under present conditions of chemical composition and amounts used, household soaps present little danger to fish in coastal environments. Ref: *J-26 27(1):45-48, Jan 1965.*

3.0 - 171
Eliassen, Rolf (1968). COLIFORM AFTERGROWTHS IN CHLORINATED STORM OVERFLOWS
--Laboratory tests were conducted on the possible bacteriological effects of combined sewer storm overflows into a tidal estuary. Bacterial growths were observed in the raw overflow and at the various dilutions. MPN values of coliforms were determined after fixed time intervals. Without chlorination MPN values increased from 10 to 40 times the value at the point of discharge, or up to 13,000,000 coliforms per 100 ml after 30 hr of mixture with estuarine water. Chlorination to 15-min chlorine demand of the overflow liquid did not stop aftergrowth but reduced the aftergrowth by 70% to 90%, with peak values of 500,000 per 100 ml in 40 hr. These studies indicate that the aftergrowth phenomenon must be studied in the determinations of design criteria for the treatment of storm overflows from combined sewer systems. Ref: *J-3 94(SA2 Paper 5913):371-380, April 1968.*

3.0 - 172
Ellis, David W. (1968). ANALYSIS OF AROMATIC COMPOUNDS IN WATER USING FLUORESCENCE AND PHOSPHORESCENCE
--Reports an investigation using a commercial spectrofluorometer/spectrophosphorimeter for analyzing aromatic compounds in water. Ref: *New Hampshire Univ. OWRR Project A-009-NH 24 p., 1968. 21 refs. (Prog. Rept. Phase I)*

3.0 - 173
Endebrock, Robert N.; D'Ardenne, Walter H. and Witzig, Watten F. (1969). UNDERSEA REACTOR SITING
--An underwater siting guide for use in international and territorial waters must be created to evaluate the consequences of the release of fission products from a nuclear reactor sited in the ocean. This paper attempts to develop the basic equations for such a guide. A very conservative fission-product-release inventory to illustrate undersea application is developed consisting of 100% of the soluble and 1% of the insoluble fission products of 66% of the gross fission-product inventory. The ocean is divided into four distinct zones for which current velocity profiles and characteristic diffusion parameters are established. Based upon a three-dimensional diffusion model incorporating shear effect and with the assumptions of no current variance, zero mean vertical current velocity, and depletion of the inven-

tory by radiological decay only, equations are presented which describe the physical transport and dispersion of the radioisotopes. A computer program, SEADIF, is applicable to a person immersed in the water and is used to determine, for both contained and uncontained systems, the distance factors and the radioisotope concentrations as a function of time and position. Ref: *J-27 7(5): 415-424, Nov 1969. 8 refs.*

3.0 - 174
Engineering-Science, Inc. (1965). OCEANOGRAPHIC AND MONITORING INVESTIGATION FOR ESTABLISHING DESIGN CRITERIA AND EVALUATING PERFORMANCE OF MARINE WASTE DISPOSAL FOR THE CITY OF OXNARD, CALIFORNIA. FINAL REPORT
--A survey of conditions at the site, near Port Hueneme, Calif., of a proposed ocean outfall sewer which will discharge sewage from the city of Oxnard after primary treatment and chlorination is reported. Factors examined include the speed and direction of prevailing winds and ocean currents, and the physical, chemical, and microbiological characteristics of the water and sediment. It was concluded that discharges from the proposed submarine pipe, which has a diffuser section of 384 ft and extends 6000 ft from the shore would not pollute nearby beaches. Ref: *Engineering-Science Inc., Arcadia. California 94 p., 1965.*

3.0 - 175
Fay, James A. (1969). SPREAD OF OIL SLICKS ON A CALM SEA
--A theoretical discussion considering the rate of spread of a finite quantity of oil on still water, the spread of a slick from a steady source in a moving stream. Theoretical considerations are compared with field observations. Ref: *Massachusetts Institute of Technology, Cambridge Fluid Mechanics Lab. Report no. PUB 69-6 16 p., Aug 1969. Also as: P-14 p. 53-63, 1969. 2 refs.*

3.0 - 176
Federal Water Pollution Control Administration (1966). DELAWARE ESTUARY COMPREHENSIVE STUDY, PRELIMINARY REPORT AND FINDINGS
--The history of the pollution problem and a physical description of the water quality and water demand requirements of the Delaware Estuary were presented. A computer simulation model was used to forecast the time varying DO profiles for various flow conditions and oxygen demanding loads. Results of the study are shown in figures and tables. Ref: *Federal Water Pollution Control Administration. Philadelphia, Pa. Preliminary Rept. and Findings 94 p., July 1966.*

3.0 - 177
Federal Water Pollution Control Administration (1968). OIL AND HAZARDOUS MATERIALS-EMERGENCY PROCEDURES IN THE WATER ENVIRONMENT
--Basic information is provided on the characteristics and effects of pollutants, and procedures to be followed in the event of significant releases to water of oil or other hazardous materials. Some general information is given on the effects of spills on aquatic life and important water uses. Pollution control measures, health hazard data, and first aid procedures are listed for each pollutant. Ref: *FWPCA Rept. CWR-10-1 137 p., Oct 1968. 8 refs.*

3.0 - 178
Federal Water Pollution Control Administration
(1969). VESSEL POLLUTION STUDY, SAN DIEGO
BAY, CALIFORNIA
--A two-year study in San Diego Bay reveals that
vessel waste discharges produce undesirable water
quality conditions in areas of concentrated vessel activity. Examined were the effects of waste
discharges representative of up to one-fourth of
the U. S. Navy's entire active fleet, more than
2500 hundred pleasure craft containing sanitary
facilities, over a hundred ships of the West
Coast commercial fishing fleet, and commercial
freight vessels carrying in excess of a million
tons of cargo to the Port of San Diego each year.
Wastes discharged were found to create conditions
that are hazardous to health, aesthetically offen-
sive and damaging to the ecological balances. Information is given on the sampling programs, the
wastes from shore sources, the wastes from water-
craft, the present water quality and the influence
of vessel wastes on water quality. Ref: _FWPCA
Pacific Southwest Region. San Francisco, Calif.
66 p., June 1969. 29 refs._

3.0 - 179
Federal Water Pollution Control Administration
(1969). CLEANING OIL CONTAMINATED BEACHES
WITH CHEMICALS
--Oil-dispersing chemicals were used for cleaning
persistent-type crude-oil from experimentally contaminated New Jersey coastal beaches and were
found to be generally ineffective. The dispersants
caused the oil to penetrate into the underlying
sand compounding the pollution problem. Ref:
_FWPCA, Edison, N.J. Research Series 30 p., Aug
1969._

3.0 - 180
Federal Water Pollution Control Administration
(1969). CHEMICAL TREATMENT OF OIL SLICKS.
STATUS REPORT
--The effectiveness and potential pollutional
effects of chemicals and other materials used to
disperse, sink or burn or otherwise dissipate oil
slicks are discussed. Considered are: dispersants,
floating sorbents, sinking agents, gelling agents
and burning agents. Some of the many commercial
products and natural materials used in connection
with recent large oil spills are reported. Ref:
_FWPCA. Water Pollution Control Research Series
WP-ORD-3 25 p., March 1969._

3.0 - 181
Finger, James H. and Wastler, T. Allen   (1969).
ORGANIC CARBON-ORGANIC NITROGEN RATIOS OF
SEDIMENTS IN A POLLUTED ESTUARY
--Most of the fresh water entering Charleston
Harbor, S. C., comes from the Cooper River system,
and this results in great amounts of inorganic
silt entering the harbor. In addition, the harbor
receives discharges of treated industrial and domestic waste waters. In the study on water quality
in the harbor, the sources and composition of the
bottom deposit were investigated. It was found
that considerable amounts of organic matter were
present. To determine the sources of the various
deposits, the carbon/nitrogen ratio of the sediments was determined and related to that of the
various waste discharges entering the harbor.
Ref: _J-1   41(R101-R109), Feb 1969. 7 refs._

3.0 - 182
Fisheries. Radiobiological Laboratory   (1967).
RADIOACTIVITY IN SURFACE AND COASTAL WATERS OF
THE BRITISH ISLES
--Detailed tabulated results are given of the
monitoring in 1966 of surface and coastal waters
in the vicinity of major nuclear sites in the
British Isles, and the data are compared with results for the years 1963-1965. The results showed
that the control of radioactive discharges is satisfactory; the highest degree of exposure for any
critical group is that for laverbread eaters in
South Wales, and in 1966 this did not exceed 18
per cent of the dose limit considered safe for
continuous exposure. Ref: _Ministry of Agriculture, Fisheries and Food, Fisheries Radiobiological
Laboratory. Tech Rept. FRL 1, Lowestoft, Suffolk
48 p., 1967._

3.0 - 183
Flemer, David A.; Dovel, William L.; Pfitzenmeyer,
Hayes T. and Ritchie, Douglas E., Jr.   (1968).
BIOLOGICAL EFFECTS OF SPOIL DISPOSAL IN CHESAPEAKE
BAY
--Field studies were made on biota of upper Chesapeake Bay under design related to shallow water
disposal of channel sediments; no gross effects
were observed on phytozooplankton, fish eggs and
fish larvae of adult fishes; some bottom animals
were smothered over wide area; several benthic
species survived deposition, and certain species
began repopulation soon after deposition. Ref:
_J-3   94 (SA 4):683-706, Aug 1968. 30 refs. Also
as Contrib. no. 329 Maryland Univ._

3.0 - 184
Foehrenbach, Jack (1969).   POLLUTION   AND
EUTROPHICATION PROBLEMS OF GREAT SOUTH BAY, LONG
ISLAND, NEW YORK
--Poor recirculation and small inflow of tidal
waters, the creek flows and groundwater flows are
helping to increase the nutrient content of the
92 sq-mile Great South Bay. Although the bay has a
large assimilative capacity for some forms of pollution, it is reaching a point where additional
loads will affect adversely its ecology, economic,
and recreational value. Ref: _J-1   41(8 Pt 1):
1456-1466, Aug 1969. 16 refs._

3.0 - 185
Foester, J. W. (1968).   PORTABLE NON-ELECTRICAL
CURRENT METER
--A description is given of a portable, easy-to-
read-instrument for measuring the velocity of
water currents in streams or estuaries. The device
consists of a weighted 'kite' of plywood suspended
by a line which crosses a board upon which a 90-
degree arc of a circle is inscribed and which enables the angle of the line with the vertical to
be measured. Current velocities are then derived
from tables. Ref: _J-25   9(1):52-55, March 1968._

3.0 - 186
Foster, R. F. and Honstead, J. F.   (1967).
ACCUMULATION OF ZINC-65 FROM PROLONGED CONSUMPTION
OF COLUMBIA RIVER FISH
--Fish caught in the Columbia River downstream
from the Hanford reactors were eaten once each
week for more than a year to obtain information on
the amount of radioactivity that might be accumulated by persons living in the neighborhood. The

accumulation of zinc-65 in the consumer was measured weekly in a whole-body counter. It was found that the maximal body burden of about 130 nc was reached on the 104th day and again on the 310th day. After the initial increase to equilibrium the body burden was about 7 times the weekly intake, and this was greater than anticipated. The reduction in zinc-65 body burden following the last meal of contaminated fish was observed for 511 days, indicating an effective half-life of 162 days. Ref: *J-73 13,:39-43, 1967.*

3.0 - 187
Fowler, S. W.; Small, L. F. and Dean, J. M. (1969). METABOLISM OF ZINC-65 IN EUPHAUSIIDS --Experiments were made on the uptake and elimination of the nuclide by the pelagic crustaceans *Euphausia pacifica* and *Thysanoessa spinifera*, both dead and alive, at temperatures in the range 5°-15°C and with 2 different concentrations of zinc-65. Under all conditions, there was a general similarity in the uptake of zinc-65 by dead animals and by live animals before moulting began. The rate of uptake was related linearly to temperature, and the body burden at any time before moulting was related directly to water temperature, animal dry weight, and initial concentration of zinc-65 in the water. Moulting accounts for a great removal of zinc-65 from the live animals but in formalin-perserved animals the rate of loss of zinc-65 varied with temperature and elimination was essentially the reverse of uptake. In both live and dead animals, and under all conditions of exposure, most of the zinc-65 was deposited in the exoskeleton and in the intercellular spaces of the myofibrils. The accumulation and loss of zinc-65 by euphausiids in sea water is not controlled metabolically; but the rapid concentration of zinc-65 from sea water and the rapid loss in non-radioactive water make these crustaceans potentially important in the cycling of radionuclides discharged into the sea. Ref: *P-3 p. 399-411, 1969.*

3.0 - 188
Foxworthy, J. E.; Tibby, R. B. and Barson, G. M. (1966). DISPERSION OF A SURFACE WASTE FIELD IN THE SEA
--Experiments performed at the Orange County, Calif., ocean outfall showed that a two-dimensional point-source mathematical model could describe the results of point-release experiments. When high winds and low stability prevailed, vertical diffusion was significant. When vertical diffusion was not significant, a one-dimensional model could be used. When the entire waste source was tagged, a model describing diffusion from a continuous volume source, based on a Gaussian distribution of material in a homogeneous, stationary, and infinite field, gave a realistic representation of the observations. Lateral variance of concentration distribution was a function of distance from the source. Ref: *J-1 38(7):1170-1193, July 1966.* 21 refs.

3.0 - 189
Frankel, Richard J. and Cumming, James D. (1965). TURBULENT MIXING PHENOMENA OF OCEAN OUTFALLS
--The turbulent mixing process that occurs when sewage is discharged into sea water was studied in the laboratory for horizontal, 15°, 30°, 45°, and vertical angles of discharge. Conductivity probes were used to measure the continuous and instantaneous change in ion concentration of the discharged effluent as it diffused into the surrounding fluid. A statistical analysis was made of the mixing process and the effects of surface proximity, angle of discharge, depth-to-diameter ratio, and Froude number on the diffusion of the effluent were studied over a large range of values common to California ocean outfalls. Ref: *J-3 91 (SA 2 Paper 4297):33-59, April 1965.*

3.0 - 190
Frankenberg, Dirk and Westerfield, Charles W., Jr. (1968). OXYGEN DEMAND AND OXYGEN DEPLETION CAPACITY OF SEDIMENTS FROM WASSAU SOUND, GEORGIA
--This study suggests strongly that severe oxygen depletion of waters in Wassau Sound could result from disturbance of the sediments during phosphate mining activities. Estimates of oxygen demand liberated by disturbance of sediments attributed to specified mining operations indicate that all the oxygen could be removed from 16 to 27 per cent of the low tide volume of Waussau Sound and its tributaries. Ref: *J-28 26(4):160-172, Sept 1968.* 32 refs.

3.0 - 191
Fukai, R. (1966). FATE OF SOME RADIONUCLIDES FIXED ON ION-EXCHANGE RESINS IN SEA-WATER MEDIUM
--Experiments were carried out on the stability of the nuclides when the spent resins are dumped at sea. Laboratory experiments on the elution of various radionuclides from ion-exchange resins when sea water was passed through the columns and when the resin particles were allowed to fall through a column of sea water showed that extensive elution of all the nuclides occurred in the case of the cation-exchange material Dowex 50W, but little or no elution occurred from the chelating resin Chelex 100. The chelating-resin particles appeared to be stable, at least for some months, after settling to the bottom of the water. Experiments were also carried out on the rate at which the resin particles sank through a column of sea water; the results were used to give a rough estimate of the probable distribution of the particles on the bottom of the sea. Ref: *P-4 p. 483-495, 1966.*

3.0 - 192
Fukai, R. (1968). SOME BIOGEOCHEMICAL CONSIDERATIONS ON THE RADIOACTIVE CONTAMINATION OF MARINE BIOTA AND ENVIRONMENTS
--The author emphasizes the importance of methods for predicting the level of radioactive isotopes in marine organisms living in a given condition of contamination and stresses the need for further accumulation of biogeochemical data on the distribution of trace elements in marine biota to assist in this prediction. The significance of the term 'concentration factor' or 'enrichment factor' is reviewed critically, and the use of the simpler term 'abundance ratio' is proposed and explained, with examples of data on the standard abundance of cobalt and chromium in various biogeochemical phases in the Mediterranean. Ref: *P-7 p. 391-394, 1966, 1968. Rome*

3.0 - 193
Fukuda, M.; Itoh, N. and Sakagishi, S. (1965). DIFFUSION PHENOMENA IN COASTAL AREAS

--30 diffusion experiments were carried out in the Pacific Ocean off the coast of Japan where it receives waste waters from the Japan Atomic Energy Research Institute and where highly radioactive material might be dumped in the event of a major accident. It was shown that diffusivity is a function of time or of area of the dye patch, and concluded that the equations used would permit a safe estimation of the diffusion of radioactivity into the sea. An equation suitable for estimating the fate of a continuous short-period discharge of low activity was also developed and the theoretical results were compared with those obtained in the present experiments. Ref: *P-10 3,:193-214, 1965.*

3.0 - 194
Gameson, A.L.H.; Barrett, M. J. and Preddy, W. S. (1965).   PREDICTING THE CONDITION OF A POLLUTED ESTUARY
--The authors outlined some of the salient features of the study of the Thames Estuary carried out by the Water Pollution Research Laboratory and considered briefly the principle of adjustment of data to half-tide conditions, especially in relation to its applicability in the Humber and Parrett Estuaries. Ref: *P-10 3,:167-192, 1964, 1965. Also in: J-57 9(10):655-664, Oct 1965. 11 refs.*

3.0 - 195
Gameson, A.L.H. and Hart, I. C. (1966). STUDY OF POLLUTION IN THE THAMES ESTUARY
--Determinations were made of the water quality of the Thames Estuary over a period of several years. It is indicated that by comparison with the accumulated data, the condition of the middle reaches of the estuary showed marked improvement in 1964 following the establishment of a secondary treatment plant at the Southern Outfall Sewage Works. Ref: *J-21 51,:2117-2123, Dec 17, 1966. 3 refs.*

3.0 - 196
Gameson, A.L.H.; Bufton, A.W.J. and Gould, D. J. (1967).   STUDIES OF THE COASTAL DISTRIBUTION OF COLIFORM BACTERIA IN THE VICINITY OF A SEA OUTFALL
--Results are given of studies on the distribution of coliform bacteria in coastal waters in the vicinity of a single outfall sewer discharging well beyond low water mark, in relation to factors such as tide, temperature, wind, sewage discharge, and discharge from a river beside the outfall. The beach was found to be only moderately polluted. Although the overall median count was low there were very wide variations from sample to sample, indicating the difficulty of assessing the level of pollution from the analysis of only a few samples. It was suggested that the most important factors causing variations in the coliform count at the water's edge are the roughness of the sea, the discharge from the river, and sunlight. Ref: *J-74 66,:501-523, 1967.*

3.0 - 197
Gameson, A.L.H.; Pike, E. B. and Barrett, M J. (1968).   SOME FACTORS INFLUENCING THE CONCENTRATIONS OF COLIFORM BACTERIA ON BEACHES
--Factors influencing the concentration of coliform bacteria on certain British beaches have been studied by the Water Pollution Research Laboratory using bromine-82, *Serratia indica,* and *Bacillus*

subtilus var. *niger* to trace discharges from nearby sewage outfalls. Details were given of the techniques employed, and some results obtained at 2 sites were presented graphically. There was a general indication that numbers of coliform bacteria on the shore were related to roughness of the sea, direction but not speed of the wind, and solar radiation. The possibility of photoreactivation of damaged cells and the effects of radiation on the two indicator organisms were investigated. Ref: *P-19 and J-59 9,:255-280, 1968. 11 refs.*

3.0 - 198
Gameson, A.L.H.; Pike, E. B. and Munro, D. (1968). STUDIES OF SEWAGE DISPERSION FROM TWO SEA OUTFALLS
--The authors describe a study of the bacterial pollution of beaches at 2 sites; one with a short (20m) outfall from which crude sewage is discharged and the other with a long (430m) outfall discharging comminuted sewage. The development and testing of mathematical models representing the dispersion of sewage in the sea was described. It was concluded that the design criteria for submarine sewage outfalls are not yet clearly defined and methods of calculating the amount of pollution that will reach the shore are not entirely satisfactory. Ref: *J-21 46,:1582-1589, Nov 16, 1968.*

3.0 - 199
Garancher, J. (1967). PROTECTION OF AN OIL PORT BY A BUBBLE SCREEN
--Describes a method of protection which provides a submerged network of pipes discharging compressed air through rows of nozzles generating vertical bubble screens forming an impenetrable barrier for oil discharged into a harbor. This method may also be used to protect beaches. Ref: (In French) *J-29 22(4):387-390, 1967.*

3.0 - 200
Garrett, William D. and Barger, William R. (1970). FACTORS AFFECTING THE USE OF MONOMOLECULAR SURFACE FILMS TO CONTROL OIL POLLUTION ON WATER
--The surface-chemical characteristics of several potential pollutants were studied to determine their behavior at the air/water interface. A number of monolayer-forming materials with varying surface-chemical properties were examined. The following properties relevant to oil pollution control were determined: the monolayer spreading velocity, the ability to resist and spread against wind, and the thickness of an oil lens supportable by a particular monolayer. Optimum characteristics were demonstrated by 'liquid' water-insoluble monolayers with high film pressures and low oil solubility. Surface films with high spreading pressures will compress thinly spread layers of pollutant oil to lenses 0.5-1.0 cm. thick, substantially reducing the area covered by pollution. Ref: *J-5 4(2):123-127, Feb 1970. 17 refs.*

3.0 - 201
Gawel, L. J. (1966). RESPIRATION CHARACTERISTICS OF OCEAN BAY SEDIMENTS AND SELECTED MARINE ISOLATES
--Studies were carried out on the respiration of bottom deposits from Yaquina Bay, at Newport, Ore. and of some of the organisms isolated from these deposits. Aerobic deposits showed a very low respiratory quotient unless supplementary glucose

and nitrate were added; addition of nitrate did not result in evolution of nitrogen gas or oxides of nitrogen, and it is assumed that the added nitrate was used in an assimilatory rather than a dissimilatory manner. Anaerobic sediments produced an equivalent of 1.3 μg of nitrogen per hour per g dry weight, and apparently contained a large number of organisms capable of using nitrate as the terminal acceptor of hydrogen. Several denitrifying bacteria were isolated and identified. Ref: *Oregon State University. Thesis 133 p., 1966.*

3.0 - 202
Genovese, S. (1967).   ON SOME PROBLEMS OF MARINE BACTERIOLOGY
--After reviewing previous work on the morphology, taxonomy, and ecology of bacteria in sea water, the author discusses the horizontal and vertical distribution of bacteria in the water and bottom deposits and emphasizes the important role of bacteria in biochemical processes and particularly their role in self-purification processes and in the antibiotic activity of sea water. Ref: *J-59 8,:41-50, 1967.*

3.0 - 203
Genovese, S.; Bruni, V. and Macri, G.   (1968). ENDOGENOUS MICROBIAL ACTIVITY AND CONTAMINATING BACTERIA IN THE SEA
--Hydrological characteristics of the Strait of Messina, Sicily, were described and the results of preliminary physico-chemical and bacteriological analyses of the water and sediment were tabulated and discussed. No evidence of serious pollution by coliform bacteria was detected. Ref: *P-19 and J-59 9,:73-81, 1968. 9 refs.*

3.0 - 204
Gerard, Robert D. (1966).   POTENTIAL FRESHWATER RESERVOIR IN THE NEW YORK AREA
--Estimates of the water budget of Long Island Sound suggest that it could become the largest reservoir in the United States, with a freshwater surplus equal to 12 times the present needs of New York City. The engineering aspects of this undertaking are within the scope of present technology. The dam structures required to isolate this area from the sea could serve as important highway links in place of highway-bridge projects presently under study. Ref: *J-6 153(3738):870-873, Aug 19, 1966.*

3.0 - 205
Gerber, H. Bruce (1967).   BIBLIOGRAPHY ON THERMAL POLLUTION
--The general categories of the bibliography include (1) general properties of heat and heat exchange between water and atmosphere, (2) effects of heated discharges on the receiving body of water, and (3) effects of heated discharges on uses made of the receiving body of water. Categories (2) and (3) contain the greater number of articles; specifically studies on cooling ponds, water supplies, lakes and reservoirs, rivers and streams, stratified flow problems, mixing and dispersion, instrumentation methods and devices, and effects on aquatic life. Ref: *J-3 93(SA3 Paper 5303):85-113, June 1967. 878 refs.*

3.0 - 206
Ghosh, B. B. and Basu, A. K. (1968). OBSERVATIONS

ON ESTUARINE POLLUTION OF THE HOOGHLY BY THE EFFLUENTS FROM A CHEMICAL FACTORY COMPLEX AT RISHRA, WEST BENGAL (INDIA)
--The Hooghly Estuary receives large volumes of untreated or inadequately treated waste waters from a variety of industries in the Calcutta area, and the results are given of a study of the effects of the waste waters from a plant upstream. It manufactures heavy chemicals, paints and varnishes, plastics and rubber chemicals, and the characteristics of some of the waste waters produced are tabulated. The waste waters are discharged to the Bager Canal, which flows into the Hooghly, and there is a marked deterioration in the canal water below the point of discharge, and also in the water of the estuary below the canal for a distance of about 3.5 km; below this, the estuary recovers from the effects of the pollution as a result of high dilution and considerable mixing. Ref: *J-76 10,:204-218, 1968.*

3.0 - 207
Gibbs, C.V. and Isaac, G.W. (1968). METROPOLITAN SEATTLE'S DUWAMISH ESTUARY WATER QUALITY PROGRAM
--The Duwamish Estuary study is the most comprehensive municipally sponsored water quality study in the Pacific Northwest. The historical development of the river problem, present water quality-monitoring effects, and results of the investigations are presented. The data collected will be used to guide the formulation of plans for future pollution-control measures. Ref: *J-1 40(3 Pt 1): 385-394, March 1968. 10 refs.*

3.0 - 208
Giese, G. L. and Barr, J. W. (1967). HUDSON RIVER ESTUARY - A PRELIMINARY INVESTIGATION OF FLOW AND WATER-QUALITY CHARACTERISTICS
--In a preliminary investigation of the flow and water quality of the Hudson River Estuary, conducted by the U.S. Geological Survey in co-operation with the New York Water Resources Commission and the New York State Department of Commerce; factors affecting flow and salinity were discussed. The future program will include investigation of the relation between flow and salinity, factors controlling the position and movement of the salt-water front, and sediment transport. Ref: *New York. State Conservation Dept. Bulletin No. 61, 1967.*

3.0 - 209
Gilmour, A. J. (1965). IMPLICATIONS OF INDUSTRIAL DEVELOPMENT ON THE ECOLOGY OF A MARINE ESTUARY
--Contains the text of evidence presented by the Fisheries and Wildlife Department to the State Development Committee at an enquiry into the development of Westernport Bay, Victoria, Australia. This bay supports important commercial fisheries and is also popular with anglers, but its topography mades it particularly susceptible to pollution, since many of the mud flats are higher on their seaward edges and thus, even at low tide, they retain large areas of shallow water, where pollutants would be likely to collect. Published information on the polluting effects of dredging and wharf construction, shipping. and urban and industrial development is reviewed, and recommendations are made for the protection of the bay from harmful effects of further development. Ref: *Australia. Victoria Fisheries and Wildlife Dept.*

State Development Committee. Fisheries Contrib. No. 20   18 p., 1965.   44 refs.

3.0 - 210
Glenn, T. R.   (1966).   EFFECTIVE ESTUARINE POLLUTION ABATEMENT PROGRAMME
--Reviews some of the work of the Interstate Sanitation Commission of New York - New Jersey - Connecticut in controlling and reducing pollution in the waters of the densely-populated New York metropolitan area.   It was not practicable to establish a single standard of purity, and the waters are divided into 2 classes, each with certain effluent standards; however, even the waters in the lower classification must not cause fish kills nor create an aesthetic nuisance, and must be suitable for many types of industrial use. Ref: *P-5 and J-23   95(4):116-120, 1966. Special Publication No. 3*

3.0 - 211
Glenne, B. and Selleck, R. E.   (1969). LONGITUDINAL ESTUARINE DIFFUSION IN SAN FRANCISCO BAY, CALIFORNIA
--The concept of one-dimensional diffusion is discussed and applied to the San Francisco Bay, California to evaluate the degree of mixing and dispersion existing within the estuarine system. The intensity of mixing and dispersion is expressed in terms of an overall, longitudinal diffusion coefficient which can be varied throughout the system.   Procedures which may be used to predict the concentrations of a water quality constituent in the Bay system are discussed briefly.   An example of a steady state computation is presented. Ref: *J-12   3(1):1-20, 1969.   16 refs.*

3.0 - 212
Goodman, Alvin S. and Tucker, Richard J.   (1969). USE OF MATHEMATICAL MODELS IN WATER QUALITY CONTROL STUDIES
--Mathematical models were utilized to study water pollution control programs in a river basin.   Sensitivity analyses, with a steady state model, showed substantial variation of cost for sewage treatment, depending upon stream purification parameter selections. An unsteady state model was developed to trace a time profile at any specified station in terms of flow and quality while upstream discharge, water temperature, and solar radiation vary.   The techniques assume that, for short reaches and/or times, steady state conditions apply without undue loss of accuracy.   A new empirical procedure was developed to route unsteady stream flow.   The time varying model was used to investigate the effectiveness of an assumed configuration of treatment plants when the stream's assimilative capacity varies with distance and time.   Susceptibility to poorer conditions increases with higher BOD releases.   Lower treatment levels also result in a greater range of river conditions than high levels.   Sensitivity analyses of stream parameters were also made with the time varying model. Ref: *Northeastern Univ., Boston, Mass. Dept. of Civil Engineering Rept. no. FWPCA-16090-07/69, July 1969.   140 p.*

3.0 - 213
Gordon, D. C.   (1966).   EFFECTS OF THE DEPOSIT-FEEDING POLYCHAETE *PECTINARIA GOULDII* ON THE INTERTIDAL SEDIMENTS OF BARNSTABLE HARBOUR
--The polychaete worm *Pectinaria gouldii* studied under laboratory conditions was found to work 6 g of sediment per day and to work continuously but at varying rates during a 24-hour period.   The working rate was inversely related to the sediment pigment concentration and decreased with decreasing temperature; worms were unable to work sediment with particle sizes larger than 1 mm.   The annual working rate of one worm, taking temperature and availability of interstitial water into account, was calculated to be 600 g of sediment. Thus the turnover rate for a flat with a population of 10 worms per m^2 and with a sediment depth of 6 cm would be 15 years.   Rapid utilization of available organic matter was suggested by the amounts of sediment pigment and organic carbon removed from the sediments. Ref: *J-41   11(3):327-332, July 1966.*

3.0 - 214
Goubet, Andre   (1969).   COOLING OF RIVERSIDE THERMAL-POWER PLANTS
--Considers power plants installed on estuaries in which the direction of the current reverses with each tide.   The discussions of JOHN E. EDINGER, G. EARL HARBECK, JR. are included. Ref: *P-30b Chapter 4:110-143, 1969.*

3.0 - 215
Graves, G. W.;   Hatfield, G. B. and Whinston, A. (1969).   WATER POLLUTION CONTROL USING BY-PASS PIPING
--Presents a mathematical model of regional water quality management using by-pass piping. The model is developed within the framework of linear programming and a large-scale problem is solved using semi-realistic data from the Delaware Estuary. The technique of generation of elements is used in conjunction with the truncated tableau to provide efficient solution. Ref: *J-16   5(1):13-47, Feb 1969.   6 refs.*

3.0 - 216
Green, Richard S.;   Dubois, Donald P. and Tutwiller, Clarence W.   (1966).   DATA HANDLING SYSTEMS IN WATER POLLUTION CONTROL
--A basic system for data processing, called STORET, has been developed for use in operations within the Division of Water Supply and Pollution Control of the U.S. Public Health Service.   The operating concepts and goals of a fully integrated data handling system necessitate prompt and continuous updating of variable information, its storage in computers for ready access and ease of subsequent mathematical analysis, and final application of the digested data in decisions affecting the pollution situation.   Mathematical models, combined with the use of automatic water quality monitoring equipment capable of telemetering data directly to centrally located computers, have important applications in this work. Ref: *J-3 92(SA 1 Paper 4652):55-67, Feb 1966.*

3.0 - 217
Greenbaum, Richard H.   (1969).   HOW SAN DIEGO CLEANED UP ITS BAY
--A brief account on steps taken to reduce pollution in San Diego Bay.   All domestic sewage from land sources which formerly discharged into the bay was collected, treated and discharged into the ocean.   Within the first year a dramatic restor-

ation of the bay had occurred. Marine life swarmed into the bay, dissolved oxygen levels rose and potentially harmful bacteriological conditions disappeared. Action is being taken to eliminate vessel pollution in the bay. See 3.0 - 178 in this bibliography for study of Vessel Pollution. Ref: *J-113   4(7):55-56, July 1969.*

3.0 - 218
Greffard, J. and Meury, J. (1967).   CARCINOGENIC HYDROCARBON POLLUTION IN TOULON HARBOUR
--The total concentration of hydrocarbons with boiling points above 55°C and the concentrations of 3,4-benzopyrene, benzofluoranthene, and perylene were determined in marine mud and in the common mussel *(Mytilus edulis)* in Toulon Harbor, France; the analytical procedures used are described. The total hydrocarbon concentration ranged from 0.108 to 0.338 g per 100 g and the concentrations of the individual compounds were 1.6-2.2 μg for benzopyrene, 0.2-0.27μg for benzofluoranthene, and 0.15-0.27 μg for perylene, per 100 g. It is thought, however, that much of the 3,4-benzopyrene in the mussel combines chemically with the protein amino acids in a quinolinic structure and loses its carcinogenic activity. Ref: *J-77 19,:457-468, 1967.*

3.0 - 219
Guizerix, J. (1968).   STUDY OF THE PHENOMENA OF DISPERSION OF WASTE WATERS BY RADIOACTIVE AND COLOURED TRACERS
--The theory of tracer transmission was outlined, and the use of dyes and radioactive tracers for predicting dispersion and dilution of waste waters discharged to sea was discussed, with particular reference to the type of tracer selected, its application by continuous or instantaneous injection, and the interpretation of data. Ref: *P-19 and J-59 9,:135-158, 1968. 14 refs.*

3.0 - 220
Gundersen, K. R. and Stroupe, D. B.   (1967). BACTERIAL POLLUTION OF KANEOHOE BAY, OAHU
--Reports an investigation of the presence and numbers of coliform bacteria, fecal streptococci and bacteria capable of growing on peptone seawater agar at 28° made in the vicinity of Kaneohoe Bay during the period June through August, 1967. Ref: *Hawaii. University. Water Resources Research Center. Tech. Rept. 12   24 p., Dec 1967.*

3.0 - 221
Gundersen, K. R.; Ohye, R. and Stroupe, D. (1970). HAND-OPERATED WINCH FOR BACTERIOLOGICAL WATER SAMPLING
--An inexpensive, winch for use in sampling off-shore waters from a boat was designed, fabricated, and used. The winch permits sampling of several 250-ml water samples at different depths from the surface to 150 m; hand operated; attachable to a small boat; and swingable in a horizontal plane, adjustable vertically. At a cost of less than $200, the sampler is made of non-corrodible materials, unaffected by seawater and is light enough to be portable by one man. Ref: *J-1 42(1):131-132, Jan 1970.*

3.0 - 222
Gunnerson, Charles G.   (1966).   OPTIMIZING SAMPLING INTERVALS IN TIDAL ESTUARIES
--Spectral analyses of dissolved oxygen and conductivity data in a tidal estuary were performed to determine the quantity of data needed to estimate the mean, max, and minimum values. Continuously recorded data from the Potomac Estuary and the Raritan Bay were used. It was concluded that: (1) sampling should be performed at more than one depth; (2) collecting data at six or twelve minute intervals yields the same amount of statistical information as data collected at two-hour intervals. Ref: *J-3   92(SA 2 Paper 4799):103-125. April 1966. 13 refs.*

3.0 - 223
Gunnerson, Charles G. (1967).   HYDROLOGIC DATA COLLECTION IN TIDAL ESTUARIES
--Spectral density, coherence, and phase relationships of stage, salinity and velocity in the Sacramento River were estimated to provide a basis for evaluating data collection and utilization. It was found that, as in the Potomac Estuary and Raritan Bay, a 2-hour sampling interval provided the essential data for engineering purposes. Ref: *J-16   3(2):491-504 Second Quarter, 1967.*

3.0 - 224
Gurnham, C. Fred (1965).   INDUSTRIAL WASTEWATER CONTROL
--The introductory chapter of this text presents brief descriptions of the parameters or properties commonly used in stream evaluation and in the study of wastewaters. The text is divided in chapters dealing successively with: food products, animal and vegetable, mining, mineral products, manufactured products and general industries such as power, atomic energy and transportation. The characteristics of the wastes produced by each are described and prevailing treatment and disposal methods are noted. Improved treatment and disposal methods are recommended in specific cases. Ref: *Industrial Wastewater Control. A textbook and reference work. Academic Press   476 p., 1965.*

3.0 - 225
Guyon, John C. and Shults, Wilbur D.   (1969). RAPID PHOSPHATE DETERMINATION BY FLUOROMETRY
--Two similar fluorometric procedures to measure phosphate contamination are proposed. Ref: *J-30   61(8):403-404, Aug 1969. 3 refs.*

3.0 - 226
Gyllander, C. (1966).   ..   WATER EXCHANGE AND DIFFUSION PROCESSES IN TVÄREN, A BALTIC BAY
--As part of the investigations being carried out on Tvären Bay to determine the effect of discharging low-level radioactive waste waters from the research centre at Studsvik, Sweden, studies were carried out on the water circulation and transport within the bay. It was found that convection processes resulted in complete renewal of the water in the bay 5 times per year, while the surface water above the sills is renewed weekly. Various methods for diffusion of the waste waters were compared, and it was shown that discharge through a pipe with a single outlet gave less effective initial dilution than discharge through a pipe with multiple diffusers. Ref: *P-4 p. 207-220, 1966.*

3.0 - 227
Gysi, Marshall and Loucks, Daniel P.   (1969).

SELECTED ANNOTATED BIBLIOGRAPHY ON THE ANALYSIS
OF WATER RESOURCE SYSTEMS
--A bibliography of the literature pertaining to
the application of systems analysis techniques to
water resources problems. Emphasis is on optimi-
zation and simulation techniques. Ref: *New York.
Water Resources and Marine Sciences Center.
Publication No. 25 177 p., Aug 1969. 500 refs.*

3.0 - 228
Halliwell, A. R. and O'Connor, B. A.   (1965).
FLOW AND SILTATION MEASUREMENTS IN THE MERSEY
ESTUARY
--Factors affecting sand and silt movements in
estuaries are outlined, and a description is given
of the equipment and methods used to measure the
strength and direction of the currents and their
pattern of movement in relation to sand banks, the
suspended solids, and salinity and temperature of
the water in the Mersey Estuary. Movements of sand
within 3 ft of the bottom were also studied. A
computer is used to process the large quantity of
data obtained and details of the analyses are
given. Results show that the bottom deposits in
Liverpool Bay are composed of medium and coarse
material with some patches of boulder clay, the
upper estuary bottom is of medium and fine sand
with mud deposits by the shores and dock entrances,
and the narrows which links these two areas has a
hard rock bottom partly covered by a thin erodable
layer of silt. Ref: *J-62   11(3):21-46, 1965.*

3.0 - 229
Halton, J. E. and Nehlsen, W. R.   (1968).
SURVIVAL OF *ESCHERICHIA COLI* IN ZERO-DEGREE
CENTIGRADE SEA WATER
--The survival of *Escherichia coli*, a common indicator organism among waste-water bacteria, was
studied in seawater at zero degree centigrade.
From the time of inoculation, about 70 per cent of
the organisms survived for 8 days, 34 percent for
15 days, and 1 percent for 35 days. The nutrient
supply was an important factor in governing the
growth of the organisms. Low seawater temperatures
favored the survival of *E. coli*. Ref: *J-1 40(5
Part 1):865-868, May 1968. 6 refs.*

3.0 - 230
Hamilton, R. D. and Carlucci, A. F.   (1966).
USE OF ULTRA VIOLET-IRRADIATED SEA WATER IN THE
PREPARATION OF CULTURE MEDIA
--The growth response of *Cyclotella nana* was determined in media prepared from irradiated sea
water to which known amounts of vitamin B_{12} had
been added, and compared with the responses of the
diatom in preparations made from charcoal-treated
sea water and irradiated sea water which had been
autoclaved. Little differences in these comparative tests were observed. Preliminary results were
obtained on the uptake of organic matter by marine
bacteria in artificial and irradiated natural sea
water. It was found that rates of uptake were
identical at lower substrate concentrations, but
that there was a slightly lower maximal rate in
media prepared from irradiated sea water. Ref:
J-7   211(5048):483-484, July 30, 1966.

3.0 - 231
Hampson, B. L. (1967).   RESTRICTED DISPERSION OF
ZIRCONIUM-95 AND OF NIOBIUM-95 AFTER RELEASE TO
THE SEA IN NUCLEAR FUEL REPROCESSING EFFLUENT

--Dispersion of the radionuclides zirconium-95,
niobium-95, and ruthenium-106 after their discharge to sea was studied, using *Porphyra umbili-
calis* as an indicator organism to integrate short-
term fluctuations in the sea-water concentrations
of the nuclides. It was found that, compared with
ruthenium-106, the dispersion of zirconium-95 and
niobium-95 was restricted and their rate of removal from the sea water to the bottom deposits by
chemical processes was greater than the rate of
mixing of the sea water immediately around the
point of discharge with more distant sea water.
Ref: *J-73   13,:1093-1103, 1967.*

3.0 - 232
Hanes, N. Bruce and White, Thomas M.   (1968).
EFFECTS OF SEAWATER CONCENTRATION ON OXYGEN
UPTAKE OF A BENTHAL SYSTEM
--Laboratory studies of the effects of percentages
of seawater varying from 0 to 100 percent on the
oxygen uptake of benthic deposits have shown that
a slight increase in oxygen-uptake rate occurs
with increased concentrations of seawater. The
time for a system to reach zero dissolved oxygen
decreases with increased seawater concentration.
The lag period of the oxygen-uptake curve was 6-
10 hr for all experiments and was unrelated to
seawater concentration. Addition of BOD nutrients
increased the oxygen uptake at all concentrations
of seawater. Exclusion of seawater from a portion
of a river should not increase the oxygen demand
of the bottom muds. Ref: *J-1   40(8):R272-R280,
Aug 1968. 14 refs.*

3.0 - 233
Hanks, R. W. (1966).   OBSERVATIONS OF "MILKY
WATER" IN CHESAPEAKE BAY
--A report of the occurrence of pollution along the
shores of Chesapeake Bay, Md., owing to the decomposition of *Ulva lactuca* (sea lettuce) which had
become detached and was concentrated in large
patches through the action of wind and tide. The
products of decomposition caused the water to become nearly opaque and cream in color, with a dissolved-oxygen content as low as 4.1 ppm. Hydrogen
sulphide liberated during decomposition caused local complaints, and fish mortalities were noticed.
Ref: *J-25   7(3):175-176, Fall 1966.*

3.0 - 234
Hansen, Donald V. and Rattray, Maurice, Jr.
(1965).   GRAVITATIONAL CIRCULATION IN STRAITS AND
ESTUARIES
--A coupled set of partial differential equations
and associated boundary condition is written to
describe circulation and salt-flux processes for
estuaries in which turbulent mixing results primarily from tidal currents. Similarity solutions,
motivated by characteristic salinity distributions
observed in estuaries, are obtained for this set
of equations and are compared with observational
data. The circulation is separated into modes ana-
logous to the barotropic, baroclinic, and Ekman
modes of oceanic circulation. The salinity distribution, although coupled to the velocity distribution, is found to vary independently of it as
well. The theoretical results are discussed in regard to: (1) correlation between the vertical variations of mean velocity and salinity, (2) the
role of this correlation in maintaining the
steady-state salinity distribution in estuaries,

and (3) some implications for computations of flushing and dispersion of contaminants. Ref: J-20 23(2):104-122, May 15, 1965. 22 refs.

3.0 - 235
Hanson, P. J. (1967). VERTICAL DISTRIBUTION OF RADIOACTIVITY IN THE COLUMBIA RIVER ESTUARY
--In studies on gamma-emitting radionuclides in the Columbia Estuary, a system was devised for the simultaneous collection of samples and in-situ measurement of salinity and turbidity; salinity and temperature were measured by a portable battery-operated induction salinometer, and turbidity by a self-contained light-transmission meter. Preliminary results indicated that particulate chromium-51 and zinc-65 increased with depth, and the percentage of radioacitve particulate matter was related to turbidity. Dissolved chromium-51 appeared to vary inversely with salinity, but dissolved zinc-65 showed no linear relation with salinity. Ref: Oregon State Univ. Thesis 77 p., 1967.

3.0 - 236
Hardy, J. P. L. (1967). SEA POLLUTION BY HYDROCARBONS AND ITS BIOLOGICAL CONSEQUENCES
--Reviews the sources of oil pollution of the sea and indicates the extent of such pollution throughout the world, including certain European coasts which suffer from chronic pollution. The effects of oil pollution are discussed, including lowering of the surface tension of the water, inhibition of gas exchange, and toxicity to algae, marine organisms, and sea birds. Ref: J-60 6(50):123-128, 1967.

3.0 - 237
Harleman, Donald R. F. (1966). DIFFUSION PROCESS IN STRATIFIED FLOW
--Presents various analytical methods for steady and unsteady one-dimensional convective diffusion in both homogeneous and stratified flow systems. In addition, analytical and experimental information on diffusion coefficients and correlations with mean-flow parameters are discussed. Ref: In Book. Estuary and Coastline Hydrodynamics. Chap. 12, p. 575-597, 1966. (See 3.0 - 270)

3.0 - 238
Harleman, Donald R. F. (1966). POLLUTION IN ESTUARIES
--This chapter is primarily concerned with the more common type of mixed estuary; however, the effect of vertical salinity gradients is an important factor in the mixing process. Since 1950 pollution analysis has developed within the framework of diffusion and mass-transfer theory. Probably the greatest single difficulty in analysis of estuarine mixing lies in recognizing the importance of distinguishing the different mixing mechanisms in regions of constant density from those in regions of variable density. Some of the analytical methods are considered in detail. Ref: In Book. Estuary and Coastline Hydrodynamics. Chap. 14, p. 630-647, 1966. (See 3.0 - 270)

3.0 - 239
Harleman, Donald R. F. (1969). MECHANICS OF CONDENSER-WATER DISCHARGE FROM THERMAL-POWER PLANTS
--This paper is concerned with the disposal of heated condenser water from thermal or nuclear-power plants into an adjacent waterway. The objective is to discuss some of the techniques and to show the degree of flexibility in controlling conditions in the waterway which is available to the engineer. Considered are the stratification of the condenser-water discharge and complete mixing. In the discussion of NORMAN H. BROOKS attention is centered on surface-spreading of hot water with minimal mixing and extensive jet-mixing of the effluent with the receiving water. Ref: P-30b Chapter 5:144-176, 1969.

3.0 - 240
Harleman, Donald R. F.; Holley, E. R. and Huber, W. C. (1967). INTERPRETATION OF WATER POLLUTION DATA FROM TIDAL ESTUARY MODELS
--Models have been developed for longitudinal concentration distributions for both instantaneous and continuous injection of pollutants into an estuarine flow. The 'slack-time' approximation, which neglects the tidal velocity, is valid in the case of instantaneous injection, but not in the case of continuous injection. The appropriate mathematical model for the concentration distribution can be fitted to the measured concentrations to determine the longitudinal dispersion coefficient for a hydraulic model. Ref: P-9 3,:49-63, 1967.

3.0 - 241
Harleman, Donald R. F.; Lee, Chok-Hung and Hall, L. C. (1968). NUMERICAL STUDIES OF UNSTEADY DISPERSION IN ESTUARIES
--A one-dimensional mathematical model is developed which describes the longitudinal concentration distribution of a pollutant in an estuary. It is applied to the upper portion of the Potomac Estuary and the results are compared with field observation. The predicted concentration distributions are in reasonable agreement with the measured values. The importance of nonlinear tidal motion effects is described in relation to the distribution of pollutants in estuaries. Ref: J-3 94(SA5 Paper 6160):897-911, Oct 1968. 9 refs.

3.0 - 242
Harvey, George W. (1966). MICRO-LAYER COLLECTION FROM THE SEA SURFACE: A NEW METHOD AND INITIAL RESULTS
--An illustrated description is given of the design and operation of an apparatus for sampling surface layers of water, approximately 60μ thick, which are collected from the surface of a rotating cylinder by means of a wiper blade. Samples collected contained considerably more bacteria and organic material than occurred in bucket samples taken at a depth of about 10 cm off the California coast. Ref: J-41 11(4):608-613, Oct 1966.

3.0 - 243
Hata, Y.; Kadota, H.; Miyoshi, H. and Kimata, M. (1965). MICROBIAL PRODUCTION OF SULPHIDES IN POLLUTED COASTAL AND ESTUARINE REGIONS
--Investigations were reported on the mechanism of the microbial production of sulphides in sea water, with particular reference to the effects of organic (pulp-mill) drainage on the distribution of sulphate-reducing bacteria in coastal regions and in estuaries in Japan. The production of sulphides

is limited by the supply of sulphates in the fresh-water part of the estuary, but mainly by the availability of organic matter in the saline part, while sulphide production is most vigorous in the brackish-water part where both sulphates and organic matter are present in high concentrations. Ref: *P-10 3,:287-302, 1965.*

3.0 - 244
Hawkes, H. A. and discussion by Welch, Eugene B. (1969).   ECOLOGICAL CHANGES OF APPLIED SIGNIFICANCE INDUCED BY THE DISCHARGE OF HEATED WATERS
--Sets forth certain fundamental ecological principles and then considers the importance of temperature as a factor determining the structure and functions of aquatic communities. The ways in which induced ecological changes may be of applied significance are considered. Results of laboratory experimental work and field surveys are reviewed in assessing the degree of change induced by thermal discharges. In the discussion of EUGENE B. WELCH observed and potential biological effects of heated water in the Tennessee Valley are described to indicate problems of data interpretation. Planned research in TVA to provide needed experimental results are briefly outlined. Ref: *P-30b Chap. 2:15-71, 1969. 84 refs.*

3.0 - 245
Hedgpeth, Joel W. (1967).   ASPECTS OF THE ESTUARINE ECOSYSTEM
--Following description of the estuarine ecosystem, it is suggested that such a value as gross photosynthesis is not a good indicator in itself of the state of this complex system. The factors which cause the decline of productivity and ecological health of several major estuarine ecosystems are identified as: alteration of river flow, changing shorelines by filling, and pollution. Ref: *P-33*

3.0 - 246
Hedgpeth, Joel W. and Gonor, Jefferson J. (1969). ASPECTS OF THE POTENTIAL EFFECT OF THERMAL ALTERATION ON MARINE AND ESTUARINE BENTHOS
--States that one of the difficulties in interpreting temperature effects is that we may not have enough information concerning the temperature regime in which many marine organisms actually live. Presents an eclectic review of the literature and evaluates the examples and approaches as they relate to an understanding of the effect of both naturally and artificially induced environmental temperature regimes on the marine benthos. Recommendations are made on the types of information and studies needed to evaluate the effects of thermal effluents on the marine biota and possibly to establish criteria for the control of such effluents. Ref: *P-30 p. 80-132, 1969. 91 refs.*

3.0 - 247
Hellmann, H.; Klein, K. and Knopp, H.   (1966). INVESTIGATIONS INTO THE SUITABILITY OF EMULSIFYING AGENTS FOR THE REMOVAL OF OIL FROM WATER
--The authors give illustrated and graphical results of studies on the degradability of various emulsified mineral oils using different emulsibying agents, in which they determined the nature of the emulsions, the emulsifying capacity of various emulsifying agents, the stability of motor-

oil emulsions in sea water and in drinking water with and without emulsifying agents, the dependence of motor-oil decay on pH value and on temperature, and the effects of oil emulsions, stabilized with a known emulsifying agent in completely demineralized waters or water containing sodium chloride or a high concentration of hydrochloric acid. Analytical results were compared with the microscopic findings, showing that there was good agreement between the analytical results and the globular structure of the emulsions. Ref: *J-78 10,:29-35, 60-70, 1966.*

3.0 - 248
Herman, S. S.; Mihursky, J. A. and McErlean, A. J. (1968).   ZOOPLANKTON AND ENVIRONMENTAL CHARACTERISTICS OF THE PATUXENT RIVER ESTUARY 1963-1965
--This study is part of a multidisciplinary effort designed to evaluate the ecological effects of heated discharge water from a steam electric station upon the Patuxent River ecosystem. Ref: *J-25 9(2):67-82, June 1968.*

3.0 - 249
Hetling, Leo J. (1968). WATER QUALITY MODELS OF THE ESTUARY
--Reviews three water quality models of the Potomac Estuary. They described the causal connections between dissolved oxygen concentrations in the estuary and the natural and man-made forces which affected them. The models were used to forecast the consequences of management activities at sewage treatment plants in the estuary. Ref: *Book. Range of Choice in Water Management: A Study of Dissolved Oxygen in the Potomac Estuary. The Johns Hopkins Press. p. 141-149, 1968.*

3.0 - 250
Hetling, Leo J. and O'Connell, Richard L. (1965). ESTIMATING DIFFUSION CHARACTERISTICS OF TIDAL WATERS
--Several proposed methods for estimating a diffusion coefficient for tidal waters are described. In each case, the turbulent analog of the Fickian coefficient of molecular diffusion is used. Ref: *J-4 112(10):378-380, Oct 1965.*

3.0 - 251
Hidu, H. (1965).   EFFECTS OF SYNTHETIC SURFACTANTS ON LARVAE OF CLAMS *M. MERCENARIA* AND OYSTERS *C. VIRGINICA*
--Reports two tests to evaluate the effect of surfactants on rapidly developing larvae of bivalve mollusks (clams and oysters). Ref: *J-1 37(2):262-270, Feb 1965.*

3.0 - 252
Hill, W. F.; Hamblet, F. E. and Benton, W. H. (1969).   INACTIVATION OF POLIOVIRUS TYPE 1 BY THE KELLY-PURDY ULTRAVIOLET SEA-WATER TREATMENT UNIT
--The use of the Kelly-Purdy ultraviolet unit to inactivate poliovirus in continuously-flowing sea water was investigated and compared with the results of a control experiment in which sea water contaminated with poliovirus was exposed in dishes to ultraviolet radiation. For a maximal flow rate of 144 litres per min and exposure for 11.7 sec, the unit effected a poliovirus reduction of over 99.9 per cent, and is considered to be suitable for treating sea water for purification of shell-

fish. Ref: J-31 17(1):1-6, Jan 1969.

3.0 - 253
Hobbie, John E. (1966). PLANKTON HETEROTROPHY
IN A NORTH CAROLINA ESTUARY
--It was found that glucose and acetate were taken
up by bacterial uptake systems and that the uptake
rate could be analyzed by the equations of enzyme
kinetics. The maximum uptake velocity was a good
indication of relative heterotrophic activity, and
reached a peak during the summer in the Pamlico
River Estuary. This parameter was a rapid and sensitive indicator of eutrophication as peaks of
activity found in a 30 km survey were correlated
with domestic wastes and effluent from phosphate
mining activity. Ref: Univ. of North Carolina.
Water Resources Research Institute Rept. OWRR
Project A-015NC 9 p., Nov 1966. 9 refs.

3.0 - 254
Hoff, J. G. (1967). LETHAL OXYGEN CONCENTRATION
FOR THREE MARINE FISH SPECIES
--The author studied the oxygen requirements of 3
species of marine fish, held in sealed jars with
and without circulation of the water. At all three
temperatures tested, the lethal oxygen levels were
similar for all three species, ranging from 1.03
to 1.36 mg per litre at 25°C, and from 0.87 to
0.93 mg at 18.5°C, and from 0.66 to 0.77 mg at
12°C. There was a statistically significant difference in oxygen consumption between winter flounder
kept at 25°C in jars in which the water was static
and those kept in jars in which the water was cir-
culated; this is attributed to the fact that this
temperature is near the 24-hr TL_m value for this
species, and that circulation of the water disturbed these fish at all temperatures, by occasion-
ally lifting them from the bottom of the jars,
thus causing additional stress and increased oxygen consumption. Ref: J-1 39(2):267-277,
Feb 1967.

3.0 - 255
Holme, Norman A. (1969). EFFECTS OF "TORREY
CANYON" POLLUTION ON MARINE LIFE
--A cargo of 118,000 long tons of Kuwait crude oil
carried by the "Torrey Canyon" was released on to
the sea March 18, 1967. The oil drifted off in
three masses. The oil polluted the north coast of
France, Guernsey and the west Cornish Coast. Brief
comments are made .on the efforts to deal with the
resulting pollution of these areas. Ref: P-14
p. 1-3, 1969. 2 refs.

3.0 - 256
Holmes, Robert W. (1969). SANTA BARBARA OIL
SPILL
--Presents a brief account of the nature of the
event and some of its effects. Notes that a number
of devices were employed to contain the oil, and a
variety of efforts were made to clean up the polluted beaches; the biological effects are being
studied. It is noted that floating oil affects the
coupling between the winds and the sea surface,
prevents evaporation, inhibits gaseous exchange
between the atmosphere and sea, changes the albedo
of the sea surface, and modifies the quality and
amount of solar radiation penetrating the sea surface. Ref: P-14 p. 15-27, 1969.

3.0 - 257

Hom, Leonard W. (1968). REMOTE SENSING OF WATER
POLLUTION
--Remote-sensing devices, primarily those based on
imaging with portions of the electromagnetic spectrum, can be valuable tools for sensing water pollution and protecting water resources. Multiband
spectral reconnaissance, in which information from
several portions of the spectrum is used to interpret the condition of land and water, is particularly useful because it enables the interpreter to
identify a feature by its 'tone signature', the
unique set of tones that feature will produce in
the several bands in which is it imaged. Bands may
include thermal infrared and radar, as well as
more usual photographic ranges. Other applications
of remote sensing to water pollution may be made
with microwaves, airborne magnetics, input electro-
magnetics, gamma-ray spectrometry, chemical vapor
detection, and fluorescent processes. This method
supplements, but does not replace, normal field
methods. Ref: J-1 40(10):1728-1738, Oct 1968.
7 refs.

3.0 - 258
Horton, Donald B.; Kueuzler, Edward J. and Woods,
William J. (1967). CURRENT STUDIES IN PAMLICO
RIVER AND ESTUARY OF NORTH CAROLINA
--Tracer studies using Rhodamine dye were made in
Pamlico River Estuary during the summer of 1967.
Studies were also made on tidal effects, river
flow, salinity, dispersion, diffusion and flushing
time. Ref: Univ. of North Carolina. Water Re-
sources Research Inst. 21 p., July 1967. 7 refs.

3.0 - 259
Hoult, David P. (1969). OIL ON THE SEA:
SYMPOSIUM ON THE SCIENTIFIC AND ENGINEERING
ASPECTS OF OIL POLLUTION OF THE SEA, PROCEEDINGS.
Sponsored by the Massachusetts Institute of Tech-
nology and Woods Hole Oceanographic Institution
and held at Cambridge, Mass., May 16, 1969.
Plenum Press. 114 pages.
--pertinent papers abstracted separately. Ref:
P-14 114 p., 1969. Book.

3.0 - 260
Hoult, David P. (1969). CONTAINMENT AND
COLLECTION DEVICES FOR OIL SLICKS
--The main engineering features of physical and
pneumatic booms operating as oil containment devices in the open sea are discussed. The oil containing capacity of a pneumatic boom is limited by
the power available to compress the air. It is
suggested that the containment capacity of physical booms is limited by the effective depth of the
boom. The results of preliminary experiments are
used to establish these ideas. A brief review of
the main types of collection systems in use is
given. Ref: Mass. Inst. of Tech. Fluid Mechanics
Lab. Pub. no. 69-8 18 p., Aug 1969. 5 refs.

3.0 - 261
Hulbert, E. M. (1968). STRATIFICATION AND MIXING
IN COASTAL WATERS OF THE WESTERN GULF OF MAINE
DURING SUMMER
--Results of a survey of the coastal waters of the
western Gulf of Maine in the summers of 1966 and
1967, during which temperatures, current veloci-
ties, and salinities were measured, are given.
Where low surface temperatures were found near
Cape Nedick, in the Sheepscot River, and adjoining

Vinalhaven Island in Penobscot Bay, these were the results of vertical mixing by tidal currents; and where high surface temperatures occurred, in the inner areas of Casco Bay and in offshore waters near Cape Ann, these were caused by reduced vertical mixing combined with favorable weather conditions. Temperature distribution profiles of coastal sections from Cape Ann to Isle au Haut Bay are shown. Ref: *J-32 25(12):2609-2621, Dec 1968.*

3.0 - 262
Hume, Norman B. and Garber, William F. (1966). MARINE DISPOSAL OF DIGESTED SCREENED WASTEWATER SOLIDS
--Study was made in relation to discharges by the Hyperion Treatment Plant of the city of Los Angeles, into Santa Monica Bay. The paper shows that the discharge of large amounts of digested solids has been accomplished with minimal measurable effect on the ocean environment. It outlines studies required to describe necessary onshore treatment procedures, and attempts to show that the present method is desirable. Finally, it outlines the direction of continuing studies and the type of additional information needed. Ref: *P-9 and J-1 38(3), March 1966.*

3.0 - 263
Hünnefeld, G. B. (1966). OIL POLLUTION IN SURFACE WATERS CAUSED BY THE OPERATION OF OUTBOARD MOTORS
--The contents including the results of investigations carried out at the Federal Institute of Hydrology, in Koblenz, Germany, have been published and were also presented at the 21st International Congress for Navigation in Stockholm, in 1965. The factors affecting water quality in rivers, lakes, and streams caused by oil, petroleum products, and water-soluble substances from outboard motors are discussed and measures introduced to prevent and control oil pollution of surface waters are summarized. (In German) Ref: *J-78 10,: 57-50, 1966.*

3.0 - 264
Ichiye, Takashi (1968). HYDROGRAPHY, TIDES AND TIDAL FLUSHING OF GREAT SOUTH BAY-SOUTH OYSTER BAY, LONG ISLAND
--Use of a tidal prism method predicts that six to eight tidal cycles are required to reduce the content ratio of a pollutant to ten per cent of the initial value in South Oyster Bay. If backflow of the pollutant is considered, 20 to 23 tidal cycles must occur. Diffusion equations averaged over cross sections of the bay system with the long channel tidal equations are applied to determine the flushing rate of South Oyster Bay. Flow charts for analog computers for determining change of pollutant concentration and transport with time are developed to predict and monitor pollution in several segments of the bay system. Ref: *P-25 p. 15-62, 1968. 29 refs. Also as: Contribution No. 1158, Lamont Geological Observatory.*

3.0 - 265
Iddings, Frank A. (1969). NUCLEAR METHODS IN AIR AND WATER POLLUTION ANALYSIS
--Basic principles and applications are discussed for the following nuclear techniques; isotope dilution, radiorelease, radioisotope derivative analysis, radiometric titration, study of analytical chemistry methods, tracing, radiation absorption, and activation analysis. Ref: *J-5 3(2):132-140, Feb 1969. 15 refs.*

3.0 - 266
Ingram, W. T. and Mitwally, H. (1966). PATHS OF POLLUTION IN NEW YORK HARBOR - MODEL STUDY
--The study utilized dye releases in model of New York Harbor to trace paths followed by pollutants discharged at particular points; influences of installed jetties and dikes on pollution paths and relationship between release concentrations of source of pollution developed by individual tests and those shown by simultaneous release from multiple sources were investigated; pollution sources were wastewater, treatment plants and stormwater overflows. This type of study is useful in predicting effects on pollution paths of changes in harbor configuration and waste discharge before such changes actually are made in prototype. Ref: *J-1 38(10):1563-1581, Oct 1966.*

3.0 - 267
Ingram, William M; Mackenthun, K. M. and Bartsch, A. F. (1966). BIOLOGICAL FIELD INVESTIGATIVE DATA FOR WATER POLLUTION SURVEYS
--This book introduces the non-biologist to the life sciences as they relate to water pollution and its control. The professional biologist inexperienced in water pollution investigations will find the book a quick introduction to field studies. A list of 467 references will provide valuable sources of information for both groups. Ref: *Federal Water Pollution Control Administration WP-13 139 p., 1966. 467 refs.*

3.0 - 268
International Atomic Energy Agency (1966). DISPOSAL OF RADIOACTIVE WASTES INTO SEAS, OCEANS, AND SURFACE WATERS
--This publication contains the full text, with discussions, of the 56 papers presented at a symposium on the disposal of radioactive wastes into sea water and surface waters, held in Vienna in May 1966. The various sessions at the symposium dealt with the physical and biological transport of radionuclides in water, evaluation of the principle routes by which radioactivity discharged to sea and surface waters can affect humans, and the possible effects of such disposal on marine and freshwater resources. Ref: *International Atomic Energy Agency STI/PUB/126 Vienna 908 p., 1966.*

3.0 - 269
International Assoc. on Water Pollution Research (1967). ADVANCES IN WATER POLLUTION RESEARCH. PROCEEDINGS OF THE 3RD INTERNATIONAL CONFERENCE HELD IN MUNICH, GERMANY, IN SEPT. 1966. VOLS 1-3
--These three volumes contain the full text, with discussions, of papers presented at the 3rd international conference on water pollution research held in Munich in Sept. 1966. Topics dealt with included the effects of pollutants on aquatic organisms, methods of sewage and waste treatment, and surveys of polluted waters. Abstracted in J-1, 39(3), 1966. Filed under individual author's names in this bibliography. Ref: *P-9 Vols. 1-3 394 p., 428 p., 374 p., 1967. (Water Pollution Control Federation Administration, Washington, D. C. $40).*

3.0 - 270
Ippen, A. T. (1966).   ESTUARY AND COASTLINE HYDRODYNAMICS
--This publication, based on a course of lectures held at the Massachusetts Institute of Technology, is intended as a textbook for those interested in problems of near-shore oceanography and coastal engineering. Aspects considered, by individual authors, include basic wave theory; generation, refraction, diffraction, and reflection of waves and their interaction with structures; hurricane surges; harbor resonance; coastal processes; seawater intrusion into rivers; tidal dynamics, pollution, mixing, and sedimentation in estuaries; and the use of coastal, estuarine, tidal and salinity models. Pertinent papers abstracted and included under individual author's name. Ref: Book. *McGraw-Hill Book Co., Inc., New York, 1966. 762 p. $28.50.*

3.0 - 271
Irukayama, Katsuro (1966). POLLUTION OF MINAMATA BAY AND MINAMATA DISEASE
--This study has shown that the causative agent of Minamata disease was methylmercury chloride, which was discharged from the acetaldehyde plant of the Minamata Factory and accumulated directly in the fish and shellfish in the bay water. Ref: *P-9 and J-1 38(3), March 1966. (abstract only)*

3.0 - 272
Isaacs, John D. and Schmitt, Walter R.   (1969). STIMULATION OF MARINE PRODUCTIVITY WITH WASTE HEAT AND MECHANICAL POWER
--Waste heat energy could be employed to raise nutrient-rich seawater from depth to the surface to enhance the production of animal protein. With dissolved phosphorus as the enrichment indicator, fertilization effects are calculated for various biological equilibria in the food chain. Ref: *J-79 33(1):20-29, Nov 1969. 10 refs.*

3.0 - 273
Iwai, S. and others   (1968).   SURVEY AND PREDICTION OF POLLUTION AT THE OMUTA INDUSTRIAL HARBOUR
--Following the enlargement of Omuta Harbor (Japan) and reclamation activities in the vicinity, models were made to predict the pollution problems to follow. Omuta is a heavily industrialized coal mining area and numerous factories utilize coal in their operations. It was feared that the additional activities would increase the pollution in the harbor and its vicinity. Ref: *P-8 and J-12 p. 126, 1968.*

3.0 - 274
Jagger, H. (1969).   WORK OF THE OIL INDUSTRY IN PREVENTING SEA POLLUTION
--Outlines the steps already taken by the oil industry both to reduce pollution of the sea by oil and to clear up any oil spills which do occur; the additional research and development which is being undertaken to reduce further the chance of pollution and minimize the effects of accidental spills; and the proposed plan to reimburse national governments when pollution is caused by tanker operations. Ref: *P-21 6 p., 1969.*

3.0 - 275
James, A. (1965).   BACTERIAL POLLUTION OF THE

RIVER TYNE ESTUARY
--A progress report of work being carried out by the Public Health Engineering Section, University of Newcastle-upon-Tyne, in connection with investigations on the pattern of bacterial distribution in the Tyne Estuary and the sea water around its mouth. It is concluded that in the lower layers there is a net movement upstream of organic matter and bacteria which are subsequently mixed with incoming fresh water at the head of the estuary and returned downstream; in the upper layers, maximal bacterial pollution occurs at high tide (with the exception of the upper parts of the estuary which are beyond the reach of the incoming polluted material). Ref: *P-1 p. 185-194, 1965.*

3.0 - 276
Jeffrey, S. W. (1965).   PAPER CHROMATOGRAPHIC SEPARATION OF PIGMENTS IN MARINE PHYTOPLANKTON
--Qualitative analyses of pigments in phytoplankton from Port Hacking, Australia, were carried out by paper chromatography. In the sea-water samples, chlorophylls a and c and carotene, fucoxanthin, and yellow zanthophylls were always found. In benthic samples chlorophylls a and c, carotene, and fucoxanthin were always present; samples from a depth of 50 m contained phytoplankton, the major pigments being carotene, chlorophyllide a, and astaxanthin; samples from depths of 100 and 200 m contained mainly diatoms and fragmented cells, the major pigments being the same as in the 50-m samples. The 2 main types of chlorophyll degradation products found in the plankton were chlorophyllides and pheophytins. Ref: *J-33 16(2):307-313, 1965.*

3.0 - 277
Jeffries, Harry Perry (1967). CHEMICAL RESPONSES BY MARINE ORGANISMS TO STRESS PHASE I.
--Responses are measured in terms of homeostatic adjustments of free amino acids, fatty acids, major lipid classes and blood proteins. Free amino acids in estuarine plankton are an index of the community's physiological condition and productive capacity. Since the important relationships in the seasonal behavior of major metabolites are understood at the community level, attention is focused on the responses of individual species to controlled conditions in the laboratory and in modified natural environments. Ref: *Rhode Island. Univ., Kingston. Ref. 67-4 76 p., 1967. 31 refs.*

3.0 - 278
Jenkins, David (1965).   DETERMINATION OF PRIMARY PRODUCTIVITY OF TURBID WATERS WITH CARBON 14
--Presents a method of productivity measurement for use in turbid waters in San Francisco Bay area. Carbon 14 is used as a tracer to measure the rate of incorporation of carbon into phytoplankton. This paper deals with a modification of older methods. Ref: *J-1 37(9):1281-1288, Sept 1965. 11 refs.*

3.0 - 279
Jenkins, David (1967).   ANALYSIS OF ESTUARINE WATERS
--Summarizes some of the methods and modifications developed for the determination in estuarine waters of suspended solids, chlorosity, dissolved silica, and nitrogen and phosphorus compounds, and for the preservation of samples for determination

of nitrogen and phosphorus. Methods have also been developed for the analysis of estuarine sediments to determine particle size distribution, total cation-exchange capacity, volatile matter, index of putrescibility, total sulphides, total nitrogen, and carbon. The accuracy and precision of these techniques when applied to the analysis of water and sediments in San Francisco Bay are summarized in tables. Ref: *J-1 39(2):159-180, Feb 1967. 27 refs.*

3.0 - 280
Jennings, C. D. (1966).   RADIOACTIVITY OF SEDIMENTS IN THE COLUMBIA RIVER ESTUARY
--The radioactivity of bottom deposits in the Columbia River was determined in situ by means of a gamma-ray detector, calibrated to give activity in pc per cm^2; the advantages of this method over those involving collection of samples and laboratory analyses are indicated. Since sediments concentrate radioactivity, those in the Columbia River contain more activity than the overlying water, and the benthic organisms are, therefore, exposed to a higher level of radiation. Chromium-51 and zinc-65 are the two most abundant artificial nuclides in the Columbia River; although the ratio between these nuclides varies, in general the chromium-51 activity of the sediments was found to be about 10 times as high as the zinc-65 activity. Other isotopes found, to a lesser extent, in the sediments were potassium-40, cobalt-60 and manganese-54. Ref: *Oregon State Univ. Thesis 62 p., 1966.*

3.0 - 281
Jennings, C. D. and Osterberg, C.   (1969). SEDIMENT RADIOACTIVITY IN THE COLUMBIA RIVER ESTUARY
--Results are given from studies on the radioactivity of sediments in the Columbia River Estuary and in a small tributary, Youngs River. The radioactivity varies widely in the estuary, as a result of the complex pattern of sediment deposition produced by the complex interactions between flow rate, salt-water intrusion, and shape of the estuary. The highest radioactivity was found in sediments in the protected areas in the upstream part of the estuary. From the mouth to the 3-km station the uptake of chromium on sediments is enhanced with respect to zinc, and an attempt is made to explain this phenomenon on the basis of the chemical behavior of chromium, since trivalent chromium is sorbed rapidly by the sediments and hexavalent chromium is sorbed more slowly; some sediments appear capable of reducing hexavalent chromium to the trivalent form and this is then sorbed rapidly. Ref: *P-3 p. 300-306, 1969.*

3.0 - 282
Johannes, R. E. (1965).   INFLUENCE OF MARINE PROTOZOA ON NUTRIENT REGENERATION
--The role of ciliates, flagellates, and bacteria in the regeneration of phosphorus from organic detritus in the marine environment is examined. Experiments showed that whereas little phosphorus was regenerated by bacteria alone, protozoa feeding on the bacteria released considerable quantities of dissolved inorganic phosphorus. Ref: *J-41 10(3):434-442, July 1965.*

3.0 - 283

Johns Hopkins University (1966).   STUDIES OF THE OCEANOGRAPHIC FACTORS AFFECTING THE USE OF NUCLEAR POWER SOURCES IN OR ADJACENT TO THE SEA. PROGRESS REPORT. OCTOBER 1, 1965 - JUNE 30, 1966.
--Studies are in progress on methods of evaluating potential hazards occurring as a result of deliberate or accidental discharge of radioactive materials into the sea from an existing or proposed nuclear installation, and present oceanographic knowledge has been used to develop equations for use in evaluating a series of offshore sites along the Atlantic coast of U.S.A. as possible locations for power sources on the ocean bottom. Studies have also been carried out on the effects of heated effluents discharged into estuarine or coastal waters on physical processes of movement and dispersion of radioactive materials, and it was concluded that maximal initial mechanical dilution of the heated effluent would be obtained by discharging the effluent as a jet having excess momentum as compared to the receiving waters. A relatively simple theoretical relation was developed for the dilution of the excess heat along the length of the plume as a function of the ratio of the discharge velocity to the velocity of the receiving waters and of the width of the discharge channel. Ref: *Johns Hopkins University. U. S. Atomic Energy Commission NYO-3109-19 9 p., 1966.*

3.0 - 284
Johnson, Bernard G. (1968).   PROPOSAL FOR A SYSTEMS ENGINEERING STUDY OF WATER POLLUTION ABATEMENT
--An outline of techniques and the approach to a water pollution abatement study of the Galveston Bay area is presented. The project approach, including the use of linear programming, simulation analysis and hydraulic modeling were discussed. Ref: *J-80 30(3):185-189, March 1968.*

3.0 - 285
Johnson, Donald W. (1968). PESTICIDES AND FISHES - A REVIEW OF SELECTED LITERATURE
--This is a review of the literature and critique of research to date on pesticide interactions in aquatic habitats. Thirty-four pesticides are discussed in terms of mean lethal concentrations. Consideration is given to: factors affecting toxicity; pesticide residues; effects of pesticides on fishes; and effects on and in aquatic food chain. Emphasis is placed on the need for studies of ecological and physiological effects of sublethal quantities, in order that realistic tolerance limits of toxic pollutants may be established. Ref: *J-23 97(4):398-424, Oct 1968. 156 refs.*

3.0 - 286
Johnson, M. G. and Matheson, D. H.   (1968). MACRO-INVERTEBRATE COMMUNITIES OF THE SEDIMENTS OF HAMILTON BAY AND ADJACENT LAKE ONTARIO
--Hamilton Bay, a natural harbor at the western end of Lake Ontario and connected to the lake by a canal, receives the run-off from a small watershed and discharges of various trade waste waters and sewage effluent. Studies were carried out to determine the distribution and abundance of benthic macro-invertebrates in the bay and in adjacent parts of Lake Ontario in relation to this pollution and to hydrodynamic factors. The deep sediments in the bay, rich in organic matter, contained considerable numbers of the oligochaetes

Limnodrilus hoffmeisteri and *Tubifex tubifex,*
while smaller numbers of 5 species of *Limnodrilus*
were found in the poorer sub-littoral sediments.
No macro-invertebrates were found in sediments
containing more than 25 per cent ferric oxide (resulting from the discharge of waste waters from 2
large steel plants). Near the canal connecting the
bay with the lake, more favorable conditions of
water chemistry, circulation, and moderately rich
sediments resulted in an increase in the biomass
of oligochaetes over that in the main basin of the
bay. In the adjacent waters of Lake Ontario there
was a more varied benthic fauna, but the specific
composition of the macro-invertebrate communities
was markedly influenced by the 'plume' of bay
water entering the lake. Ref: *J-41 13(1):99-
111, Jan 1968.*

3.0 - 287
Johnson, V. G. (1966). RETENTION OF ZINC-65 BY
COLUMBIA RIVER SEDIMENT
--The relative importance of ion exchange and
specific sorption as mechanisms of the uptake of
zinc-65 by sediments in the Columbia River was investigated, and the exchangeable zinc-65 fraction
and the effect of sea water on gamma-emitters
sorbed on the sediment were determined simultaneously be elution with synthetic sea water in the
field immediately after collection of the samples,
while specifically-sorbed zinc-65 was determined
by elution with a dilute solution of copper sulphate. Less than 5 per cent of the zinc-65 sorbed
on the sediment was found to be exchangeable, but
35-54 per cent could be displaced with copper sulphate. This was shown to be due to the greater affinity of copper for the specific sorption sites
rather than to ion-exchange displacement or effects of pH value. Ref: *Oregon State Univ.
Thesis 56 p., 1966.*

3.0 - 288
Josa, Fernando (1966). BASES FOR OUTFALL DESIGN
ON THE MEDITERRANEAN COAST
--Reports an investigation to provide information
on the nearshore characteristics in the vicinity
of Barcelona to guide the engineer in the improved
design of outfall systems. Ref: *P-9 and J-1
38(3), March 1966. (abstract only).*

3.0 - 289
Josephs, Walter J. (1970). TIDAL FLUSHING SYSTEM
--A system for the environmental improvement of a
bay or similar body of water subject to tidal flow.
The system includes a circulation channel extending along the periphery of the bay, with the channel having controllable gates, permitting selective ingress and egress of water to and from the
channel. At high tide, for example, water may enter the channel adjacent the closed end of the
bay, pass thru the channel, and be discharged at
the open end of the bay when the water level between the channel and this latter portion of the
bay permits such egress. Conversely, water can be
accumulated in the channel at high tide at the
closed end of the bay and discharged through the
same gates at the closed end of the bay at low
tide. In the first instance, improved circulation
of the water in the bay will result, and in the
second instance, build-up of sand or silt due to
incoming tides are pushed back, and a harbor
mouth, for example, may be kept open for shipping.

Ref: *U. S. Patent No. 3,492,822. Not assigned.
1970.*

3.0 - 290
Juliano, David W. (1969). REAERATION
MEASUREMENTS IN AN ESTUARY
--Measurements of surface reaeration are presented
for the Sacramento-San Joaquin Delta. Estimates of
reaeration were computed from observed diurnal
dissolved oxygen changes in the estuary. The reaeration constants computed in this manner varied
between 0.16 and 3.91 grams per cu m per hr at 0%
saturation. Independent in-situ measurements using
gasometeric and disturbed equilibrium methods were
conducted for comparison. Reaeration constants
varied from 0.64 to 2.84 gm per cu m per hr using
the gasometeric method. The disturbed equilibrium
method yielded reaeration constants between 0.62
and 1.70 gm per cu m per hr. The independent methods showed reaeration constants to be highly variable. Surface turbulence proved to be the most
important mechanisms controlling reaeration constants in the estuary. Wind velocity was the sing-
ularly most significant parameter in causing surface turbulence. Ref: *J-3 95(SA6 Paper 6987):
1165-1178, Dec 1969.*

3.0 - 291
Kadota, H. and Miyoshi, H. (1965). HETEROTROPHY
OF SULPHATE-REDUCING BACTERIA IN MARINE AND
ESTUARIAL SEDIMENTS
--Studies were made to determine the role of organic material in the nutritional physiology and
heterotrophic metabolism of sulphate-reducing bacteria. Results are summarized, including the amino
acids and other substances required for maximal
growth. It appeared that differences between the
fresh- and salt-water strains as regards their
pattern of utilization of organic compounds as
sources of carbon or as electron donors were
closely related to the differences between the two
groups as regards the permeability of cell mem-
branes. From tracer experiments using radioactive
carbon, it was found that some organic acids were
utilized by these bacteria as substrates for the
biosynthesis of cell constituents. The results of
these experiments explain the mechanism by which
organic matter participates in the microbial production of sulphides in marine and estuarine sediments. Ref: *P-1 p. 205-206, 1965.*

3.0 - 292
Kaelin, Joseph Richard (1969). SYSTEM FOR
SURFACE AERATION OF LIQUID
--A system for surface aeration of water, particularly for aeration or cleaning the waters in
rivers, lakes, creeks, or along beaches and
shores, by means of an aeration rotor mounted on
a floating carrier frame for at least partial immersion into the water to be aerated, said carrier
frame being arranged to be anchored at any desired
location along a shore where the water is to be
aerated. Ref: *U. S. Patent No. 3,462,132. Not
assigned. 1969.*

3.0 - 293
Kahn, Lloyd and Brezenski, Francis T. (1967).
DETERMINATION OF NITRATE IN ESTUARINE WATERS.
COMPARISON OF A HYDRAZINE REDUCTION AND A BRUCINE
PROCEDURE AND MODIFICATION OF A BRUCINE PROCEDURE
--A hydrazine reduction method and a brucine me-

thod were evaluated for the determination of nitrate in estuarine waters. This method gave low results in many instances, which were attributed to the consumption of the available hydrazine by environmental impurities, resulting in the incomplete reduction of the nitrate to nitrite. The brucine method as described by JENKINS and MEDSKER was modified to give more consistent analytical calibration curves which followed the Beer-Lambert law from 0 to 0.6 mg of nitrate nitrogen per liter. The devious behavior of the calibration curves obtained by alternative brucine procedures is explained. The precision of the recommended procedure is better than 0.03 mg of nitrate nitrogen per liter. Ref: *J-5 1(6):488-491, June 1967. 18 refs.*

3.0 - 294
Kahn, Lloyd and Brezenski, Francis T.   (1967). DETERMINATION OF NITRATE IN ESTUARINE WATERS. AUTOMATIC DETERMINATION USING A BRUCINE METHOD
--This paper indicates that automation of the brucine method for nitrate determination described by KAHN and BREZENSKI on the Technicon Auto-Analyzer resulted in a twofold improvement of precision. The automated procedure is capable of analyzing 100 samples in 7 hours with a standard deviation of less than 0.01 mg of nitrate nitrogen per liter. Ref: *J-5 1(6):492-494, June 1967. 9 refs.*

3.0 - 295
Karinen, J. F.; Lamberton, J. G.,; Stewart. N.E. and Terriere, L. C. (1967).   PERSISTENCE OF CARBARYL IN THE MARINE ESTUARINE ENVIRONMENT. CHEMICAL AND BIOLOGICAL STABILITY IN AQUARIUM SYSTEMS
--Colorimetric and radiometric analyses were used to study the persistence of carbaryl (1-naphthyl-N-methylcarbamate) in estuarine water and mud in laboratory aquaria at 8° and 20°C. In the absence of mud there was a 50 per cent decrease in carbaryl concentration in 38 days at 8°C, most of the decrease being due to the production of 1-naphthol. At 20°C the carbaryl had almost completely disappeared after 17 days, with about 43 per cent being converted to 1-naphthol. In the presence of mud the concentrations of both carbaryl and 1-napthol in the sea water fell to less than 10 per cent in 10 days, and both compounds were adsorbed by the mud, in which decomposition continued more slowly. Tests with carbaryl labeled with carbon-14 showed that decomposition occurred by hydrolysis of the carbamate and oxidation of the naphthyl ring; only 40 per cent of the radioactive carbon was recovered as carbon dioxide and it is thought that the remainder was evolved as methane. In a preliminary field experiment in which part of a mud flat was treated with carbaryl at rates similar to those used to control pests in oyster beds, carbaryl could be detected in the mud for 42 days but 1-naphthol persisted in significant amounts for only 1 day. Ref: *J-81 15(1):148-156, 1967.*

3.0 - 296
Kariya, Teiji; Akiba, Reiko; Suzuki, Shuko and Tsuda, Tsutomu (1967). STUDIES ON THE POST-MORTEM IDENTIFICATION OF THE POLLUTANT IN THE FISH KILLED BY WATER POLLUTION. IV. DETECTION OF CYANIDE IN THE FISH
--A study of lethal doses of potassium cyanide.

The Pirizin-Pirazoren method was used in the identification of cyanide in dead fish. (In Japanese) English abstract. Ref: *J-28 33(4):311-314, April 1967.*

3.0 - 297
Kautsky, H. (1966).   POSSIBLE ACCUMULATION OF DISCRETE RADIOACTIVE ELEMENTS IN RIVER MOUTHS
--It was found that limited areas of increased radioactivity were present in the bottom deposits at certain points in the outer mouth of the Elbe Estuary. The isotopes identified included barium-140 and zirconium-95 and it was assumed that these isotopes originated from fallout and had been transported out to sea by the river. The main deposition of suspended solids, however, takes place upstream from Cuxhaven, in the area of mixing of river and sea waters. To explain the increased deposition of radioactive material in the outer estuary, it was assumed that elements of low solubility, such as zirconium, barium, and cerium, are mostly associated with the finer particles of suspended matter and these are deposited mainly in the outer Elbe; this was confirmed by examination of suspended solids from the river and of the radioactivity associated with them. Many of these sparingly soluble isotopes are among the biologically-essential heavy metals, and may, therefore, cause an increased radiation hazard to marine flora and fauna in the mouths of estuaries. Ref: *P-4 p. 163-175, 1966.*

3.0 - 298
Kehrer, W. S. (1966).   AERIAL SURVEY OF THE CONTAMINATED OCEAN SURFACE AT OPERATION WIGWAM, WITH DOSE RATE CONTOUR LINES THROUGH D+4 DAYS
--Aerial survey was utilized to measure the radiation intensities above the contaminated pool at Operation Wigwam. These field data were used to provide a detailed analysis of the radiation field at 3 ft. above the surface through D+4 days, and to determine the hazard to personnel on board ships traversing the area. Ref: *U. S. Naval Radiological Defense Lab., San Francisco, Calif. Rept. no. USNRDL-TR-981, Feb 1966. 54 p.*

3.0 - 299
Keil R. (1966). BACTERIAL STATE OF HARBOUR WATER
--Bacteriological examination of samples of water from Rostock Harbor, Germany, from October 1963 to August 1964, showed that 37 out of 64 samples contained salmonellae, *Salm. paratyphi B* being the type most often detected. Types of phage present in the harbor water corresponded well with strains from chronic carriers. Faecal *Esch. coli* were found in 34 out of 42 samples. The average colony count was lower during the colder months of the year. Ref: *J-83 58(4):49-53, 1966.*

3.0 - 300
Keller, Alan (1968). BAHAMAS BEACHES SAVED FROM OIL POLLUTION
--Reports that chemical dispersants were used to prevent oil, discharged during a tanker accident, from reaching the beaches of the Eleuthera Island. The companies that participated in the clean up are identified. Ref: *J-84 49(573):100-102, July 1968.*

3.0 - 301
Kempf, T.; Lüdemann, D. and Pflaum, W.   (1967).

POLLUTION OF WATERS BY MOTORIZED OPERATIONS, ESPECIALLY BY OUTBOARD MOTORS
--Details are given of extensive investigations into the polluting effects of underwater exhausts from outboard motors and mineral oils, carried out under the auspices of the Bundesministerium für Gesundheitswesen, Germany. Tabulated and graphical data from field and laboratory experiments show the damage to fish and other aquatic organisms caused by motor and diesel oils, petrol and other organic solvents and their immiscibility with water. The ecological differentiation of microorganisms, such as diatoms and rotatoria, showed that oil-tanker accidents, liberating diesel oil, resulted in either total destruction of aquatic organisms or reduction of some species, but in certain favorable locations some species survived while others were able to tolerate the oil-water emulsion, resulting in only a small reduction in numbers, considered over the period of the annual cycle. Ref: *J-85 (26):48, 1967.*

3.0 - 302
Kennedy, V. S. and Mihursky, J. A. (1967). BIBLIOGRAPHY ON THE EFFECTS OF TEMPERATURE IN THE AQUATIC ENVIRONMENT
--Lists more than 1200 references on the effects of temperature in the aquatic environment. Ref: *Maryland. University. Natural Resources Institute Contribution No. 326, 1967.*

3.0 - 303
Kingsbury, A. William (1966). DEVELOPMENT OF AN OILY WATER SEPARATOR
--An oily-water separator for treating water-ballast discharges from ship fuel tanks utilizes a capacitance probe of sensitivity sufficient to detect oil concentrations of about one percent. Water with greater oil concentrations is retained in a slop tank, while water with lesser concentrations is treated in a two-stage separator. In the first stage, much of the oil coalesces after passage of the mixture through Dutch-weave screens, and then is drawn off to the slop tank. Second-stage coalescence is achieved with fiberglas layers. This system can meet International Convention standards of 100-mg/l maximum oil concentration in ship discharges. Ref: *J-1 38(2):236-240, Feb 1966. 5 refs.*

3.0 - 304
Kinne, O. (1966). PHYSIOLOGICAL ASPECTS OF ANIMAL LIFE IN ESTUARIES WITH SPECIAL REFERENCE TO SALINITY
--The literature on the physiology of estuarine animals is reviewed and the ecological factors governing physiological responses are discussed. Salinity is by far the most important; it has limiting effects on embryonic and larval development, temperature resistance and reactions to abnormal proportions of solutes, and modifying effects on rates and efficiency of metabolism, activity, growth and reproduction. Various compensatory devices can reduce the effects of salinity on the organisms; these are escape, reduction of contact, regulation of osmotic state of the body, and adaptation which is visualized as an adjustment of organisms to alterations in the pattern of variables in their environment which ultimately results in an increase in their capacity for survival. Ref: *J-34 3,:222-244, 1966. 88 refs.*

3.0 - 305
Klingeman, P. C. (1965). TRANSPORT OF RADIONUCLIDES IN SURFACE AND ESTUARINE WATERS
--Results are given of studies on the transport of fission products in the waters and sediments of river-estuary systems, the changing distribution of these radionuclides in estuarine waters, and factors affecting these changes with particular reference to zirconium-niobium-95 and other fission products of recent fallout origin. Studies in San Pablo Bay, a major component of the San Francisco Bay system, many fundamental relations determining the desposition, resuspension, and redistribution of flocculant radionuclide-sorbed sediments within estuaries were observed. Certain parts of the estuary were found to be particularly susceptible to the accumulation of radionuclide-sorbed sediments. Ref: *Univ. of California Thesis 424 p., 1965.*

3.0 - 306
Koeman, J. H. and others (1969). CHLORINATED BIPHENYLS IN FISH, MUSSELS AND BIRDS FROM THE RIVER RHINE AND THE NETHERLANDS' COASTAL AREA
--Describes the occurrence and distribution of PCBs. Methods used were chromatography and mass spectrometry. Beside being a hazard to fish, shellfish and birds, they interfere with the detection of organochlorine insecticides such as DDT. Ref: *J-7 221(5186):1126-1128, March 22, 1969.*

3.0 - 307
Kolesnikov, A. G. and Nelepo, B. A. (1967). INVESTIGATION INTO THE SPREAD OF RADIOACTIVE CONTAMINATION AS A RESULT OF THE DISCHARGE OF RADIOACTIVE WASTE INTO THE IRISH SEA
--From a study of transfer processes in the northeastern part of the Atlantic Ocean, the authors suggest that radioactive contamination in this area is caused by waste waters discharged to the Irish Sea and carried by the North Atlantic Current. Ref: *Gosud. Kom. Ispol. Atomn Energii. SSSR Moscow 14 p., 1967.*

3.0 - 308
Komaki, Shigeshi and others (1967). EXAMPLES OF SEA WATER POLLUTION IN HOKKAIDO - CONCERNING SEA WATER POLLUTION BY WHALE FACTORY WASTE AT KIRITAPPU, HAMANAKA BAY WITH REGARD TO MASS FISH MORTALITY
--Wastes discharged from a whale processing plant situated in Hamanaka Bay pollute the waters near the factory. Neritic fish are found floating on beaches. They are found with opened mouths, discolored gills apparently caused by lack of oxygen in the sea water. A breakwater westward of the factory restrains the westward flow of the polluted water. (In Japanese. English Summary). Ref: *J-86 32,:62-81, March 1967*

3.0 - 309
Kopp, J. F. and Kroner, R. C. (1967). TRACING WATER POLLUTION WITH EMISSION SPECTROGRAPH
--Reports experience in tracing water pollution with an emission spectrograph in the U.S. surveillance program since 1957. Results of studies on various rivers in the Eastern and Midwestern areas are noted. Ref: *J-1 39(10 Pt 1):1659-1668, Oct 1967.*

3.0 - 310

Kott, Yehuda and Ari, H. B.   (1968).
BACTERIOPHAGES AS MARINE POLLUTION INDICATORS
--Laboratory studies showed that the survival rate
of T bacteriophage in mixtures of sea water and
sewage was higher than that for coliform bacteria.
Now that a rapid, simple MPN technique for estimating T bacteriophage has been developed it would
prove a useful indicator of sewage pollution.
Ref: *P-19 and J-59 9,:207-217, 1968.*

3.0 - 311
Kott, Yehuda and Gloyna, E. F.   (1965).
CORRELATING COLIFORM BACTERIA WITH *E. COLI*
BACTERIOPHAGES IN SHELLFISH
--To obtain new criteria for indicating estuarine
pollution, the degree of correlation was investigated between coliform MPN and *Escherichia coli*
bacteriophage MPN in oysters (*Crassostrea virginica*) placed in a bay at various distances from
the point of discharge of a sewage-works effluent.
A table is given, showing that the number of coliform organisms decreases as the distance from the
outfall increases. Probability graphs for each of
three stations show that curves for coliform bacteria and *Esch. coli* bacteriophage were almost
parallel with about one order of magnitude difference between MPN, the numbers of the bacteriophage
being lower. Counts were also carried out on raw
and shelled commercial oysters; again the numbers
of the bacteriophage were found to be lower than
those of coliform bacteria. Ref: *J-4 112,:
424-426, 1965.*

3.0 - 312
Krenkel, Peter A. and Parker, Frank L.   (1969).
ENGINEERING ASPECTS, SOURCES AND MAGNITUDE OF
THERMAL POLLUTION
--This discussion deals with engineering problems
associated with the discharge of heated waters to
our environment and considers reasonable methods
for preventing these heated waters from adversely
affecting receiving waters. Adverse effects on
water quality caused by both natural and artificial addition of heat have been demonstrated. Various means of dissipating the excessive heat were
examined, and it may be concluded that, while it
is possible to reduce the temperature of cooling
water to its original temperature, it cannot be
done without excessive additional costs. Ref:
P-30 p. 10-52, 1969. 30 refs.

3.0 - 313
Krenkel, Peter A. and Parker, Frank L.   (1969).
BIOLOGICAL ASPECTS OF THERMAL POLLUTION
--A collection of papers constituting the proceed-
ings of the national symposium on thermal pollution
sponsored by the Federal Water Pollution Control
Administration and Vanderbilt University. This
section was devoted to biological aspects of ther-
mal pollution. The symposium was held in Portland,
Oregon, June 3-5, 1968. Ref: *P-30 Book. 1969.*
(See also 3.0 - 417).

3.0 - 314
Krishnamoorthy, T. M. and Viswanathan, R. (1968).
CO-PRECIPITATION STUDIES IN THE DETERMINATION OF
COBALT IN SEA WATER
--Both radioactive and stable cobalt could be de-
termined in a single sample of sea water by co-
precipitation with magnesium hydroxide which gives
an overall recovery of 93 percent. The cobalt con-

tent of the precipitate is determined spectropho-
tometrically using the nitroso-R-salt method; and
the activity due to cobalt-58 is determined in a
hydrochloric acid solution of the precipitate
using a gamma scintillation counter. Tabulated results from the analysis of sea water from Bombay
Harbor Bay show that the cobalt content of sea
water may very widely and rapidly in the same locality. Ref: *J-35 6,:169-170, 1968.*

3.0 - 315
Krolewski, H.   (1966).   CONSTRUCTION OF A
COMPRESSED-AIR OIL TANK FOR INLAND HARBOURS
--Difficulties and problems associated with the
construction of compressed-air oil tanks increase
with decreasing depth of water. The minimal and
optimal values of dimensions for oil tanks in inland harbors are included. Special consideration
is given to both theoretical deductions and original experiments. Ref: *J-87 56,:333-336,
1966.*

3.0 - 316
Kujala, N. F. (1966).   ARTIFICIAL RADIONUCLIDES
IN PACIFIC SALMON
--Pacific salmon concentrate certain gamma-emitting radionuclides (zinc-65, manganese-54, potas-
sium-40, and caesium-137) in their viscera. In
some cases, the pattern of concentration of the
nuclides appears to be related to the position of
the Columbia River 'plume'; thus fish whose migra-
tory paths are far south of the river contain more
zinc-65 and less manganese-54. In other cases the
nuclide concentrations can be explained, at least
in part, by differences in feeding habits; the
more carnivorous chinook and coho salmon accumulate the highest concentrations of zinc-65, man-
ganese-54 and caesium-137, while sockeye salmon,
which feed on plankton, accumulate less radioactivity, with manganese-54 the dominant nuclide,
some zinc-65, but no caesium-137. The effects of
diet on concentration of radioactivity in salmon
were investigated by analysing stomach contents;
crab larvae concentrated manganese-54 and zinc-65
while euphausiids concentrated only zinc-65. Ref:
Oregon State Univ. Thesis 62 p., 1966.

3.0 - 317
Kuhl, H. and Mann, H. (1967).   TOXICITY OF
VARIOUS OIL-COUNTERACTING AGENTS FOR SEA- AND
FRESHWATER ANIMALS
--This study suggests that a layer of crude oil
alone on the surface of the water is less detrimental than a mixture of crude oil and emulsifying
agents. As far as beaches and harbors are concerned a decision must be made as to whether damages
to the local flora and fauna can be accepted.
Ref: *J-106 16(4):321-327, Dec 1967. 4 refs.*

3.0 - 318
Lackey, James B. (1967).   NUTRIENT AND POLLUTANT
RESPONSE OF ESTUARINE BIOTAS
--The behavior of microbiota - algae and protozoa
as affected by commercial, recreational, and metropolitan uses of estuarine waters is outlined.
Silt, it was found, sharply reduces the microscopic
populations. The role of engineers is to assure
that adequate studies of the biology are made so
that they in turn might design and construct the
necessary treatment plants and outfalls which
would prevent overenrichment or pollution. Ref:

3.0 - 319
Lagarde, E. and Castellvi, J. (1965). ASPECTS OF BACTERIAL POLLUTION IN A BRACKISH REGION ON THE MEDITERRANEAN COAST
--A systematic qualitative and quantitative study was made of the bacteria in the water and sediments in the northern part of the Bages-Sigean Pond, part of a large complex of coastal lagoons in Aude, France. Counts of coliform bacteria, *Escherichia coli*, enterococci, and *Clostridium perfringens* (all indicators of faecal pollution) decreased during the summer in spite of the larger discharges of waste waters from the increased population along the banks. To explain this anomaly, an attempt was made to determine the factors in the lagoon environment which could contribute to the destruction of pathogenic bacteria, particularly enterococci which gave negative tests thruout June, July, and August. Tests showed that the destruction of pathogenic bacteria in summer could not be attributed to the increased salinity. Other tests showed that a concentration of 750 p.p.m. would be required to inhibit the growth of *Esch. coli* and *Streptococcus faecalis* and it is not feasible that these concentrations could occur in the pond, even in summer. The bactericidal action of the pond water must be attributed to physico-chemical changes affecting the ionic equilibrium and the oxidation-reduction potential. It is recommended that, wherever possible, all analyses, particularly physico-chemical determinations, should be made at the time of sampling, to avoid the changes which occur during storage. Ref: *P-1   p. 43-54, 1965.*

3.0 - 320
Lager, John A. and Tchobanoglous, George (1967). USE OF HYDRAULIC AND MATHEMATICAL MODELS FOR DETERMINING EFFLUENT DIFFUSION IN SOUTH SAN FRANCISCO BAY
--A comparison was made of the effectiveness of a physical hydraulic model and a mathematical model for assessing the waste assimilative capacity of San Francisco Bay. Specific effects studied were: mixing and dilution, waste dispersion, and the decay of waste material. DO and BOD were measured. The mathematical model yielded more reliable results than the hydraulic model. Ref: *P-2 p. 384-422, Aug 1967.*

3.0 - 321
Lager, John A. and Tchobanoglous, George (1968). EFFLUENT DISPOSAL IN SOUTH SAN FRANCISCO BAY
--The effects of discharging effluent from a proposed primary treatment plant to the South San Francisco Bay estuary system are evaluated using both the Corps of Engineers' hydraulic model of San Francisco Bay and a specially developed mathematical model. Results obtained from both the hydraulic and mathematical models indicate that the BOD concentration will decrease logarithmically along the deep-water channel in both directions from the point of discharge. Steady-state BOD concentrations over the proposed discharge location were estimated to be 7.0 mg per l and 2.0 mg per l using the mathematical and hydraulic models respectively. Starting with an initial DO value of 7.6 mg per l and using the mathematical model, the steady-state dissolved oxygen concentration directly over the outfall was estimated to be 6.7 mg per l. Ref: *J-3   94(SA2 Paper 5891)213-236, April 1968.*

3.0 - 322
Lai, M. G. and Goya, H. A. (1966). RADIOACTIVITY RELEASE FROM RADIONUCLIDE POWER SOURCES. III. RELEASE FROM PLUTONIUM METAL TO SEA WATER
--Plutonium metal reacts completely with natural sea water to produce solid reaction products, believed to be plutonium oxide and/or hydroxide, and a gaseous product whose major component is hydrogen; the reaction occurs fairly rapidly, 90 per cent of a 60-mg sample reacting in less than 5 hours. The rate at which the solid reaction products of plutonium enter into 'solution' in sea water is very slow, about $1.5-2.0$ μg per 50-70 mg of solids per day. The equilibrium (or maximal) concentration of dissolved plutonium in 3 samples of natural sea water was found to be 67 μg per litre, but this concentration may vary with differences in the concentration of complexing anions present. Ref: *U. S. Atomic Energy Commission USNRDL-TR-1050   45 p., 1966.*

3.0 - 323
Lalou, C. (1965). CONCENTRATION OF 3,4-BENZOPYRENES BY HOLOTHURIANS IN THE REGION OF VILLEFRANCHE AND ANTIBES
--To determine the role of marine animals in the passage of 3,4-benzopyrene through the aquatic food chain, studies were made on samples of holothurians and the sediments and beds of *Posidonia* in which they live near the coasts of Antibes and Villefranche, France. Data obtained before and after saponification with alcoholic potassium hydroxide show that the benzopyrene is not only loosely adsorbed on the holothurians but that it penetrates into the cell structure; the fluorescence spectra, however, remained unchanged showing that the hydrocarbon is not metabolized. Contrary to results previously obtained for the uptake of radioactive isotopes, the uptake of benzopyrene was not related to the concentration in the sediments, possibly owing to the uneven distribution which depends on the currents, so that the sand collected close to the animals will not contain exactly the same concentration of benzopyrene as that which has already been ingested. The results show that it is impossible to predict the degree of pollution by 3,4-benzopyrene. Ref: *P-1   p. 363-366, 1964-1965.*

3.0 - 324
Leeds, J. V. (1967) ACCURACY OF DISCRETE MODELS USED TO PREDICT ESTUARY POLLUTION
--Considers that a significant problem is to determine the closeness of the solution of the ordinary differential equation to the solution of the partial differential equation, the spacing, and the number of sections. The closeness of the solution can be judged by examining the magnitude and phase of the frequency response of the partial differential equations and the set of ordinary differential equations. From the knowledge of the frequency response of the system the roles developed give the number of sections and spacing to meet specified errors in the approximation. Ref: *J-16 3(2):481-490, 1967.   4 refs.*

3.0 - 325

Leeds, J. V. and Bybee, H. H. (1967). SOLUTION OF ESTUARY PROBLEMS AND NETWORK PROGRAMMES
--Equations for estimating the distribution of pollution in an estuary can be solved by using existing digital computer programs. Transient and frequency responses may be obtained. Ref: *J-3 93(SA3 Paper 5277):29-36, June 1967.*

3.0 - 326
Leffel, Ernest R. (1967). ESTUARINE POLLUTION OF THE CHAO PHRAYA RIVER, AT BANGKOK, THAILAND
--The sources of pollution in the Chao Phraya River are identified. A mathematical model is used to calculate dissolved oxygen relationships in the estuary. It was found that the pollution conditions do not conform to assumptions employed in the development of previous formulations of oxygen sag relationships. Ref: *P-2 p. 370-383, 1967.*

3.0 - 327
Leffel, Ernest R. (1968). POLLUTION OF THE CHAO PHRAYA RIVER ESTUARY
--The estuary of the Chao Phraya River, Thailand, is polluted with sewage and drainage discharged from Bangkok through a series of canals and ditches; owing to the low flow in the canals during dry weather, this organic pollution depletes the content of dissolved oxygen in the water. A new sewerage system is to be constructed, and studies were carried out on the condition of the estuary to determine whether a combined or separate system would be most suitable. Studies on the dissolved oxygen in the estuary showed that the self-purifying capacity is limited and a combined sewerage system discharging overflows of storm sewage would add to the pollution problem; a separate system is therefore proposed. Ref: *J-3 94(SA2 Paper 5903):295-306, April 1968.*

3.0 - 328
Legin, V. K.; Kuznetsov, Y. V. and Lazaref, K. F. (1966). CONCENTRATION OF URANIUM IN MARINE DEPOSITS
--A solution of sodium bicarbonate with a pH value close to that of sea water was used as a leaching agent to investigate the mobility of uranium in marine deposits from the Azov and Black Seas. It was found that only 4-6 per cent of the uranium could be extracted from the deposits from the Azov Sea, while most of the uranium was extracted from the Black Sea deposits, indicating that the uranium in the latter was originally dissolved in the sea water while the uranium in the Azov Sea deposits was of terrestrial origin. Ref: *J-88 5,:606-608, 1966.*

3.0 - 329
Leighton, David; Nusbaum, I. and Mulford, S. (1967). EFFECTS OF WASTE DISCHARGE FROM POINT LOMA SALINE WATER CONVERSION PLANT ON INTERTIDAL MARINE LIFE
--Studies were made to determine the polluting effects of the waste waters from the Point Loma (San Diego, Calif.) conversion plant. It was found that both the salinity and the temperature of the waste waters had adverse effects on the intertidal organisms, and the combined effects may be more severe than those indicated for each alone. Most of the intertidal animals were killed by short periods of exposure to temperatures of 30°-35°C, and full-strength effluent at 16°-18°C. was lethal to most species within 24 hours; effluent diluted to 20 per cent with sea water, at 16°-18°C. was lethal only to sea urchins. Orphiuroids (brittle starfish), which are distributed widely in the intertidal zone in southern California, were used as indicators of the areal influence of the discharge; they were affected by moderate concentrations of the effluent and were killed by a temperature of 37°C. A bioassay technique for conditions such as those existing at Point Loma, using the purple sea urchin (*Strongylocentrotus purpuratus*)as test animal, has been developed and is described. Since the Point Loma plant was shut down, the affected tidepool area has recovered rapidly from the effects of the pollution. Ref: *J-1 39(7):1190-1202, July 1967.*

3.0 - 330
Le Meur, A. (1968). PRACTICAL MEASURES TAKEN AGAINST OIL POLLUTION IN PORTS
--In ports as well as on open sea, the main sources of pollution are tankers, cargoes, port vessels or machinery, and land machinery; unfavorable factors are to be found mainly in considerable increase in volume of hydrocarbons handled; favorable factors result from - application of London Conventions of 1954 and 1962 which prescribe providing of apparatus for treatment of offal water in ports and installing separators on more tankers and even cargo-vessels. (In French) Ref: *P-28 6 p., 1968.*

3.0 - 331
Le Petit, J. and Barthelemy, M. H. (1968). LES HYDROCARBURES EN MER: LE PROBLEME DE L'EPURATION DES ZONES LITTORALES PAR LES MICROORGANISMES
--A qualitative and quantitative analysis of the gas-oil degradation by microorganisms in coastal sea-area was carried out. Fast disappearance of gas-oil compounds occurs when the microorganisms are supplied with sources of nitrogen and phosphorus. It is noted that interesting results are observed in the presence of inorganic compounds such as $PO_4H(NH_4)_2$ or more complex substances such as sewages. (In French, English Summary) Ref: *J-89 114(2):149-158, Feb 1968. 11 refs.*

3.0 - 332
Levin, Gilbert V. (1968). THE NEW POLLUTION
--Notes the emergence of nutrient pollution or eutrophication as a major problem in lakes and estuaries. Sewage treatment produces this form of pollution. Organic material present in the sewage is more thoroughly degraded with the result that the subsequent offending nutrients are released as soluble minerals such as phosphate and nitrogen. Ref: *P-11 3,:934-941, 1968.*

3.0 - 333
Lewis, G. B. and Seymour, A. H. (1965). DISTRIBUTION OF ZINC-65 IN PLANKTON FROM OFFSHORE WATERS OF WASHINGTON AND OREGON 1961-1963
--Principle sources of zinc-65 are the Hanford Nuclear reactors. Analyses of 238 samples of unsorted plankton indicate significant, seasonal but not annual, changes and a close relationship between zinc-65 in the river water and plankton. Ref: *P-15 2,:956-967, 1965. 6 refs.*

3.0 - 334
Lidz, Louis (1966). PLANKTONIC FORAMINIFERA IN

THE WATER COLUMN OF THE MAINLAND SHELF OFF NEWPORT BEACH, CALIFORNIA
--Plankton tows were taken off Newport Beach, California, along with temperature, salinity, and transparency measurements. Nearshore conditions and foraminiferal populations are modified by upwelling in Newport Submarine Canyon and domestic effluent waste discharge from the Orange County Sewer outfall. Foraminifera range in size from 50 to 250μ; therefore, use of a 62-μ mesh net is necessary. *Globigerina bulloides* and *G. quinqueloba* compose 90% or more of the samples. Right-coiling specimens of *G. pachyderma*, characteristic of deep-water tows, and *Bolivina vaughani*, usually considered benthic, were also found. Ref: *J-41 11(2):257-263, April 1966. 16 refs.*

3.0 - 335
Liebman, Jon C. and Marks, David H. (1967). 'BALAS' ALGORITHM FOR ZONED UNIFORM TREATMENT
--Discusses the complexities of the problem of finding appropriate treatment levels for waste discharges located along an estuary on which quality standards are imposed. A zoned solution is proposed wherein waste producers are divided into categories, and treatment levels are found which minimize the cost-subject to the requirement that all members of the category provide the same treatment. A branch-and-bound algorith is developed to obtain the solution. Ref: *P-2 p. 44-59, 1967.*

3.0 - 336
Livingstone, D. J. (1969). APPRAISAL OF SEWAGE POLLUTION ALONG A SECTION OF THE NATAL COAST
--The distribution and occurrence of coliforms and pathogenic indicators was studied along the coast of Natal before the use of submarine outfalls began. Pollution was studied in areas called clean and in areas considered grossly polluted. The method used was based on Escherichia coli 1 counts, parasitic units, staphylococci, salmonellas and salinity. The pollution was related to sanitary installations on shore. The monitoring of changes in water quality will be of value in studies in future developments in the area. Ref: *J-114 67,:209-223, 1969. 18 refs.*

3.0 - 337
Livingstone, Robert, Jr. (1965). PRELIMINARY BIBLIOGRAPHY WITH KWIC INDEX ON THE ECOLOGY OF ESTUARIES AND COASTAL AREAS OF THE EASTERN UNITED STATES
--This bibliography, which contains more than 5,470 references, is an initial effort to bring together references on the ecology of estuaries and coastal water of the eastern U.S. It encompasses the period 1900-1960. Ref: *U. S. Fish & Wildlife Service Report, May 1965.*

3.0 - 338
Logan, Campbell F. (1970). FLUID RECOVERY SYSTEM AND METHOD
--A method and system for recovering a fluid leaking from a crack in a submerged flowline or the like, in a flowing body of water wherein the fluid has a specific gravity less than the specific gravity of water and substantially immiscible therewith, the system included a chamber positioned adjacently above the crack, and means are attached to the chamber to fix the relative position between the chamber and the crack. Ref: *U. S. Patent Number 3,500,843. Not assigned. 1970.*

3.0 - 339
Lowe, Jack I. (1965). CHRONIC EXPOSURE OF BLUE CRABS, *CALLINECTES SAPIDUS*, TO SUBLETHAL CONCENTRATIONS OF DDT
--Juvenile blue crabs, *Callinectes sapidus*, were reared in flowing seawater containing sublethal concentrations of DDT. Crabs fed, molted, and grew for 9 months in seawater containing 0.25 ppb (micrograms/liter) DDT but could survive only a few days in water containing DDT in excess of 0.5 ppb. Ref: *J-90 46(6):899-900, Autumn 1965. 4 refs.*

3.0 - 340
Lowman, F. G.; Phelps, D. K. and others (1966). INTERACTIONS OF THE ENVIRONMENTAL AND BIOLOGICAL FACTORS ON THE DISTRIBUTION OF TRACE ELEMENTS IN THE MARINE ENVIRONMENT
--Preliminary results are given of studies carried out in Puerto Rico on the distribution of stable isotopes in 3 watersheds and the adjoining estuaries which drain areas of different geological origin and on radioactive isotopes from fallout in marine organisms and sea water, to determine the effect of the stable isotopes on the accumulation of radioactivity in the marine food chain. Although, on the basis of the simple addition of fallout material to the coastal waters of Puerto Rico, it was expected that marine organisms on the west coast would accumulate much more radioactivity than those on the south coast, the difference between the two areas was less than anticipated. This is attributed to the combined effects of chemical and physical form of the radionuclides, the degree of dilution and co-precipitation by stable nuclides, and differences in the method of biological uptake by different groups of organisms. Ref: *P-4 p. 249-266, 1966.*

3.0 - 341
Lowton, R. J.; Martin, J. H. and Talbot, J. W. (1966). DILUTION, DISPERSION AND SEDIMENTATION IN SOME BRITISH ESTUARIES
--The authors summarize the results of studies on the Solway Firth and the estuaries of the Severn and Blackwater to investigate factors affecting the distribution of radioactive waste waters discharged to them. In the Blackwater estuary, the most important factors affecting subsequent dispersal of the radioactivity are the comparatively large tidal oscillations, the low river run-off, and the presence of mud flats. In the Solway Firth tidal oscillations are the most important factor, but transfer and deposition of sediments varies markedly with the coarseness of the sediment, and since this also affects the amount of radioactivity adsorbed by the particles the distribution of radioactivity in the bottom deposits varies. There was also evidence in the Solway that sedimented material was being transported into the estuary from the neighboring discharge site at Windscale, Cumberland. Ref: *P-4 p. 189-206, 1966.*

3.0 - 342
Lyon, R. J. and Lee, Keenan (1968). INFRARED EXPLORATION FOR COASTAL AND SHORELINE SPRINGS
--Reports that an infrared scanning system is

being developed to detect, delineate and evaluate discharge of coastal and shoreline springs. An infrared radiometer was used for absolute temperature measurement and was correlated with pertinent ground control measurements. Unexpected findings on imagery include an apparent expression of shallow sublake topography and a secondary plume of colder surface water offshore from warm springs. Ref: *Stanford University. Remote Sensing Lab. Tech. Rept. No. 68-1, Oct 1968. 68 p. 83 refs.*

3.0 - 343
McCarty, James C. and Harris, Howard S. (1967). FUTURE OF AN ESTUARY
--Discusses existing and future water quality in San Francisco Bay and outlines means to cope with pollution's adverse effects on beneficial uses of the Bay water. A mathematical model is employed to predict future water quality in terms of total nitrogen and total dissolved solids. A major obstacle to the implementation of any control program will be coordinating the diverse interests of the many agencies concerned with water quality in San Francisco Bay. Ref: *P-2 p. 335-369, 1967.*

3.0 - 344
McCrone, A. W. (1966). HUDSON RIVER ESTUARY: HYDROLOGY, SEDIMENTS AND POLLUTION
--Reports a study of the Hudson River from Kingston to Dobbs Ferry to identify the radioactive pollutants in the river and to determine the effect of their accumulation in the bottom muds and in organisms such as fish. It was found that radioactivity concentrated in fish was insignificant in so far as public health was concerned. Ref: *J-36 56(2):175-189, 1966.*

3.0 - 345
McCullough, Charles A. and Vayder, Jerry D. (1968). DELTA-SUISUN BAY WATER QUALITY AND HYDRAULIC STUDY
--Fluorescent dye tracers were used to determine the Impact of waste discharges at sensitive locations in the San Francisco area. A mathematical model was superimposed on a hydraulic model to predict conditions resulting from changes in the location and quantities of water released into the Delta. It was concluded that saline intrusion and other water quality control problems could be controlled by releases of fresh water from storage areas located in points around the delta. Ref: *J-3 94(SA5 Paper 6143):809-827, Oct 1968. 2 refs.*

3.0 - 346
McDermott, James H.; Ballinger, Dwight G. and Sayers, William T. (1969). FUTURE OF INSTRUMENTATION IN WATER POLLUTION CONTROL
--A discussion on automatic instrumentation available and required for the near future. The need for field, laboratory and aerial instrumentation capable of evaluating and controlling waste sources and the water receiving these wastes. Ref: *Analysis Instrumentation 6,:97-104, 1969. 13 refs.*

3.0 - 347
Machler, Claude Z. and Greenberg, Arnold E. (1968). IDENTIFICATION OF PETROLEUM IN ESTUARINE WATERS
--A simple sequential scheme of analysis suitable for the unequivocal demonstration of petroleum products present as pollutants in the estuarine environment is described. It involves the use of gas chromatographic analysis of head space vapor and solvent extraction of samples followed by infrared spectrophotometric and paper chromatographic examinations. Ref: *J-3 94(SA5 Paper 6172):969-978, Oct 1968. 8 refs.*

3.0 - 348
Machler, Claude A. and Greenberg, Arnold E. (1967). IDENTIFICATION OF PETROLEUM PRODUCTS IN ESTUARINE WATERS
--To identify petroleum products in estuarine waters a simple sequential scheme is proposed. It includes gas chromatographic analysis of vapor space gas and solvent extraction followed by infrared spectrophotometric and paper chromatographic examinations. (See previous abstract) Ref: *P-2 p. 517-536, Aub 1967.*

3.0 - 349
Mackay, D. W. and Fleming, G. (1969).CORRELATION OF DISSOLVED-OXYGEN LEVELS, FRESHWATER FLOWS AND TEMPERATURES IN A POLLUTED ESTUARY
--Following a survey of the Clyde Estuary, data on dissolved oxygen, freshwater input, and temperature were analysed, and equations relating these parameters were formulated for various stations in the estuary. Dissolved-oxygen levels varied significantly with freshwater flow rising rapidly in the upper reaches as the flow increased above drought levels, but tending to diminish again in spate conditions. Ref: *J-12 3(2):121-128, Feb 1969.*

3.0 - 350
McKay, H. A. C. (1967). OIL POLLUTION AT SEA. STUDIES IN CONNECTION WITH THE TORREY CANYON EPISODE
--A summary of work carried out as a result of the Torrey Canyon disaster, on methods of preventing and controlling pollution of sea water and beaches by oil, including studies on the adsorption of oil on straw, on the use of coagulants, on the sinking of oil with agglomerates of solids, on the concentration of oil slicks by means of towed booms, and on the removal of oil from sea water by pumping. Ref: *U. K. Atomic Energy Authority AERE-R5550, 1967. 44 p.*

3.0 - 351
McLean, D. M. and Brown, J. R. (1968). MARINE AND FRESHWATER VIRUS DISPERSAL
--Results are given of studies on the dispersal of virus in a relatively quiet land-locked body of sea water and at an open sea beach, and at comparable sites in freshwater lakes; and on the viricidal effect of adding chlorine to creek water. At 4°C poliovirus-2 persisted in fresh water for 12 days, but in sea water the infectivity decreased 100-fold over the same period and was negligible after 5 days at 25°C. In both sea water and fresh water the virus remained infective at beaches and in open water for 5-10 min; the virus was recovered after 65 ft of lateral drift at a freshwater beach and after 25 ft of drift at a sea beach. Dispersal of the virus was relatively unaffected by wave action. Addition of free residual chlorine to creeks infected with virus pulses resulted in rapid inactivation of the virus when mixing was adequate but with incomplete mixing virus could be

detected downstream. Ref: *J-37 59,:100-104, 1968.*

3.0 - 352
McNulty, J. K. (1966). RECOVERY OF BISCAYNE BAY FROM POLLUTION
--Results are given of studies on benthic organisms, zooplankton, fouling organisms, and dissolved inorganic phosphate in northern Biscayne Bay, Fla., before and after abatement of pollution by domestic sewage. Within 100 m of outfalls, the bottom fauna was poor both with and without pollution; at distances greater than 370 m seaward of outfalls there were more polychaete species and fewer lamellibranch species with pollution than without pollution. In hard bottom, at distances of 185-740 m from outfalls pollution again had a marked fertilizing effect on the benthic fauna, but at 20 m from outfalls the number of species and the number of individuals was greater in the absence of pollution. The concentration of inorganic phosphate fell considerably after abatement, particularly in areas least flushed by tidal currents, and in these areas zooplankton volumes also decreased, but remained at pre-abatement levels in areas with considerable tidal flushing. Neither the total displacement volume of all fouling organisms nor the number of barnacles settling per month showed any clear relation to the occurrence of pollution. Ref: *University of Miami. Thesis 192 p., 1966.*

3.0 - 353
Magee, R. J. and Rahman, A. K. M. (1965). DETERMINATION OF COPPER IN SEA WATER BY ATOMIC ABSORPTION SPECTROSCOPY
--Investigations were carried out with a spectrophotometer, to determine the optimal conditions of operation and the minimal amount of copper which can be determined. A new approach was made based on the selective extraction of copper complexes into organic solvents and spraying of the organic extract into the flame. Using ammonium pyrrolidine dithiocarbamate as the complexing agent and ethyl acetate as the solvent, a marked increase in sensitivity was obtained. In tests with sea water, interference by traces of heavy metals can be overcome by addition of EDTA before formation of the complex. Water from the Irish Sea at Belfast Lough was found to contain, on average, 1.85 μg of copper per litre, which is similar to the value previously reported for the Pacific Ocean. Ref: *J-38 12 (Part 1):409-416, 1965.*

3.0 - 354
Majori, L.; Morelli, M. L. and others (1968). STUDIES ON THE POLLUTION OF SEA WATER IN THE GULF OF TRIESTE
--Concentrations of *Esch. coli* and anionic detergents, and the BOD of sea water were determined at more than 70 sampling points in the Gulf of Trieste and average values were presented on charts showing 5 degrees of pollution ranging from very clean to very polluted. The results indicated highly polluted areas in and adjacent to the port of Trieste and off Monfalcone where mussels are cultivated. Salmonella were also isolated at some points. The effects of synthetic detergents on marine life and their significance as indicators of pollution were discussed, and methods for controlling pollution of the sea were considered. Ref:

P-19 and J-59 9,:83-98, 1968. 16 refs.

3.0 - 355
Mallet, L. (1965). POLLUTION OF THE MEDITERRANEAN COAST OF FRANCE AND MORE ESPECIALLY OF VILLEFRANCHE BAY BY HYDROCARBONS PARTICULARLY OF THE 3,4-BENZOPYRENE TYPE
--The origin of hydrocarbons found in the marine environment was discussed and the results of studies on the presence of 3,4-benzopyrene along the French Mediterranean coast were summarized. The concentrations of this hydrocarbon in the sediments, generally proportional to those in the marine flora and fauna, were greatest in the region of Villefranche and were also important in the Gulf of Fos, Etang de Berre, and River Rhone and its delta, but were lower in the Gulf of Prado at the south of the Gulf of Marseilles. Ref: *P-1 p. 325-330, 1965.*

3.0 - 356
Mangin, J. P. (1968). "NATURAL" SEDIMENTARY AND GEOCHEMICAL TRACERS IN THE STUDY OF MARINE POLLUTION
--In studies on the pollution of sea water, measurements of pH value, oxidation-reduction potential, salinity, and temperature provide simple and rapid means for tracing coastal discharges. Similar information may be obtained by the more complex method of determining concentrations of elements characteristic of terrestrial waters and by physical examination of suspended solids and sediments. Ref: *P-19 and J-59 9,:159-166, 1968.*

3.0 - 357
Mann, H. (1965). EFFECTS ON THE FLAVOUR OF FISHES BY OILS AND PHENOLS
--The author reviews information on the production of undesirable flavors in fish by exposure to polluting materials in water, particularly phenolic compounds, tar derivatives, and mineral oils, and the enhancement of these flavors by the simultaneous presence of synthetic detergents. Ref: *P-1 p. 371-374, 1965. 20 refs.*

3.0 - 358
Marshall, A. R. (1967). PRACTICES AFFECTING SOUTH ATLANTIC AND GULF COAST MARSHES AND ESTUARIES DREDGING AND FILLING
--Reports on the direct and indirect effect of dredging and filling on the fish and wildlife resources of Florida's estuarine and freshwater habitats. The aspects discussed are the effects of: siltation, reduction of light penetration, creation of anaerobic bottom conditions, reduction of nutrient outflow from marshes and swamps. Examples cited are for Boca Ciega Bay, Tampa; Biscayne Bay, Indian River; and St. John's River. Ref: *Florida. Bureau of Sport Fisheries and Wildlife, Vero Beach, Fla. 1967.*

3.0 - 359
Martin, J. H. (1968). PHYTOPLANKTON-ZOOPLANKTON RELATIONSHIPS IN NARRAGANSETT BAY. III. SEASONAL CHANGES IN ZOOPLANKTON EXCRETION RATES IN RELATION TO PHYTOPLANKTON ABUNDANCE
--Laboratory experiments using freshly-caught phytoplankton and zooplankton from Narragansett Bay were carried out to determine the excretion of nitrogen and phosphorus by zooplankton in relation to the amount of food available and to estimate

the importance of the excreted compounds for phytoplankton growth. Excretion of both nitrogen and phosphorus was minimal when phytoplankton was abundant; possible reasons for this are discussed. During periods of phytoplankton abundance, zooplankton provide only a small fraction of the nitrogen and phosphorus required by the phytoplankton, and during periods of phytoplankton scarcity, when plant nutrient requirements are low and zooplankton excretion rates are high, the nitrogen and phosphorus provided by the zooplankton exceeds the phytoplankton demands. Ref: J-41 13(1):63-71, Jan 1968.

3.0 - 360
Martin, W. W. (1969).   RADIOECOLOGY AND THE FEASIBILITY OF NUCLEAR CANAL EXCAVATION
--In consideration of the proposed use of nuclear explosives in the construction of a sea-level canal across the isthmian region of Central America, extensive studies were made to predict the kinds and quantities of radionuclides to be expected in the environment and the ecological effects of the radioactive contamination. The work includes studies on the water, sediments, and freshwater organisms in rivers of east Panama and northwest Colombia; the use of hydrological models of the freshwater systems and of the proposed canal to provide estimates of the time-specific concentrations of radionuclides at specific points on different streams, following pulse inputs to the watersheds from each nuclear detonation, and to provide estimates of the radionuclide input to the marine environment after the canal is opened at both ends; and studies on marine and estuarine ecology along the Pacific and Caribbean coast of Panama and Colombia to assess the potential radiological hazards. The potential radiological hazards of nuclear canal excavation may be less than those associated with the previous testing of nuclear weapons. Ref: P-3 p. 9-22, 1969.

3.0 - 361
Martino, P. A. and Marchello, J. M.   (1968).
USING WASTE HEAT FOR FISH FARMING
--Considers the possibility of utilizing industrial waste heat, such as from a coastal nuclear power plant, for convectively pumping up nutrient-rich deep water for fish farming. Thermo-nutrient pumping conditions are described. A proposed scheme involves a joint program encompassing nuclear and desalination plants, offshore oil fields and a fish farming project. Ref: J-110 3(4): 36-39, April 1968. 12 refs.

3.0 - 362
Matalucci, Rudolph V. and Abdel-Hady, Mohamed (1968).   INFRARED AERIAL SURVEYS IN ENVIRONMENTAL ENGINEERING
--To obtain full advantage of the techniques involved in remote IR sensing, the basic principles related to the nature of IR radiation and the problems associated with its atmospheric attenuation are reviewed and illustrated. Some of the basic differences between IR photography and imagery are analyzed. Illustrations are provided which illuminate the techniques that have been used to locate thermal water pollution by IR sensing. Further illustrations indicate the facility of IR imagery to display stream valleys and subsurface drainage patterns. The location of buried conduits and util-

ity systems are illustrated to highlight another valuable use of IR sensing in revealing near surface features. Ref: J-3 94(SA6 Paper 6277): 1071-1084, Dec 1968.

3.0 - 363
Mattson, James S. and Mark, H. B., Jr.   (1969).
APPLICATION OF INTERNAL REFLECTANCE ·SPECTROSCOPY TO WATER POLLUTION ANALYSES
--The use of internal reflectance spectroscopy, circumvents separation steps which must be employed with optically opaque samples. With this technique, direct spectrophotometric analyses of marine sediments, water filtrates, aqueous suspensions, etc. can be carried out. Both visible colorimetric and infrared spectrophotometric methods are described, along with some representative data and the experimental apparatus, pointing out the potentialities of this technique. Ref: J-5 3(2):161-164, Feb 1969. 8 refs.

3.0 - 364
Mazieres, J.   (1965).   BACTERIAL TESTS OF CONTAMINATION AND EVALUATION OF THE BACTERIOLOGICAL QUALITY OF OYSTERS
--Further data are given from the bacteriological analysis of water and oysters from the River Auray, France with reference to 3 groups of bacteria, *Escherichia coli*, other true coliform bacteria(*Esch. intermedium, Citrobacter*, and *Cloaca*), and paracolon bacilli (*Paracoli coliforme, Hafnia*, and *Providencia*); and the significance of each group as an indicator of pollution in marine areas is considered. Data obtained at stations intermediate between the very polluted water at the port of Auray and the very clean water at Rolay in the open sea were used to develop systems for classifying the bacteriological quality of the water and the oysters according to the *Esch. coli* count; water having a count of 601-1200 and oysters with a count of 2501-5000 per litre must be considered doubtful and counts higher than 1200 for water or 5000 for oysters indicate heavy contamination and are unacceptable in oyster culture. An international standard is considered necessary. Ref: P-1 p. 265-275, 1965.

3.0 - 365
Mecarini, G. and Piety, J. (1967). THE OCEAN, TOO, COULD BECOME POLLUTED
--An illustrated description is given of techniques used during an oceanographic survey off the southern coast of Long Island, N.Y. to study factors affecting the proposed discharge of sewage, and the effects of such disposal on marine plants and animals. The methods used included dye-tracking studies after the discharge of Rhodamine B from specific locations, combined with current measurements, the use of a seismic profiler to provide data for the location of a buried outfall and the collection of sediment cores by a device which vibrated into the sediments and was capable of recovering 20-ft-long cores. Ref: J-91 4(8): 42-44, 1967.

3.0 - 366
Mediterranean Association of Marine Biology and Oceanography. (1968).   PROCEEDINGS OF THE THIRD INTERNATIONAL COLLOQUIUM ON MEDICAL OCEANOGRAPHY
--The first and second sessions of the third international colloquium on medical oceanography,

held at the Centre d'Études et de Recherches de Biologie et d'Océanographis Médicale, Nice, France, in September 1967, comprised papers on the behavior of terrestrial bacteria after discharge to the sea and on tracer studies on the dispersion of waste waters. (See pertinent papers under author's name in this publication). Ref: *P-19 and J-59   9,:1-283, 1968.*

3.0 - 367
Medsker, Lloyd L.; Jenkins, David and Thomas, Jerome F. (1969). ODOROUS COMPOUNDS IN NATURAL WATERS - 2-EXO-HYDROXY-2-METHYLBORNANE, THE ODOROUS COMPOUND PRODUCED BY SEVERAL ACTINOMYCETES
--A survey of 28 species of actinomycetes indicated three organisms as producers of the compound 2-exo-hydroxy-2-methylbornane. These are: Streptomyces antibioticus, Streptomyces praecox, and Streptomyces griseus. Ref: *J-5 3(5):476-477, May 1969. 5 refs.*

3.0 - 368
Metcalf, T. G. and Stiles, W. C. (1968). VIRAL POLLUTION OF SHELLFISH IN ESTUARY WATER
--It is indicated that increased levels of chlorination accompanied by prolongation of retention time lead to reduction in number of viral isolations made from treated effluents. Enterovirus occurs in oysters collected from seawater containing less than 70 Coliform median most probably number/100ml. Reduction of viral pollutants to undetectable levels in oysters by depuration in estuary waters requires 3 to 6 days; depuration efficacy was adversely affected by large numbers of viral pollutants in oysters, by water temperatures falling below 10°C, or both. Ref: *J-3 94(SA4 Paper 6063):595-609, Aug 1968. 18 refs.*

3.0 - 369
Middleton, F. M.; Rosen, A. A. and Burttschell, R. H. (1969). MANUAL FOR RECOVERY AND IDENTIFICATION OF ORGANIC CHEMICALS IN WATER
--This is a manual prepared for use by persons interested in recovering and analyzing small amounts of organic contaminants in water or wastes. It is based on material prepared for a training course given at the Robert A. Taft Sanitary Engineering Center in May, 1957. (Report published 1969).
Ref: *Robert A. Taft Sanitary Engineering Center, Cincinnati, Ohio. 1969.*

3.0 - 370
Mihursky, Joseph A. (1967).   POSSIBLE CONSTRUCTIVE USES OF THERMAL ADDITIONS TO ESTUARIES
--Thermal loading in estuaries can cause damage in some ecosystems. It can also be used constructively to maintain warm temperatures for the development of food items for commercially important species, and to stimulate growth of commercially important fish and shellfish. Ref: *J-39 17(10): 698-702, Nov 1967. 31 refs.*

3.0 - 371
Mihursky, Joseph A. (1969).   PATUXENT THERMAL STUDIES - SUMMARY AND RECOMMENDATIONS
--Reports a study made in the period 1962-1967 to understand the physical, chemical and biological effects of heated water releases into the Patuxent Estuary. An effort was made to determine quantitatively the effects of installing a major power unit. Studies were made on the biological role of temperature and temperature change, uses and potential uses of the estuary. Recommendations for control, regulation, power plant operating procedures, and future studies are summarized. Ref: *Maryland. University. Solomons. Natural Resources Institute Spec. Rept. No. 1   20 p., Jan 1969. 82 refs.*

3.0 - 372
Mihursky, Joseph A. and Kennedy, V. S.   (1967). WATER TEMPERATURE CRITERIA TO PROTECT AQUATIC LIFE
--The ecological significance of temperature in the aquatic habitat is discussed in relation to the thermal loading of ecosystems by electric power plants. Effects of temperature on behavior, metabolism, and mortality of aquatic organisms are described to indicate the difficult problems involved in determining acceptable standards for a healthy fish population. A multivariate analysis of interactions between temperature and other environmental factors is suggested. Standards for temperature regulation are described for three ecosystems: (1) cold-water salmonid streams, (2) warm-water centrarchid environments, and (3) estuaries. Ref: *P-32 and J-23 96(1):20-32, (Supp. Special Publication No. 4), 1967. 42 refs.*

3.0 - 373
Mikkelsen, Trygve (Norway) (1970).   BOOM FOR SCREENING IN AND COLLECTING UP OF POLLUTION ON WATER
--A boom construction for closing off and collecting up oil from the surface of sea water. A boom which comprises a plurality of floatable and foldable flat sections linked together in the form of a zig-zag rail and provided with one or more purse lines arranged to fold said flat sections on being drawn in. In the water the boom will provide an upstanding barrier above the surface of the water. The boom can be set up in a ring in the water and by hauling in the purse lines, the closed-off area will be decreased. The boom is manufactured of individual plates of porous plastic covered and linked together by a pliable material which is durable to sea water and oil. The purse lines are guided by rings at alternate links. Between adjacent links are connected bands to limit the flattening out of the boom. Ref: *U. S. Patent No. 3, 499, 291. Not assigned, 1970.*

3.0 - 374
Miller, Denny M.; Wetherall, J. A. and Lenarz, William H. (1967). MODERN APPROACH TO THE STUDY OF ESTUARIES, WITH SPECIFIC REFERENCE TO THE DUWAMISH RIVER, WASHINGTON
--A systhesis of new and old methods is providing an effective approach to the study of complex ecological problems in the organically enriched Duwamish Estuary, Washington. Simulation models may be used to estimate bias and to design sampling strategies that will reduce bias in survival estimates. Ref: *P-12 p. 165-173, March 1967. 4 refs.*

3.0 - 375
Mitchell, R. (1968).   LYSIS OF INTESTINAL AND OTHER NON-MARINE MICRO-ORGANISMS BY MARINE BACTERIA
--This study is concerned with the contribution of the indigenous marine microflora to the killing of intestinal bacteria, represented by *Escherichia coli* and of fungi represented by *Pythium debary-*

anum. The results show a direct relationship between the use of the marine microflora and the rate and extent of die-off of *E. coli* in sea water. Ref: *P-8 and J-12   2(1):113, Jan 1968. (abstract only)*

3.0 - 376
Mitchell, R. (1968).   FACTORS AFFECTING THE DECLINE OF NON-MARINE MICRO-ORGANISMS IN SEA WATER
--Work related to the decline in sea water of sewage-borne bacteria, yeasts, fungi, and enteric viruses, is reviewed. Some factors considered in the case of bacteria include sedimentation, adsorption, temperature effects, heavy metals, the production of toxins by plankton, and lysis by marine organisms. Regarding yeasts, temperature effects and the activities of anti-yeast marine bacteria were investigated; in the case of fungi the fungistatic properties of marine algae were tested, and in the case of viruses the part played by shellfish in their survival was studied. Ref: *J-12 2(8):535-543, Sept 1968.*

3.0 - 377
Mitchell, R. and Nevo, Z. (1965). DECOMPOSITION OF STRUCTURAL POLYSACCHARIDES OF BACTERIA BY MARINE MICRO-ORGANISMS
--Investigations were carried out to determine whether micro-organisms capable of degrading both agar and bacterial structural materials could be isolated from sea water. When enrichment cultures were prepared by inoculating natural Mediterranean sea water into an artificial sea-water medium in which the sole source of carbon comprised capsules of *Flavobacterium, Azotobacter, Rhizobium,* or *Arthrobacter,* or cell walls of *Escherichia coli B,* in each case a marine bacterium capable of utilizing the respective structural material was isolated and the isolate also caused liquifaction of agar. The marine *Pseudomonas* isolated from *Flavobacterium* capsule medium was also capable of metabolizing cell walls of *Esch. coli;* and studies showed that polysaccharidases active against *Flavobacterium* capsular material and agar were produced extracellularly, but the enzymatic system active against the cell walls of *Esch. coli* was intracellular. In comparative studies on the survival of *Arthrobacter* and *Esch. coli* in artificial sea water, both these non-marine bacteria were suppressed markedly in the presence of a lytic marine *Pseudomonas; Arthrobacter* was the more resistant to lysis, possibly owing to its capsular layer. Ref: *J-7   205(4975):1007-1008, March 6, 1965.*

3.0 - 378
Modin, John C. (1969).   CHLORINATED HYDROCARBON PESTICIDES IN CALIFORNIA BAYS AND ESTUARIES
--Analyses of oysters, mussels, and clams sampled revealed DDT, DDD, and DDE, dieldrin, and endrin in concentrations from 10 to 3,600 ppb. Levels in king crabs, ova of king salmon, prawn, flounder, halibut and sole were high. Ref: *J-40   3(1): 1-7, June 1969. 7 refs.*

3.0 - 379
Momma, T. and Iwashima K. (1967).   SCAVENGING OF RADIONUCLIDES IN SEA WATER BY THE USE OF MANGANESE DIOXIDE AND OTHERS (SIC).
--The efficiences of various scavenging materials for concentrating traces of cobalt-60, ruthenium-106, and zinc-65 from sea water were compared. Ferric hydroxide was found to be inefficient for cobalt-60; hydroxides of ferric iron with magnesium and ferric iron with manganese were efficient, but difficult to filter. The best results were obtained with a commercial granular a-manganese dioxide; a concentration of 0.2 g removed the trace elements completely from 50 ml of sea water after stirring for 1 hour. Ref: *J-92   16(2):68-72, 1967.*

3.0 - 380
Moore, P. (1967).   ASPECTS OF SEWAGE DISPOSAL BY SEA OUTFALL
--Pollution in and near the Tyne Estuary caused by sewage discharges and the effect of the discharge into the North Sea were investigated. Measurements were made of bacterial decay rates, density changes, and densimetric flow, and the results of a previous investigation of wind-induced currents were combined with an examination of wind records to determine the occurrence of critical winds which would have caused beach pollution. Ref: *J-93 94(5):161-165, May 1967.*

3.0 - 381
Morrison, G. E. (1966).   AN INVESTIGATION OF THE DISTRIBUTION OF *NEPHTYS CAECOIDES* IN YAQUINA BAY
--A study of the distribution of the polychaete worm, *Nephtys caecoides,* in Yaquina Bay, Ore., during the summer of 1964 showed that it was distributed evenly from just offshore to a point about 8 km into the bay. None of the environmental factors examined (salinity, temperature, and sediment composition) appeared to be the single one limiting distribution of the worm, but it is possible that, in summer, the sediment porosity, organic content, and temperature combine to produce unfavorable conditions. Ref: *Oregon State Univ. Thesis   35 p., 1966.*

3.0 - 382
Moskovits, G. and Flanagan A. (1967).   GROWTH OF MARINE BACTERIA ON SOME ORGANIC ACIDS AND ITS APPLICATION TO THE SELECTIVE ISOLATION OF PSEUDOMONADS
--The ability of heterotrophic marine bacteria to utilize some organic acids as a source of carbon for growth is reported. Organic acids could be used for the selective isolation of pseudomonads, although in the experiments described selection was not complete. Ref: *J-19   13,:1561-1563, 1967.*

3.0 - 383
Mount, Donald I. (1967).   CONSIDERATIONS FOR ACCEPTABLE CONCENTRATIONS OF PESTICIDES FOR FISH PRODUCTION
--All quality requirements for aquatic life must protect even the most sensitive developmental stages and the most sensitive species including necessary food chain organisms. Requirements based on data derived from exposures of at least one generation are minimal; multi-generation exposures are certainly preferable. When more than one pollutant is present, the acceptable concentrations for individual pollutants must be revised. In estuarine and marine waters, invertebrates as well as fish are frequently harvested for consumption and recreation. The establishment of satisfactory concentrations of pesticides for fish pre-

sents problems such as (1) substantial food-chain accumulation; (2) tissue residues rendering the fish unfit for consumption; (3) potential hazard to the fish from readsorption of fat-stored pesticides; and (4) off-taste or tainting from certain types of pesticides. Concentrations of pesticides that appear to be acceptable under continuous exposure may not be adequate to protect the fish when pesticides are present in their food. Also, unacceptable residues in edible portions may result from exposure of the fish to the water concentrations that are not directly harmful to the fish themselves. Safe pesticide concentrations should be based on continuous exposure experiments to protect against those instances in which exposure is continuous. Ref: *P-32 and J-23 96(1): 3-6, (Supp. Special Publication No. 4), 1967. 5 refs.*

3.0 - 384
Mukherjee, Shishir K. (1969). ECONOMIC EVALUATION OF WATER QUALITY. A MULTICOMPONENT MODEL OF OPTIMAL QUALITY CONTROL IN ESTUARINE WATERS
--The overall objectives of the study, were to utilize the techniques of operations research to determine the economic effects of changing the water quality requirements of an estuarine water basin. The specific objectives were: to study the transportation, dispersion, and degradation of waste constituents in an estuarine basin; to develop dispersion models for optimal allocation of water quality in an estuary to achieve various related objectives; to develop discrete versions of the dispersion models as linear programs; to develop an integrated multicomponent model of dispersion and waste treatment which will simultaneously provide an optimal plan of waste treatment; and to study various modifications of the model and the economic effects of various alternative quality-improvement projects. Ref: *California. Univ., Berkeley. Sanitary Engineering Research Lab. Rept. no. 4 (Annual). 109 p., Jan 1969.*

3.0 - 385
Munson, Frederick J. (1970). EFFLUENT DISPOSING SYSTEM
--This invention pertains to systems for disposing of sewage into large bodies of water such as the oceans. It comprises a long outfall which extends from a sewage processing plant into the ocean. The extended end portion of the outfall is formed with orfices for discharging the effluent into diffusers aligned with such orifices. The diffusers are spaced a predetermined distance from the orfices to entrain sea water with the effluent as it is forces under pressure into the diffusers. The diffusers are formed with diffuser openings for letting the sewage and intermixed sea water seep into the ocean for dissipation therein with normal ocean currents. Ref: *U. S. Patent No. 3,490,485, Not Assigned. 1970.*

3.0 - 386
Murchelano, R. A. (1968). HETEROTROPHIC BACTERIA IN NARRAGANSETT BAY AND THEIR ABILITY TO REGENERATE PHOSPHATE FROM *SKELETONEMA COSTATUM*
--Studies on bacteria in Narragansett Bay, R.I., showed that the viable heterotrophic population ranged from 1.5×10^3 to 5.0×10^4 per ml. More proteolytic than lipolytic or amylolytic bacteria were found, and most of the bacteria were able to

grow at 9°, 18° and 27°C. All the bacteria were able to utilize *Skeletonema* substrates, but there was no evidence that they subsequently released inorganic phosphate to the medium. Ref: *Rhode Island University Thesis 101 p., 1968.*

3.0 - 387
Murphy, R. S. and Miller, A. P. (1968). WASTE-INDUCED OXYGEN UPTAKE OF AN ALASKAN ESTUARY
--In Knik Arm, Alaska, oxygen consumption in 2°C waters inoculated with settled domestic sewage was measured over 20-day period. Oxygen uptake in natural waters alone was substantial at this temperature, and addition of sewage considerably increased demand for oxygen. It was demonstrated that the oxygen consumption observed could not be directly related to increase in bacterial numbers but rather to effect (on bacterial growth) of planktonic organisms in natural waters. Ref: *J-3 94(SA2 Paper 5908):345-354, April 1968.*

3.0 - 388
Nakatani, R. E. (1969). EFFECTS OF HEATED DISCHARGES ON ANADROMOUS FISHES
--Reviews some of the highlights of biological research at Hanford on the effects of elevated water temperatures, especially on salmonids. Emphasis is placed on the Pacific salmon and rainbow trout because of their sensitivity to warm waters and their economic importance. The problem of evaluating and assessing the biological effect of the relatively small heat increments added by the Hanford reactors to the Columbia River or added heat from any source on the health of salmon populations defies a direct, definitive answer at this time because of large gaps in our knowledge about those complex factors which determine survival. Ref: *P-30 p. 294-317, 1969. 29 refs.*

3.0 - 389
Naylor, E. (1965). EFFECT OF HEATED EFFLUENTS UPON MARINE AND ESTUARINE ORGANISMS
--Discusses the biological effects of heated effluents on estuarine life. It is suggested that there may be many situations where siting power plants in estuaries could be beneficial to the marine environment, as well as other situations where such would be detrimental. Ref: *Advances in Marine Biology Vol. 3 p. 63-104 Academic Press, 1965.*

3.0 - 390
Nishiwaki, Y.; Honda, Y. and others (1968). STUDIES ON THE RELEASE OF RADIOACTIVITIES FROM THE ION-EXCHANGE RESINS INTO THE SEA WATER
--The release of various radioactive isotopes from ion-exchange resins was studied in a water bath containing natural sea water from Osaka Bay, Japan. Results show that the isotopes were released rapidly from the resins; nearly 100 per cent of the cobalt-60 and strontium-89 were released but chromium-51 and iron-55 were not released so easily. The percentage of activity released increased with decreases in the weight ratio of ion-exchange resin to sea water but there were no marked differences for weight ratios less than 10^{-4}. With a fixed weight ratio there was a tendency for the percentage of activity released to decrease with increases in the initial amount of adsorbed activity, but there was no marked effect when the weight ratio was

less than 10⁻³. The accumulation and distribution of isotopes in the suspended matter were also studied by fractional filtration. The concentration factor often used in calculating the hazard of accumulation of radioactivity by biological material is discussed critically, and the advantages of using a proposed 'sample accumulation fraction' or 'sample concentration factor' are explained. Ref: *P-7 p. 681-699, 1966. Published 1968.*

3.0 - 391
North Carolina. University. Chapel Hill. (1966). PROCEEDINGS. SYMPOSIUM ON ESTUARINE ECOLOGY OF THE COASTAL WATERS OF NORTH CAROLINA
--Includes papers describing the estuarine research and action programs of the N.C. Dept of Conservation and Development, Water and Air Resources, and Health; N. C. Wildlife Resources Commission and State Recreation Commission; the U.S. Fish and Wildlife Service, National Park Service, Public Health Service; the University of North Carolina at Chapel Hill and North Carolina State University at Raleigh. Ref: *North Carolina. Univ. Chapel Hill OWRR Project A-999-NC 111 p., May 1966.*

3.0 - 392
North, Wheeler J.; Neushul, M.; and Clendenning, K. A. (1965). SUCCESSIVE BIOLOGICAL CHANGES OBSERVED IN A MARINE COVE EXPOSED TO A LARGE SPILLAGE OF MINERAL OIL
--Observations, with tabulated data, are reported on the general changes in flora and fauna in a small cove on the Pacific coast of Lower California, Mexico, since 1957 when a loaded oil tanker ran aground, blocking the entrance to the cove, restricting wave action until the hull was later disintegrated, and liberating diesel oil both at the time of the wreck and sporadically during the next 8 months. Oil was the primary factor causing the destruction of organisms, either by killing them directly or by forcing them to release their attachment to the bottom when they could be cast ashore by the surf. Most of the plant species became re-established within a few months but the animal species re-appeared more gradually over a period of several years, and 7 years afterwards the populations of certain organisms such as grazing sea urchins, abalones, and filter-feeding mussels were still considerably reduced and some species present before the shipwreck have still not been reported. Of the animals which survived the shipwreck, the periwinkle (*Littorina planaxis*) probably owed its survival to its location in the spray zone and its ability to isolate itself inside the shell for a month or more, but the large anemones (*Anthopleura sp.*) and some other coelenterates must have been exposed to oil or oil-water emulsions and presumably can tolerate oil pollution. Laboratory studies were made on the toxicity to kelp (*Macrocystis*) and urchins (*Strongylocentrotus purpuratus*) of diesel and other fuel oils supplied as a surface film or in emulsions with sea water. Tabulated results show the effects on the photosynthetic capacity of juvenile kelp blades; irreversible damage occurred after exposure to 0.1 per cent emulsion of oil for 6-12 hours. When urchins were exposed to 0.1 per cent diesel oil emulsion, their tube feet were soon withdrawn and they could no longer cling to the

bottom; during subsequent exposure for up to 1 hour they remained motionless but shed no spines; the period required for recovery in clean sea water increased with the period of exposure, and recovery was still possible after exposure for 1 hour. Ref: *P-1 p. 335-354, 1965.*

3.0 - 393
Oakley, H. R. (1965). STUDY OF BEACH POLLUTION IN TIDAL WATERS
--Reports an investigation of sewerage and sewage disposal in Tyneside in order to prepare a design to overcome pollution. Using coliform bacteria as the main indicator, the beaches were found to be grossly polluted. The beaches were polluted by local short outfalls and in part by the discharge of the polluted river water in which wind-induced currents were important. Ref: *P-10 3,:85-116, 1965.*

3.0 - 394
O'Connor, B. A. and Croft, J. E. (1967). POLLUTION IN A TIDAL ESTUARY
--Water from the Mersey Estuary was analysed to determine the nature and origin of organic matter and the degree and manner of its association with suspended solids. The results indicated a close relation between the organic and inorganic fraction throughout the tide and that much of the organic matter associated with solids was comprised of nitrogenous matter. As the turbidity of the estuary prevents the development of marine algae, it was apparent that it came from sewage and trade effluents; the wide distribution of *Esch. coli* in both surface and bottom water samples confirmed this. The presence of a secondary density circulation in an estuary such as the Mersey causes the retention of organic material in the system which in turn may encourage deposition of coarse sediments and cause silting-up of the estuary. Ref: *J-94 7,:365-374, 1967.*

3.0 - 395
O'Connor, Donald J. (1965). ESTUARINE DISTRIBUTION OF NONCONSERVATIVE SUBSTANCES
--Various mathematical analyses and methods are presented to define water quality and pollution conditions in a one-dimensional estuary, characteristic of many estuaries on the eastern coast of the United States. Three common coordinate systems are used to describe the geometry of various estuarine systems; different types of spatial and temporal pollutional loadings are included in the analysis. Final equations are used to define longitudinal distribution of various pollution parameters in estuaries of the Delaware, East and James Rivers. Ref: *J-3 91(SA1 Paper 4225):23-42, Feb 1965. 12 refs.*

3.0 - 396
O'Connor, Donald J. (1966). ANALYSIS OF THE DISSOLVED OXYGEN DISTRIBUTION IN THE EAST RIVER
--Analysis of water quality in the East River, New York, by a mathematical model consisting of linear differential equations produced results agreeing generally with observation of actual conditions. Storm overflows and sludge deposits appear to have significant effects. The spatial profile of DO is directly related to wastewater discharges and temporal distribution is established primarily by the temperature distribution during the summer. Ref:

J-1 38(11):1813-1830, Nov 1966. 6 refs.

3.0 - 397
O'Connor, Donald J.; St. John, John P. and DiToro,
D. M. (1968).   WATER QUALITY ANALYSIS OF THE
DELAWARE RIVER ESTUARY
--A mathematical model was developed for the Delaware River which assesses the efficiency of various proposals for water quality improvement. Emphasis is on the importance of nitrification in
the river that may become intensified by future
reduction in carbonaceous demand due to increased
treatment. It is concluded that basin-wide collection and treatment facilities with downstream
disposals may be a realistic alternative. Ref:
J-3 94(SA6 Paper 6318):1225-1252, Dec 1968.
16 refs.

3.0 - 398
Oglesby, R. G. and Jamison, D. (1968). INTERTIDAL
COMMUNITIES AS MONITORS OF POLLUTION
--Ecological surveys of intertidal zones are proposed as an economical way in which biologic impact of many wastes discharged into estuarine and
coastal marine environments can be assessed.
Species diversity and community structure are measures selected and these are determined through a
carefully designed and statistically valid program
of sampling. Aerial photography is used in developing a sampling program with infrared Ektachrome
film providing information on distribution and
nature of intertidal flora. Ref: J-3 94(SA3
Paper 6008):541-550, June 1968. 14 refs.

3.0 - 399
Ogura, Norio and Hanya, Takahisa   (1968).
ULTRAVIOLET ABSORBANCE AS AN INDEX OF THE
POLLUTION OF SEAWATER
--Study of several bays in Japan show that ultraviolet absorption can be used effectively as an
indicator of organic pollution in coastal waters.
Transparency and chemical oxygen demand are used
to determine pollution. Absorbance of seawater is
due mainly to organic matter and bromides, and
absorbance of coastal water is higher than that of
the open sea. Ref: J-1 40(3 Part 1):464-467,
March 1968. 7 refs.

3.0 - 400
Oka, T. and Katsuta, K. (1969).   NEW-TYPE HIGH-
EFFICIENCY OIL SEPARATOR FOR SHIP AND PORT USE
--An illustrated description is given of an oil
separator which can reduce the oil concentration
in oily water to less than 100 p.p.m. It consists
of 3 chambers in series, two for sedimentation,
with the intermediate stage filled with a coal-
escing medium in the form of small-diameter tubes
made of plastic material such as polyvinylchlor-
ide or polypropylene. The mechanism of separation
of oil globules is explained theoretically. Performance is good even with hot or very cold water.
Test results are given for engine bilge, and the
separator can also be used to treat dirty ballast
and tank-cleaning water; flow diagrams are given
of commercial installations in Japan, and the advantages of the system are outlined. Ref: P-21
19 p., 1969.

3.0 - 401
Oliff, W. D.; Berrisford, C. D. and others (1967).
ECOLOGY AND CHEMISTRY OF SANDY   BEACHES AND

NEARSHORE SUBMARINE SEDIMENTS OF NATAL. I.
POLLUTION CRITERIA FOR SANDY BEACHES IN NATAL. II.
POLLUTION CRITERIA FOR NEARSHORE SEDIMENTS OF THE
NATAL COAST
--Chemical characteristics and fauna were studied
on beaches and in offshore marine sediments in 4
localities along 60 miles of coastline in Natal,
and the observations in specific and different localities were compared in order to obtain criteria
for the assessment of pollution. The effects of
organic enrichment on the fauna of the beaches are
discussed. Analyses were made of dehydrogenase
activity, humic acids, sulphides, and faunal biomass. No uniform background levels of parameters
were found for all the locations, and there were
changes with time in a particular location; considerably increased levels of chemical parameters
and high faunal densities were associated with organic pollution, harpacticoid copepods being well
represented, and the polychaete Capitella capitata
was specifically associated with pollution. Maximal monitoring levels are suggested for perman-
ganate demand, dehydrogenase activity, humic acid,
and animal density. Ref: J-12 1(2):115-129,
131-146, Feb 1967.

3.0 - 402
Olson, T. A. and Burgess, Frederick, J. (1967).
POLLUTION AND MARINE ECOLOGY (Book)
--This book contains the full text of 20 papers,
and related discussions, presented at a conference
in Texas, March 1966, sponsored by Texas A & M
University and the University of Minnesota, and
dealing with the status of knowledge, critical research needs, and potential research facilities relating to ecology and pollution problems in the
marine environment. The papers, provided with a
subject index are classified into sections on (1)
man's resources in the marine environment; (2) dynamics of the littoral marine community; (3) ecological systems; (4) energy transfer; (5) interactions between the biota and the chemical-physi-
cal environment; and (6) parameters of marine pollution. Ref: P-16 380 p. John Wiley and
Sons, New York, 1967.

3.0 - 403
O'Neal, G. L. (1966).   DEGRADATION OF KRAFT
PULPING WASTES IN ESTUARINE WATERS
--The waste waters from a combined pulp and paper
mill were mixed with sea water to give waste concentrations of 3, 7, and 10 per cent, and measurements were made on 5-day BOD, Pearl-Benson index,
and toxicity to bay mussels (Mytilus edulis). It
was found that degradation of the waste water, as
measured by the rate of change of BOD, followed
first-order kinetics, and that degradation was
more rapid in more dilute solutions. For a given
concentration of waste water, the rate of degradation appeared to be independent of salinity, but
the ratio of BOD to salinity appeared to be related to the degradation rate at 20°C. The toxicity of the waste water to mussels was found to be
biologically degradable. There was no apparent relation between the reductions in BOD, Pearl-Benson
index, and toxicity. Ref: Oregon State Univ.
Thesis 134 p., 1966.

3.0 - 404
Orlob, G. T.; Selleck, R.; Yeiser, A.; Walsh, R.
and Stann, E. (1968).   MODELING OF WATER QUALITY

BEHAVIOR IN AN ESTUARIAL ENVIRONMENT
--Research and development efforts extending more than five years on the complex estuary of the Sacramento and San Joaquin Rivers have yielded several specialized mathematical models for characterization of quantity changes in such systems. The development of these models to be used as essential tools of the San Francisco Bay - Delta Study is described and examples of their application to specific problems are given. Ref: P-8 and J-12 2(1):122, Jan 1968. (abstract only).

3.0 - 405
Orlob, G. T.; Shubinski, R. P. and Feigner, K. D. (1967). MATHEMATICAL MODELING OF WATER QUALITY IN ESTUARIAL SYSTEMS
--Presents the theoretical and practical basis for the development of a mathematical model for digital computer simulation of quality changes, concentrating on the distribution in space and time of conservative constituents. This model was extended in a subsequent study for the Federal Water Pollution Control Administration as a part of its comprehensive investigation of the San Joaquin Master Drain and its effects on water quality in San Francisco Bay and the Delta. Ref: P-2 p. 646-675, 1967.

3.0 - 406
Osterberg, Charles (1965). RADIOACTIVITY FROM THE COLUMBIA RIVER
--States that the influence of river water at sea inferred by the zinc-65 content of marine organisms, is widespread. Fishes from California to Alaska carry a faint but distinct radioactive souvenir of their contact with Columbia River water. While the horizontal extent of the river's influence is great, vertical penetration appears to be limited. Ref: P-15 2,:968-979, 1965.

3.0 - 407
Osterberg, C. L.; Cutshall, N. and others (1966). SOME NON-BIOLOGICAL ASPECTS OF COLUMBIA RIVER RADIOACTIVITY
--Studies on the distribution of radioactivity in the Pacific Ocean, originating from the reactors at Hanford and carried out to sea by the Columbia River, are summarized. A probe, developed to measure gamma-ray emission in situ, showed that the concentrations of zinc-65, manganese-54, and cobalt-60 are higher in sediments than in the overlying water. It was concluded that ion exchange is not important in the retention of sediment-sorbed zinc-65, and that a considerable amount is bound by a mechanism involving the formation of a co-ordination complex. Large-scale equipment has also been developed for determining chromium-51, used to trace the dispersion of the river 'plume' at sea. Ref: P-4 p. 321-335, 1966.

3.0 - 408
O'Sullivan, A. J. and Richardson, Alison J. (1967). TORREY CANYON DISASTER AND INTERTIDAL MARINE LIFE
--Following the Torrey Canyon disaster, the effects of the oil and detergent on the intertidal marine life were examined at two areas of the Cornish Coast. In an effort to clean up the oil roughly 22,500 gallons of detergent were used each day. The report paints a dismal picture. Ref: J-7 214(5087):448, 541-542, April 29, 1967.

3.0 - 409
Ozmidov, R. V. and Popov, N. I. (1966). SOME DATA ON THE DIFFUSION OF SOLUBLE CONTAMINANTS IN THE OCEAN
--Data on the distribution of strontium-90 in the seas and oceans of the world have been used to predict the transport of soluble contaminants by water circulation. The distribution of a contaminant for the ocean as a whole can be calculated by means of a simple vertical transport equation with a constant coefficient of turbulent diffusion and a zero mean vertical rate of movement of the ocean water. Using this equation it was estimated, and confirmed by observation, that the change in the concentration of strontium-90 in the surface layers of the ocean is proportional to the square root of the period since global fallout began in 1954, and the co-efficient of turbulent diffusion was estimated to be 30 cm^2 per sec. Ref: P-4 p. 451-460, 1966.

3.0 - 410
Padilla, George M. and Bragg, R. J. (1968). ACCUMULATION OF A HEMOLYTIC FACTOR BY ESTUARINE SHELLFISH IN THE FIELD AND LABORATORY
--Reports a study to establish base levels of toxicity in estuarine filter feeders by the localization of chronic infections among shellfish; with special reference to the content of hemolytic factors in oysters. The study is being made in cooperation with the Division of Commercial Fisheries of the Department of Conservation and Development of the State of North Carolina and the Institute of Marine Sciences of the University of North Carolina at Morehead City. Ref: P-17 p. 193-204, 1968. 13 refs.

3.0 - 411
Palausi, G. (1968). STUDY OF THE DISPERSION OF COLOURED FLOATS IN THE BAY OF CANNES
--A fluorescein tracer and small expanded polystyrene floats were used to indicate the superficial currents in the Bay of Cannes, and the dominant influence of locally prevailing winds on these currents was described. Ref: P-19 and J-59 9,:191-205, 1968. 19 refs.

3.0 - 412
Pall, David B. and Rosenberg, David (1969). MARINE SEWAGE DISPOSAL METHOD AND APPARATUS
--A method and apparatus are provided for rapidly disposing of marine sewage in which human body waste is pulverized in the presence of a disinfectant into colloidal size particles to form a stable colloidal suspension that within a very short period can be safely dumped overboard. Ref: U. S. Patent No. 3,472,390. Assigned to Pall Corporation. 1969.

3.0 - 413
Paoletti, A. (1965). PATHOGENIC ORGANISMS IN THE MARINE ENVIRONMENT
--Reviews and discusses the occurrence of various pathogenic organisms in municipal waste waters, with individual sections on tubercle bacteria, salmonellae, and enteroviruses; the behavior and survival of the principle pathogens, namely enterobacteria and enteroviruses, when discharged to sea water; self-purification in sea water, including the role of absorption, sedimentation, solar radiation, temperature, aeration, nutrients, salts,

bactericidal or antibiotic substances, bacteriophage, and animal predators; problems encountered
in the sampling and study of pathogenic organisms;
diseases of bathers caused by polluted water; methods for overcoming the aesthetic, disease, and
putrefactive-odor problems associated with the
disposal of sewage at sea; and different standards
necessary for bathing waters according to the conditions in different countries. In an appendix, a
study is reported on the pollution caused by sewage from Naples which, to protect the Gulf of
Naples, is discharged through an intercepting sewer to coastal waters off Cumes. Ref: P-1
p. 134-184, 1965. 355 refs.

3.0 - 414
Paoletti, A. (1965).   HYGIENIC PROBLEMS OF
SHELLFISH
--The author discusses the diseases which may be
caused by shellfish, owing to the presence of
toxic substances or pathogenic enterobacteria or
viruses; hygienic precautions to be taken in
shellfish culture; methods for the purification of
polluted shellfish; and procedures for bacteriological analysis. Ref: P-1 p. 251-264, 1965.
73 refs.

3.0 - 415
Paoletti, A. (1966).   FAECAL POLLUTION OF THE
COAST OF CUMES AND CONSIDERATIONS ON THE SELF-
PURIFYING POWER OF THE MARINE ENVIRONMENT
--During a detailed study from 1961 to 1964 of the
pollution of the coastal waters of Cumes, which
receive sewage from the suburbs of Naples, samples
of sewage from the outfall and of the sea water at
various distances from the point of discharge were
analysed for Salmonellae, coliform bacteria, total
micro-organisms growing in agar at 22° and 37°C,
and coliform bacteriophages. The results are given
in a table and graphs: the outfall discharges
large amounts of bacterial pollution which decreases with dispersion. However, this continuous load
has not affected the stability of the biological
equilibrium of the sea, and the bacteriological
condition of the local water is not considered to
be dangerous. The author stresses the need for
further research into the survival of enterobacteria and viruses ingested by other organisms.
Ref: J-59 1,:44-55, 1966.

3.0 - 416
Parker, Bruce C. (1967).   BIODIALYSTAT: NEW
SAMPLER FOR DISSOLVED ORGANIC MATTER
--The biodialystat is used for collection of cell-
free water for content analysis of dissolved organic matter. The device functions by permitting
dialysis of ambient natural water against sterilized distilled water contained in the chamber.
Ref: J-41 12(4):722-723, Oct 1967.

3.0 - 417
Parker, Frank L. and Krenkel, Peter A. (1969).
ENGINEERING ASPECTS OF THERMAL POLLUTION
--A collection of papers constituting the pro-
ceedings of the National symposium on thermal pol-
lution sponsored by the Federal Water Pollution
Control Administration and Vanderbilt University.
This part of the symposium was held at Nashville,
Tennessee, Aug 14-16, 1968. Ref: P-30b 351 p.,
1969. See also: 3.0 - 313, Krenkel

3.0 - 418
Parker, P. L. (1966).   MOVEMENT OF RADIO-ISOTOPES
IN A MARINE BAY: COBALT-60, IRON-59, MANGANESE-54,
ZINC-65, SODIUM-22
--Reports on studies of the distribution of trace
elements within the ecosystem in Redfish Bay, Tex.
The uptake and release of added radioactive cobalt, iron, manganese, zinc, and sodium by the
marine grass Thalassia testudinum were measured.
Most of the sodium remained in the water, but the
other elements were quickly taken up by the grass
and were later partly released. Results of experiments with cobalt-60 indicated a diurnal transfer
of this element between the grass and the sediment, the maximal concentration in the grass occurring at about midnight, whilst the concentration in the water gradually decreased. Ref:
Texas University. Institute of Marine Science Publication 11 p. 102-107, 1966.

3.0 - 419
Parkhurst, John D.; Haug, Lester A. and Whitt,
Malcolm L. (1967).   OCEAN OUTFALL DESIGN FOR
ECONOMY OF CONSTRUCTION
--Design requirements for submarine outfalls for
disposal of metropolitan sewage wastes are des-
cribed. Specification data and costs of construc-
tion are given for five major submarine outfalls
on the Pacific Coast of the United States. Ref:
J-1 39(6):987-993, June 1967.

3.0 - 420
Pastuhov, Alexis V. (1969). COMBATING POLLUTION
CREATED BY OIL SPILLS. VOLUME ONE: METHODS
--Provides information on the state-of-the-art of
available methods for combating oil spills along
with their basic technology. The effectiveness of
each method has been rated on the basis of technical, ecological, and operational considerations
and qualitative cost information associated with
actual oil spill clean-up operations. Ref: Arthur
D. Little, Inc. Cambridge, Mass. Rept. no. ADL-
71386 (R) 164 p., June 1969.

3.0 - 421
Patrick, Ruth (1967).   DIATOM COMMUNITIES IN
ESTUARIES
--The diatom types that compose estuarine communities are usually benthic and neritic species, although some plankton species may be brought in by
tidal action or wind. Light and temperature seem
to be important environmental factors which influence diatom abundance. Salinity affects the number
of species, and particularly the kinds of species.
There appears to be a high consistency in the diversity which any particular area will support as
long as environmental characteristics do not
change radically. Radical changes may be brought
about naturally but often occur as a result of
pollution. Ref: In book: Estuaries, Lauf, G. H.
757 pages. AAAS.

3.0 - 422
Patrick, Ruth (1968).   WATER RESEARCH PROGRAMS
- AQUATIC COMMUNITIES
--Knowledge of the effects of various types of
pollution on aquatic ecosystems is discussed.
Fields of research which need to be pursued to
understand the structure and functioning of aquatic ecosystems and the effects of pollution or
perturbation are outlined. Ref: U. S. Dept. of

the *Interior. Office of Water Resources Research Contr. no. 14-01-0001-1569   22 p., March 1968. 9 refs.*

3.0 - 423
Patten, B. C. and Chabot, B. F. (1966). FACTORIAL PRODUCTIVITY EXPERIMENTS IN A SHALLOW ESTUARY: CHARACTERISTICS OF RESPONSE SURFACES
--Experiments on productivity in York River, Va. are described, using a factorial design in which samples of water collected from seven depths down to 22 ft were suspended vertically in pairs of dark-and-light bottles. Data on gross production, respiration and net production relative to collection and suspension depths were obtained between June and August, 1963, and the characteristics of the respective response surfaces are discussed. Analyses of the phytoplankton are tabulated. Since, in most cases, negative values of integral net production were calculated although the station had no unusual factors, the accuracy of measurement of production was doubted, but it was confirmed that data on cell abundance and species composition were of no use in assessing levels of production and respiration. Ref: *J-25 7(3): 117-136, Fall 1966.*

3.0 - 424
Paulson, Richard W. (1968). PRELIMINARY REMOTE SENSING OF THE DELAWARE ESTUARY
--The potential applications of remote sensing techniques for estuarine hydrology are discussed in a review of infrared imagery and aerial photography of the Delaware Estuary. It is concluded that infrared imagery can be an important estuarine reconnaissance tool. Ref: *NASA Tech Letter 128 22 p., Oct 1968. 12 refs.*

3.0 - 425
Paulson, Richard W. (1969). LONGITUDINAL DIFFUSION COEFFICIENT IN THE DELAWARE RIVER ESTUARY AS DETERMINED FROM A STEADY-STATE MODEL
--Because the form of the diffusion coefficient allows 2 degrees of freedom in fitting the solution of the diffusion equation to data from a real estuary, it is possible to determine the magnitude of the diffusion coefficient as well as the effect, on the distribution of the conservative substance, assuming a constant coefficient. Data from the Delaware Estuary were used to test the solution. Ref: *J-16 5(1):59-67, Feb 1969. 6 refs.*

3.0 - 426
Pearcy, W. G. and Osterberg, C. L. (1967). DEPTH, DIEL, SEASONAL AND GEOGRAPHIC VARIATIONS IN ZINC-65 OF MIDWATER ANIMALS OFF OREGON
--Macroplankton and micronekton at one station off the coast of Oregon were sampled over a 2-year period to obtain information on variations in the uptake of zinc-65. Animals collected in the upper 150 m showed marked seasonal variations in the content of zinc-65 per g of biomass, with summer maxima related to the seasonal occurrence of Columbia River 'plume' waters off Oregon; these variations were less noticeable in animals from depths of 150-500 m, and no seasonal variations were found in animals at greater depths. Although the concentration of zinc-65 in animals collected at all depths during winter was low, it was higher than in samples collected further offshore, indicating that even in winter more of the zinc activity or-

iginated from the Columbia River water than from fallout and that some of the river water is retained off Oregon throughout the year. Vertically migrating animals may play a major role in the movement of certain radioactive isotopes, and other materials, through density gradients in the open sea. Ref: *J-42 1,:103-116, 1967.*

3.0 - 427
Pearcy, W. G. and Osterberg, C. L. (1968). ZINC-65 AND MANGANESE-54 IN ALBACORE *THUNNAS ALALUNGA* FROM THE WEST COAST OF NORTH AMERICA
--A study was made to determine the major gamma-emitting radio-isotopes found in the livers of albacore, *Thunnus alalunga*, taken from the coastal waters off northwest America during the summers of 1962-1966. Zinc-65 and manganese-54 were found to be the dominant artificial radionuclides and their concentration and specific activities changed considerably during the summer. Levels of zinc-65 in albacore taken off Oregon and Washington increased during the summer and were directly related to their association with the Columbia River plume; zinc-65 content of fish taken from Baja California was only 10 per cent of fish taken further north and showed no seasonal trends. There was no evidence of migration between the northern and southern fisheries. The radioactivity and specific activity of manganese-54 decreased during the summer, indicating that manganese-54 is more readily available in offshore waters than in coastal waters. The main source of manganese-54 is fallout from nuclear weapon tests. Ref: *J-41 13(3): 490-498, July 1968. 25 refs.*

3.0 - 428
Pearson, E. A. (1966). SOME DEVELOPMENTS IN MARINE WASTE DISPOSAL
--Describes methods and equations for analysing the dispersion of waste waters discharged into the sea, including the initial mixing in the vicinity of the discharge point and the subsequent transport and dispersion of the waste water in the dispersion plume. The methods used to determine current speed, frequency, direction, distribution and diffusion using drift cards, including methods of releasing and recovering the cards, and analysing the data obtained are explained. Much more attention should be paid to the estimation and control of floatable matter in waste waters and to the determination of the rates of 'die-away' of bacteria, particularly coliform organisms, since this is of importance in determining the length of outfall required to produce an acceptable bacterial concentration on the shore. Californian practice is based largely on an average T_{90} value for the coliform die-away rate of 4 hours for primary sewage effluent, but recent studies off the coast of Ghana showed an average decay rate for these tropical waters of 80 min. Ref: *J-74 p. 223-234, 1966.*

3.0 - 429
Pearson, C. R. and Pearson, J. R. A. (1965). SIMPLE METHOD FOR PREDICTING DISPERSION OF EFFLUENTS IN ESTUARIES
--A simplified mathematical method, based on the principle of retention time with emphasis on its relation to physical processes of mixing discharges into tidal estuaries is described. It can be used by a small pollution control agency, an individual trader, or a local authority. Ref: *Amer-*

ican Institute of Chemical Engineers. New Chemical Engineering Problems in Utilization of Water. Paper 9.9   p. 39-45, June 1965.

3.0 - 430
Pence, George D., Jr.; Jeglic, John M. and Thomann, Robert V. (1967). DEVELOPMENT AND APPLICATION OF A TIME-VARYING DISSOLVED OXYGEN MODEL
--A one-dimensional time varying mathematical model for the simulation of dissolved oxygen in an estuary is developed along with a numerical integration procedure for computer solution. Some applications of the model are presented. Ref: P-2 p. 537-585, 1967.

3.0 - 431
Pence, George D.; Jeglic, John M. and Thomann, Robert V. (1968). TIME-VARYING DISSOLVED OXYGEN MODEL
--A mathematical model was developed to simulate the dissolved oxygen in a one-dimensional estuary using mass balances on finite sections. The solution requires integration on a computer. The determination of parameters is analyzed and the results of a verification of one year of data as well as several hypothetical control programs are presented graphically. Ref: J-3 94(SA2 Paper 5915):381-402, April 1968.

3.0 - 432
Pescod, M. B. (1969). PHOTOSYNTHETIC OXYGEN PRODUCTION IN A POLLUTED TROPICAL ESTUARY
--Interference with light transmission by turbidity restricts photosynthetic oxygenation in the Chao Phya River Estuary in Thailand. Studies showed that oxygen production by phytoplankton was normally from 0.5 to 1.3 mg/day at the river surface and fell off to 0 at a depth of 1.0 to 1.5 m. In polluted sections it ranged from 0.20 to 0.78g/day/sq m, supplying only 1.25 to 4.6 per cent of the oxygen demand. Ref: J-1 41(8 Pt 2):R309-R321, Aug 1969.

3.0 - 433
Petit, J. L. and Bianchi, A. (1965). STUDY ON SOME CHARACTERISTICS OF POLLUTION OF THE WATERS OF THE OLD PORT OF MARSEILLES
--Pollution in the old port of Marseilles arises not only from the numerous and frequent discharges of waste waters and polluting material from the dense population but also from many pleasure boats and trawlers and from the commercial port. Preliminary physico-chemical and bacteriological observations were made at 13 sampling points and results are tabulated and discussed in relation to the meteorological conditions. The water is polluted all the time, with the exception of a few zones where a temporary improvement may result from the circulation of water caused by winds. The various winds have considerable influence in spreading the waste-water discharges, reducing the bacterial count at some sampling points and increasing it at others. The commercial port seems to be the principle source of pollution. However, the repair dock, outside this area, contains rather stagnant water and is the most polluted part of the Old Port; but this affects the main body of water only in the vicinity of the approach channel. The results are discussed in relation to current hygienic practices and a careful survey of bathing places is recommended. Ref: P-1

p. 67-70, 1965.

3.0 - 434
Pilpel, N. (1968). NATURAL FATE OF OIL ON THE SEA
--The processes of dispersal and destruction of oil in the ocean are described. Evaporation, emulsification and sinking after becoming coated with sediment and small pebbles are the main forms of dispersal. Spontaneous oxidation plays a small part in the destruction of oil but the major factor in its decomposition at sea is microbial oxidation. The oxygenated, nitrogenated, and sulphuretted hydrocarbons are the constituents most rapidly attacked; the rate of oxidation is dependent on many environmental factors including temperature and oxygen content of the sea water. Anaerobic oxidation does occur in oil which sinks but it is always a much slower process; the production of gases tends to re-float the submerged oil so that aerobic oxidation once again takes place and this cycle may be repeated several times before the oil is completely destroyed. Treatment of floating oil patches with detergents may delay the final destruction of the oil as it also destroys the bacteria. Ref: J-43 27(100):11-13, 1968.

3.0 - 435
Poliakoff, Melvin Z. (1969). OIL DISPERSING CHEMICALS, A STUDY OF THE COMPOSITION, PROPERTIES AND USE OF CHEMICALS FOR DISPERSING OIL SPILLS
--This review of chemicals used to disperse oil begins with a history of the development of oil spill dispersants, then considers emulsion chemistry, and the nature and properties of surface active agents. Ref: Federal Water Pollution Control Administration. Edison, N.J., Water Pollution Control Research Series 33 p., 1969.

3.0 - 436
Polikarpov, G. G. (1966). RADIO-ECOLOGY OF AQUATIC ORGANISMS
--The translation of a book originally published in U.S.S.R. Discusses the importance of marine radio-ecology in determining the effect of radioactive contamination of sea water on commercial fisheries, in predicting the risk to humans from contaminated sea food, and in developing measures for controlling radioactive contamination of seas and oceans. Factors affecting the accumulation of radionuclides by marine organisms are discussed and the effects of nuclear radiation on marine organisms are described. The author points out that strontium-90 accumulated during life is returned to the environment from dead marine plants; in addition to being more hazardous to man than other isotopes in food, strontium-90 is also more mobile in the sea. Ref: Book. 340 p., 1966. Reinhold Book, N. Y.

3.0 - 437
Pomeroy, L. R.; Smith, E. E. and Grant, C. M. (1965). EXCHANGE OF PHOSPHATE BETWEEN ESTUARINE WATER AND SEDIMENTS
--Results are given of experiments, using phosphorus-32 as tracer, on the exchange of phosphate between estuarine water and bottom deposits from Doboy Sound, Ga.: these showed that exchange is the result of two-stage ion exchange between clay minerals and water, plus an exchange between interstitial micro-organisms and water, and tends

to maintain a concentration of phosphate in the water of 1 μmole per litre. In undisturbed sediments the biological exchange is small, but in suspended sediments biological exchange moves almost as much phosphate as does the exchange with clay minerals. The rates of exchange and the exchange capacity of the sediments are large enough to be of ecological significance. Ref: *J-41 10(2):167-172, April 1965.*

3.0 - 438
Pomeroy, L. R.; Odum, E. P.; Johannes, R. E. and Roffman, B. (1966). FLUX OF PHOSPHORUS-32 AND ZINC-65 THROUGH A SALT-MARSH ECOSYSTEM
--Zinc-65 and phosphorus-32 were introduced simultaneously into the waters of a tidal creek flowing through a salt marsh on the east coast of U.S.A., and the distribution of radioactivity in the various components of the ecosystem was observed over a period of several months. The isotopes were taken up rapidly by the clay sediments and also by the bacteria in these sediments; higher plants in the marsh did not take up either of the isotopes, and populations of diatoms and algae did not become as radioactive as the sediments in which they lived, but a dinoflagellate bloom did accumulate appreciable amounts of radioactivity. The isotopes were removed from the sediments by animals which consumed the sediments either as their food or incidentally during feeding, and it is thought that digestion of bacteria from the sediments by sediment-feeding animals is an important step in the transport of radioactivity from sediments to biota. Ref: *P-4 p. 177-188, 1966.*

3.0 - 439
Porges, Ralph (1969). REGIONAL WATER QUALITY STANDARDS
--Water quality management concepts applied in the development of regional water quality standards included protection of clean streams, abatement of polluted waters, a minimum required degree of wastewater treatment and the equitable apportionment of stream assimilative capacity. The Delaware River Basin Commission adopted water quality standards and regulations setting forth water uses to be protected, water quality criteria necessary to protect water uses, effluent quality requirements, and allocation of stream assimilative capacity. Ref: *J-3 95(SA3 Paper 6596):423-437, June 1969.*

3.0 - 440
Powell, Robert M. and Van Heuit, Robert E. (1968). OCEAN OUTFALL MAINTENANCE AND REPAIR
--The County Sanitation Districts of Los Angeles County own a complex system of trunk sewers, treatment plants, and ocean outfalls serving an area of approximately 700 sq miles with an estimated population of 3.4 mil people. Discussed are the maintenance and repair problems of the Districts' 4 outfalls varying in size from 60 in. to 120 in diam etc. and handling up to 450 mgd (1,705,000 cu m/day). Items to be maintained and methods thereof are included. Solution of specific area outfall problems also is covered. Conclusions indicate that periodic inspection and surveillance are the keys to proper maintenance. Ref: *J-1 40(11):1900-1904, Nov 1968. 2 refs.*

3.0 - 441

Presnell, M. W.; Miescier, J. J. and Hill, W. F. (1967). *CLOSTRIDIUM BOTULINUM* IN MARINE SEDIMENTS AND IN THE OYSTER *(CRASSOSTREA VIRGINICA)* FROM MOBILE BAY
--Samples of marine sediment and oysters from Mobile Bay, Ala., were tested by the mouse bio-assay method for *Clostridium botulinum;* 4.1 per cent of the sediment samples and 2.7 per cent of the oyster samples were positive. Types C, D and E were found in sediments and type E in oysters, with only one type isolated from each positive sample. Ref: *J-31 15(3):668-669, May 1967.*

3.0 - 442
Preston, A. and Jeffries, D. F. (1969). I.C.R.P. CRITICAL GROUP CONCEPT IN RELATION TO THE WINDSCALE SEA DISCHARGES
--The critical exposure pathway limiting radioactive discharges of waste waters to sea from the Windscale Plant, Cumb., involves *Porphyra* which is used in manufacture of laverbread, for human consumption, the critical nuclide is ruthenium-106, and the critical organ is the lower large intestine. The critical group, which is determined statistically, should be representative of the more highly exposed individuals and should also be reasonably homogeneous with respect to those factors which affect the dose received. In the critical group determined for the Windscale area, the median rate of consumption of laverbread, suggested as a basis for controlling the Windscale discharge, is 160 g per day and based on this figure the estimated average dose of radioactivity to the lower large intestine over the last 6 years is 0.4-0.7 rem per year, compared with the I.C.R.P. recommended dose limit of 1.5 rem per year. Ref: *J-73 16,:33-46, 1969.*

3.0 - 443
Pringle, Benjamin H., Hissong, Dale E. and others (1968). TRACE METAL ACCUMULATION BY ESTUARINE MOLLUSKS
--A series of studies were initiated to investigate the mechanics of concentration of trace metals. Data were obtained on a number of mollusk species. There is a wide variation in species ability to take up and concentrate zinc, lead, nickel, cobalt, iron, manganese, copper, cadmium, and chromium within their natural (estuarine) environment. Uptake rates in a controlled, simulated-environment system using various concentrations of lead, copper, cadmium and zinc indicate that all of the species studied varied in their selectivity for the particular metal taken up. The rate of uptake, and the tissue level attained, were found to vary with time, and the particular metal concentration used. Using various lead concentrations it was observed that of the various anatomical areas, the muscle, mantle edge, mantle, remainder, gill, gonad, and digestive gland accumulated increasing tissue levels in the order given. Depletion is a relatively slow process in most cases. Ref: *J-3 94(SA3 Paper 5970):455-475, June 1968. 37 refs.*

3.0 - 444
Pritchard, Donald W. (1969). DISPERSION AND FLUSHING OF POLLUTANTS IN ESTUARIES
--The fate of a pollutant introduced into an estuary depends upon the relative density of the effluent and the receiving water, the vertical density structure, the strength of the tidal cur-

rents, the nontidal circulation pattern, and the intensity of turbulent diffusion. Effluents having lower density than the receiving waters, and discharged from an outfall on the bottom, ascend to the surface as a buoyant plume, entraining diluting water en route. Tidal currents advect the polluted volume as an oscillating plume, and turbulent diffusion leads to further dilution of the pollutant. Numerical solutions to time dependent theoretical advection-diffusion equations can be used to depict the probable distribution of a pollutant in a tidal segment of the estuary centered on the outfall. Exchange of pollutant between tidal segments in the estuary and the ultimate flushing of the pollutant from the estuary are best treated using a two-dimensional segmented mathematical model. Ref: *J-18 95(HY1 Paper 6344):115-124, Jan 1969. 3 refs.*

3.0 - 445
Pritchard, Donald W. and Carter, H. H.   (1965).
PREDICTION OF THE DISTRIBUTION OF EXCESS TEMPERATURE FROM A HEATED DISCHARGE IN AN ESTUARY
--Treats the specific case of the heated effluent from the PEPCO Chalk Point Power plant on the Patuxent Estuary in Maryland. The authors believe that the techniques they describe will have general application. Ref: *The Johns Hopkins Univ. Chesapeake Bay Institute Tech. Rept. No. 33 Feb 1965.*

3.0 - 446
Pritchard, Donald W.; Okubo, A. and Carter, H. H. (1966). OBSERVATIONS AND THEORY OF EDDY MOVEMENT AND DIFFUSION OF AN INTRODUCED TRACER MATERIAL IN THE SURFACE LAYERS OF THE SEA
--Tracer studies, using Rhodamine B, were carried out on movement and diffusion of surface layers off the east coast of Florida, near Cape Kennedy. Experimental procedure and results are described and theories are developed to describe the decrease in peak concentration with time and the observed horizontal elongation of the dye patch. Ref: *P-4 p. 397-424, 1966.*

3.0 - 447
Prych, E. A.; Hubbell, D. W.; and Glenn, J. L. (1965). MEASUREMENT EQUIPMENT AND TECHNIQUES USED IN STUDYING RADIONUCLIDE MOVEMENT IN COLUMBIA RIVER ESTUARY
--Radioactivity sorbed on bed sediments are obtained with a radiation detector mounted on an underwater sled. Samples of water and suspended sediment are obtained with a high volume sampler. A newly devised portable vibratory sampler is used to core samples of bed sediment. Ref: *P-34 p. 683-704, Oct 1965.*

3.0 - 448
Public Health Service, Washington, D. C. (1965).
NITROGEN AND PHOSPHORUS IN WATER: AN ANNOTATED BIBLIOGRAPHY OF THEIR BIOLOGICAL EFFECTS
--A selected and annotated bibliography of 171 entries intended for engineers and scientists faced with predicting changes resulting from plant nutrient loadings. Emphasis is placed on critical concentration values for algal development and effects of fertilization upon aquatic life. Ref: *U. S. Public Health Service. Publication No. 1305 111 p., 1965. 171 refs.*

3.0 - 449
Purpura, J. A. and Thornton, E. B.   (1966).
TRACING OF SPECIAL MATERIAL TRANSPORT IN THE OCEAN AT CAPE KENNEDY. PROGRESS REPORT
--Fluorescent tracers were used to study the movement of waste products in the ocean at Cape Kennedy, Fla. The tracer mixed with cement was allowed to set and was then broken up with a hammer mill with exchangeable screens and provision for operating at different speeds to give tracer particles of various sizes. The tracer was then injected into the ocean to simulate the movement of fissionable material; the average particle velocity was found to be 408 ft per day. The distribution of tracer particles at various sites on the beach was also observed. Ref: *U. S. Atomic Energy Commission Rept. No. ORO-3298-2 32 p., 1966.*

3.0 - 450
Putnam, H. D.   (1967).   LIMITING FACTORS FOR PRIMARY PRODUCTIVITY IN A WEST COAST FLORIDA ESTUARY
--Tabulated and graphical results are given of studies on primary productivity and factors limiting algal photosynthesis in Waccasassa Estuary, an unpolluted estuary in Florida.   There are marked seasonal fluctuations in photosynthesis; photosynthetic activity is maximal in late June and early October. Diatoms are the most abundant organisms; only in January and February do they comprise less than 50 per cent of the phytoplankton population. There is no evidence of an increasing concentration gradient of nitrogen or phosphorus with depth; bottom water incubated at the surface in productivity experiments was no more fertile than surface water, and salinity gradients do not develop in the bay except during periods of very high river flow. The productivity of the phytoplankton appears to be regulated by the available nigrogen and phosphorus. Production does not appear to be influenced by run-off from rain, since there is no statistical relation between stream flow and amount of photosynthesis; the soils in this region are sandy and the high annual precipitation continually leaches out the few available nutrients. There are large standing crops of attached algae and spermatophytes in the estuary, and decomposition of these releases nutrients which are used by the phytoplankton, but it is possible that some, at least, of the nitrogen is lost to the estuary by reduction of oxidized substances to nitrogen gas. The probable effects on the estuary of any future pollution by organic waste waters are discussed. Ref: *P-9 3,:121-152, 1967.*

3.0 - 451
Qasim, S. Z.; Wellershaus S. and others   (1969).
ORGANIC PRODUCTION IN A TROPICAL ESTUARY
--This study indicates that in a highly turbid and polluted estuary the C-14 assimilation is near to net production and the diurnal rhythm in photosynthesis is associated with the increase and decrease in daily illumination. Ref: *J-45 69(2 Sec. B):51-94, Feb 1969. 64 refs.*

3.0 - 452
Rae, B. B.; Johnston, R. and Adams, J. A. (1965).
INCIDENCE OF DEAD AND DYING FISH IN THE MORAY FIRTH, SEPTEMBER 1963

--An investigation into the causes of fish mortalities which occurred in the Moray Firth during the first fortnight of September 1963 is reported. Numerous dead fish, dead lugworms were found on many beaches. Examination of the water in the locality revealed below-normal oxygen content and large numbers of the dinoflagellate *Peridinium foliaceum* at certain points. The toxicity of the water was confirmed by laboratory tests, using shrimps as indicators. Ref: *J-2 45(1):29-47, April 1965.*

3.0 - 453
Rambow, C. A. and Hennessy, P. V.   (1965).
OCEANOGRAPHIC STUDIES FOR A SMALL WASTEWATER OUTFALL
--Reviews the considerations involved in locating and designing an ocean outfall and describes how a relatively inexpensive oceanographic survey was applied to the design of one such outfall. Ref: *J-1 37(11):1471-1480, Nov 1965. 3 refs.*

3.0 - 454
Ramsdale, S. J., and Wilkinson, R. E.   (1968).
IDENTIFICATION OF PETROLEUM SOURCES OF BEACH POLLUTION BY GAS-LIQUID CHROMATOGRAPHY
--Beach pollution may originate from the discharge of crude oils, fuel oils, or cargo residues at sea. A gas-liquid chromatographic procedure has been developed for the examination of pollution samples in an attempt to assess the relative contributions made to pollution by these sources. Samples containing up to 90 per cent sand and others with 80 per cent water have been analysed rapidly without pre-treatment. The three major sources of beach pollution can be recognized from the chromatograms obtained. Ref: *J-8 54(539): 326-332, Nov 1968.*

3.0 - 455
Raney, Edward C. and Menzel, Bruce W.   (1969).
HEATED EFFLUENTS AND EFFECTS ON AQUATIC LIFE WITH EMPAHSIS ON FISHES
--A bibliography on the effects of heated effluents on aquatic life with emphasis on fishes. References given to 1870 papers. KWIC Indexes included. Ref: *U. S. Dept. of the Interior, Water Resources Science Information Center. Bibliographic Publication 470 p., April 1969.*

3.0 - 456
Rawls, C. K. (1965).   FIELD TESTS OF HERBICIDE TOXICITY TO CERTAIN ESTUARINE ANIMALS
--Fish and shellfish in tidal waters of Virginia and Maryland were exposed to various concentrations of 2,4-D formulations of weedkillers which were thought capable of controlling *Myriophyllum spicatum* but no mortalities occurred as a result of the exposure. Ref: *J-25 6(3):150-161, Sept 1965.*

3.0 - 457
Ray, P. and David, A. (1966).   EFFECTS OF INDUSTRIAL WASTES AND SEWAGE UPON THE CHEMICAL AND BIOLOGICAL COMPOSITION AND FISHERIES OF THE RIVER GANGA AT KANPUR (U.P.)
--The effect of sewage and trade waste waters on fish in the river Ganges at Kanpur, and physical, chemical and biological conditions in the river are reported. Observations were made at 8 stations on water color, turbidity, pH value, dissolved-oxygen content, BOD, alkalinity, dissolved solids, nitrogen, nitrate, chloride, and phosphate; comprehensive quantitative and qualitative data were obtained for plankton for particular months, and the concentrations found were differentiated between locations on either bank of the river; bottom and marginal biota were also studied. Locations of fisheries were noted, and a list of fish and their relative abundance in zones of varying degrees of pollution is given. Except for 2 locations, no major ill effects were caused to fish by pollutional discharge. Crude sewage was found to be dispersed rapidly and homogeneously several km below the outfall in conditions of considerable dilution, helping to stimulate aquatic growth and to provide a location for large carp and catfish. Conditions of fast currents and high dilution of sewage generally limited zones of pollution, and fish, after feeding in such zones, could always escape into cleaner zones. Previously-noted toxicity due to textile and tannery waste waters was almost eliminated as a result of dilution with sewage in the trunk sewer. Ref: *J-46 8,:307-339, 1966.*

3.0 - 458
Reed, R. J. (1966).   SOME EFFECTS OF DDT ON THE ECOLOGY OF SALMON STREAMS IN SOUTHEASTERN ALASKA
--Results are given of a 4-year study in Alaska to investigate the risk to fish and aquatic insects in salmon streams caused by spraying forested watersheds with DDT to control budworm and hemlock sawfly. The DDT was applied to selected areas in fuel oil at a rate of 0.28 kg per hr. After treatment there was an immediate marked increase in the numbers of aquatic insects drifting in the stream, and insects were completely killed within 3 days. The insects began to appear again a few weeks after spraying, but did not approach normal numbers until the following summer. The condition of fish declined, apparently as a result of the reduction in the food supply and it is concluded that aerial spraying with DDT to control forest insects, could, therefore, have adverse effects on trout and on coho, sockeye, and king salmon. Ref: *U.S. Fish and Wildlife Service. Special Scientific Fisheries Report No. 542 15 p., 1966.*

3.0 - 459
Reimold, R. J. and Daiber, F. C.   (1967).
EUTROPHICATION OF ESTUARINE AREAS BY RAINWATER
--Tabulated and graphical results are given of analyses of total phosphorus in rain water at Lewes, Delaware from February 1966 to January 1967. Possible causes of the sudden increase after April and the reason for the unusual phosphorus cycles in bay waters and marshes along the east coast of U.S.A. are discussed. Ref: *J-25 8(2): 132-133, June 1967.*

3.0 - 460
Reish, Donald J. (1965).   EFFECT OF OIL REFINERY WASTES ON BENTHIC MARINE ANIMALS IN LOS ANGELES HARBOUR, CALIFORNIA
--Observations were made on the benthic fauna in the Consolidated Slip-East Basin region of Los Angeles harbor before and after dredging to remove accumulated polluting material largely derived from the discharge of oil refinery waste waters. Comparative studies are reported in other parts of the Los Angeles-Long Beach harbors to in-

vestigate the relations between the number of species of animals and certain environmental factors. The number of species decreased whenever the concentration of organic carbon in the sediments exceeded 4.5 per cent and above this concentration the number of species was inversely related to the carbon concentration; the number of species was also directly related to the concentration of dissolved oxygen in the water. Similar relations were found for the species in sediments collected in bottles suspended in different ecological areas of the harbors for periods of 28 days, but in this case the limiting concentration of carbon was higher, 8 per cent, probably owing to the short period of exposure. These large concentrations of organic carbon occurred near the outfalls from oil refineries and are also associated with low concentrations of dissolved oxygen in the water. Ref: *P-1 p. 355-361, 1965.*

3.0 - 461
Reish, Donald J. (1966).   RELATIONSHIP OF POLYCHAETES TO VARYING DISSOLVED OXYGEN CONCENTRATIONS
--Laboratory investigations on the environmental requirements of polychaetes (pollution indicator species) were made to determine the effect of several factors on these organisms. Emphasis was placed on the effect of different concentrations of dissolved oxygen on the polychaetes indicative of semi-polluted conditions. Ref: *P-9 and J-12 39(3) (abstract only), March 1966.*

3.0 - 462
Remirez, Raul (1968).   THERMAL POLLUTION: HOT ISSUE FOR INDUSTRY
--Discusses the problem of thermal pollution and presents current information on the subject. About 70 per cent of the industrial thermal-pollution load is attributed to the steam electric power industry. Nuclear plants reject about 50 percent more heat than fossil fuel plants. Reservoirs or cooling towers could alleviate the problem but might increase the cost of electricity one to five per cent. Reuse of wasted heat is considered. Ref: *J-47 75(7):48-52, March 25, 1968.*

3.0 - 463
Renfro, W. C. (1968).   RADIO-ECOLOGY OF ZINC-65 IN AN ARM OF THE COLUMBIA RIVER ESTUARY
--Studies were made on the concentrations of zinc-65 in water, bottom deposits, plants, and animals in Alder Slough, a small ecosystem in the Columbia River Estuary. There were temporary fluctuations in the activities of zinc-65 and in the concentrations of total zinc in all components of the ecosystem. There were also variations between individual fish. In general, individuals with high zinc-65 activities also had high total zinc concentrations. Following the shut-down of the nuclear reactors at Hanford for 45 days, the rates of decrease in zinc-65 activity in several organisms varied with the trophic level of the organism and with changes in prevailing ecological conditions Ref: *Oregon State Univ. Thesis 94 p., 1968.*

3.0 - 464
Renfro, W. C. and Osterberg, C. (1969).   RADIO-ZINC DECLINE IN STARRY FLOUNDERS AFTER TEMPORARY SHUT-DOWN OF HANFORD REACTORS
--During studies on zinc-65 in Alder Slough, a

small arm of the Columbia River Estuary, the dynamics of zinc-65 in starry flounders was examined over a 1-year period under the conditions prevailing before and after the 45-day shut-down of the nuclear reactors at Hanford. When the amount of radioactivity entering the ecosystem was reduced, there was a considerable reduction in the specific activity of zinc-65 in the flounders; for juvenile starry flounders the 'ecological half-life' of zinc-65 was 139 days. The rate of loss of zinc-65 was compared in the field and laboratory tests; the effective half-life of zinc-65 in flounders in the laboratory ranged from 56 to 162 days and appeared to vary as a function of the initial concentration of zinc-65. Ref: *P-3 p. 372-379, 1969.*

3.0 - 465
Rice, T. R.; Baptist, J. P. and Price, T. J. (1965).   ACCUMULATION OF MIXED FISSION PRODUCTS BY MARINE ORGANISMS
--Phytoplankton, scallops, shrimps and croakers were exposed to sea water containing mixed fission products, and oysters were fed on *Carteria* cells grown in such water; and the uptake and subsequent losses of β- and γ-activity were measured. Results were presented in tables and graphs. Much of the β-activity became associated with phytoplankton cells by non-metabolic processes, probably adsorption and exchange. *Carteria* cells appeared to remove a greater percentage of cerium-144/praseodymium-144 than of other radioactive isotopes with weaker energies. There appeared to be a rapid uptake of isotopes of short half-life, with the uptake of isotopes with longer half-lives proceeding more slowly. These results were discussed in relation to the possible hazards to man. Further studies are to be made including pilot-scale experiments in large tanks and ponds. Ref: *P-10 3,:263-286, 1965.*

3.0 - 466
Richards, F. A. (1965). CHEMICAL OBSERVATIONS IN SOME ANOXIC, SULPHIDE-BEARING BASINS AND FJORDS
--The author explains the differences in chemical composition and biological environment caused by decomposition of organic matter; accumulation of organic decomposition products; physiological toxicity of sulphides, which also form highly insoluble compounds with metal ions at the pH value of sea water causing low concentrations of metals in the water; and the lower oxidation-reduction potentials in anoxic waters which permit greater accumulation of organic debris, as indicated by the higher concentrations of organic carbon and chlorophyll in the sediments. Consideration was also given to the effects of seasonal mixing of anoxic and oxygen-bearing waters which appears to be important in some of the waters studied, such as Saanich Inlet, B.C., Dramsfjord, Norway, and possibly the Gulf of Cariaco, Venezuela. Laboratory experiments to investigate the reaction between sulphide and oxygen when anoxic and oxygenated waters are mixed showed that about 30 hours would be required for the complete oxidation of sulphide originally present in a concentration of 30 μg-atom of sulphide-sulphur per litre. A stoichiometric model was devised for the decomposition of organic matter of marine plankton origin, both in the presence and absence of free oxygen, and observations were made in several anoxic environ-

ments to confirm the validity of the model particularly as regards the relations between oxygen consumption and the concentrations of phosphate and carbonate-carbon, and also between the concentrations of sulphide-sulphur and ammoniacal nitrogen. Ref: *P-10 3,:215-243, 1965.*

3.0 - 467
Robinson, J.; Richardson, A. and others (1967). ORGANOCHLORINE RESIDUES IN MARINE ORGANISMS
--Concentrations of *pp'*-DDE and dieldrin in marine organisms from the eastern British Coast, and in eggs of sea birds nesting in Northumberland, Berwickshire, or Fife were determined by gas-liquid chromatography. Residues tended to be greater in organisms at higher trophic levels, but there were exceptions; considerable variation in the concentrations of residues occurred in species in the same family and within the same genus. In breeding birds, concentrations were found to be independent of age, with the exception that an age-dependent trend was found in the liver, for *pp'*-DDE; a relation was found between standard deviations of residues in the eggs of the 6 species of sea bird examined, and arithmetic means of concentrations.
Ref: *J-7 214(5095):1307-1311, June 24, 1967.*

3.0 - 468
Roger, E. (1965). CONTRIBUTION TO THE STUDY OF THE POLLUTION OF MUSSELS BY PETROLEUM PRODUCTS
--After enumerating the sources, types and polluting characteristics of various petroleum products discharged into sea water and rivers, the author discusses the conditions under which these products cause pollution of mussels, the nature of the damage caused, the removal of petroleum products by self-purification and methods for preventing this type of pollution. Ref: *P-1 p. 367-369, 1965.*

3.0 - 469
Roper, Harry McK., Jr. (1967). ROLE OF THE PHYSICAL HYDRAULIC MODEL OF SAN FRANCISCO BAY AND DELTA IN POLLUTION STUDIES
--Discusses the use of a physical hydraulic model developed by the Corps of Engineers for studying pollution in San Francisco Bay. Ref: *P-2 p. 423-440, 1967.*

3.0 - 470
Rosenberger, Richard L. and Walsh, Raymond (1967). ESTUARINE WATER QUALITY MANAGEMENT IN THE SACRAMENTO-SAN JOAQUIN DELTA
--Presents a summary of the San Francisco Bay-Delta Water Quality Control Program. Vast water development projects which would ultimately result in the complete control of inflow to the Delta and Bay are discussed. Ref: *P-2 p. 23-25, 1967.*

3.0 - 471
Rosenberger, Richard L. and Walsh, Raymond (1968). ESTUARINE WATER QUALITY MANAGEMENT
--The Bay-Delta Water Quality Control Program is a comprehensive study designed to develop a water quality control program for the San Francisco Bay-Delta area of California. The Program's planning studies cover a period of 50 yrs into the future. The Bay-Delta system water quality is influenced not only by steadily increasing waste loads but also by upstream water development which is changing the hydraulic regimen of a substantial por-

tion of the system. The scope and organization of the Program is described as well as its approach to the development of a comprehensive water quality control plan. Particular emphasis is placed on the influence water resource development projects, located upstream from the estuary, have on the planning process. Ref: *J-3 94(SA5 Paper 6164): 913-926, Oct 1968.*

3.0 - 472
Rosenthal, Harold and Gunkel, W. (1967). EFFECTS OF CRUDE OIL-EMULSIFIER MIXTURES ON MARINE FISH FRY AND THER FOOD ANIMALS
--Reports tests of the effects of crude oil-emulsifier mixtures on the larvae of *Clupea harengus L.* and *Agonus cataphractus L.* Lethal concentrations were determined. Crude oil alone did not cause damage to herring larvae during the four day observation period. Ref: *J-106 16(4):315-320, Dec 1967. 4 refs.*

3.0 - 473
Roskopf, Robert F. (1968). COMPOSITE-GRAB OF WATER POLLUTION CONTROL SAMPLING
--The importance of sampling in water pollution control activities is explained. Ref: *J-1 40(3 Part 1):492-498, March 1968. 9 refs.*

3.0 - 474
Rouet, J. and Danon, F. (1968). POLLUTION OF SEAS BY HYDROCARBONS. MEANS AND METHODS OF PROTECTION
--The use of absorbents, emulsified surface-active materials, and barrages to control oil pollution at sea and along coasts is reviewed, with examples of the successful application of such methods during recent incidents. Improvised straw barrages and sawdust adsorbent, which were used to prevent oil from the Torrey Canyon reaching the French Coast, are considered unsatisfactory. Ref: *J-48 21,:279-283, 1968.*

3.0 - 475
Rubelt, Christian (1967). ANALYTICAL METHODS REGARDING THE MINERAL OIL-WATER-SOIL-COMPLEX
--Presents examples of analyses and methods of identification of oil contaminants. A method was developed for qualitative and quantitative estimation of bacterial oil degradation products depending upon bacterial flora, limitation factors and different hydrocarbons or mineral oil products. Ref: *J-106 16(4):306-314, Dec 1967. 20 refs.*

3.0 - 476
Ruggles, C. P. (1967) EFFECT OF WATER POLLUTION ON MARITIME FISHERIES
--The effects of pollution of rivers and coastal waters on fisheries, fish, shellfish and fish-processing industries in the Maritime provinces of Canada, are discussed briefly. Subjects include the effect on salmon and trout of aerial spraying of forests with DDT, and of the misuse of agricultural chemicals; the effects on fish migration of pulp mill waste waters and metal ions from mining; the effects of sewage on shellfish industries; and the pollution by sewage of harbor waters used by fish-processing plants. Ref: *J-37 58,:77-79, 1967.*

3.0 - 477
Rützler, Klaus and Sterrer, Wolfgang (1970).

OIL POLLUTION

--Damage observed in tropical communities along the Atlantic seaboard of Panama is reported. Ref: J-39 20(4):222-224, Feb 1970. 4 refs.

3.0 - 478
Salkowski, Martin J. (1967). DETECTION OF OIL CONTAMINATION IN SEA WATER. VOL. I. EXPERIMENTAL INVESTIGATIONS: APRIL 19, 1965 THROUGH DECEMBER 31,1966.
--Presents a detailed discussion of a laboratory study, and the design, construction, and calibration of a prototype marine oil contamination monitor. The instrument is a split-beam infrared absorption system, which continuously monitors and permanently records contamination levels. Ref: IIT Research Institute. Technology Center, Chicago, Ill. Summary Rept. No. IITRI-C6065-22 Vol. I 117 p., Feb 1967. (268 refs. in Vol. II).

3.0 - 479
Salkowski, Martin J. (1967). DETECTION OF OIL CONTAMINATION IN SEA WATER. VOL II
--This is the second volume reporting on a study of oil contamination monitoring system. Drawings of the equipment are presented. An annotated bibliography of 268 references is the main content of this volume. Ref: IIT Research Institute. Technology Center, Chicago, Ill. Summary Rept. No. IITRI-C6065-22 Vol. II 202 p., Jan 1967. 268 refs.

3.0 - 480
Salo, E. O. and Leet, W. L. (1969). CONCENTRATION OF ZINC-65 BY OYSTERS MAINTAINED IN THE DISCHARGE CANAL OF A NUCLEAR POWER PLANT
--Cooling water and low-level radioactive waste waters from Humboldt Bay nuclear power plant, near Eureka, Calif., are discharged into a short canal leading into Humboldt Bay. Pacific oysters (Crassotrea gigas) were reared for periods up to 13 months on trays suspended on a raft in the discharge canal, and the uptake of zinc-65 was studied by removing oyster samples as fresh groups were added. Changes in the concentration in the water were reflected in changes in the concentration in the oysters. Oysters maintained on rafts can be used as long-term indicators for zinc-65. As regards public health, the maximal body burden that could be derived from eating the oysters is well within the maximal permissible concentration. Ref: P-3 p. 363-371, 1969.

3.0 - 481
Santini, D. B. (1965). EFFECT OF POLLUTION ON SOME SURFACE POPULATIONS OF ROCKY SUBSTRATUM
--Animal and plant populations living on the surface of rock materials were sampled to study the effects of pollution in the inner Gulf of Marseilles and to compare these with populations in clean water from the outskirts of the Gulf. The adverse effects of pollution on color, density and diversity of the populations; the elimination of species sensitive to pollution and the establishment of more resistant species are indicated. Ref: P-1 p. 127-131, 1965.

3.0 - 482
Saunders, J. W. (1969). MASS MORTALITIES AND BEHAVIOR OF BROOK TROUT AND JUVENILE ATLANTIC SALMON IN A STREAM POLLUTED BY AGRICULTURAL

PESTICIDES

--Observations were made of the behavior of brook trout and juvenile Atlantic salmon, following spillage of endrin and nabam into the upper reaches of Mill River, Prince Edward Island, Canada. Mass mortalities of trout occurred for several miles downstream within 4 days after the spillage. Electric fishing in a section of the river just above the head of the tide caused trout and salmon to fall to the bottom of the river and die; trout and salmon were observed together in pools, and the young salmon were found near or at the surface of pools. A week after the spillage, trout, salmon, and fry were trapped at the head of the tide in movement to brackish water, and many fish died in the trap. Ref: J-32 26,:695-699, 1969.

3.0 - 483
Saunders, R. L. and Sprague, J. B. (1967). EFFECTS OF COPPER-ZINC MINING POLLUTION ON A SPAWNING MIGRATION OF ATLANTIC SALMON
--Studies of the effects of pollution by copper and zinc in the Northwest Miramichi River, N.B., included observations on the avoidance reactions of migrating Atlantic salmon (Salmo salar). The results showed that metal concentrations of less than half the lethal threshold value caused a considerable reduction in the number of salmon reaching the spawning grounds above the polluted zone and a marked increase in the number returning downstream without spawning. Ref: J-12 1(5):419-432, May 1967.

3.0 - 484
Saville, T. (1966). STUDY OF ESTUARINE POLLUTION PROBLEMS ON A SMALL UNPOLLUTED ESTUARY AND A SMALL POLLUTED ESTUARY IN FLORIDA
--This report contains extracts of detailed studies made by a variety of scientists and engineers associated with the Dept. of Bioenvironmental Engineering at the University of Florida. It comprises studies by the same group and by similar methods on two generally comparable estuaries, one virtually unpolluted and the other heavily polluted. The project which continued over a period of about 3 1/2 years was designed to develop measures for evaluating ability of such estuaries to assimilate wastes under natural and controlled conditions. Ref: Univ. of Florida. Engineering Progress 20(8): Bulletin Ser. No. 125 210 p., 1966.

3.0 - 485
Sawyer, Clair N. (1965). SEA LETTUCE PROBLEM IN BOSTON HARBOR
--Growths of sea lettuce are prevalent in three areas of Boston Harbor. These waters were found to be highly contaminated by sewage discharges from an outfall sewer. Coliform and total bacterial numbers were excessive on occasion and the fertilizing elements, nitrogen and phosphorus, were present in excess of amounts in normal seawater at all times. Sewage discharges into tidal waters were directly responsible for furnishing the nutrients responsible for supporting the extensive growths of sea lettuce. Ref: J-1 37(8):1122-1133, Aug 1965. 2 refs.

3.0 - 486
Saxena, K. L.; Chakrabarty, R. N. and others

(1966). POLLUTION STUDIES OF THE RIVER GANGES NEAR KANPUR

--In a survey by the Central Public Health Engineering Research Institute, samples were taken from 4 stations along a dredged channel supplying water for the power station and water works of the city, and from 8 stations between the confluence of this channel with the Ganges and Kishanpur. The water quality was reasonably satisfactory at Bhairon Ghat water works but deteriorated after pollution by discharges of sewage and textile industry waste waters in the dredged channel. Improvement in water quality occurred at the confluence of the channel and the Ganges, but gross pollution occurred further downstream owing to discharges of tanneries waste waters. It was considered desirable to maintain a dissolved-oxygen concentration greater than 5 mg per litre during the year, and this could be achieved by substantial reduction of the BOD from all sources; therefore further remedial measures are proposed, including stopping the discharge of the textile mill waste waters in the dredged channel; provision of treatment plants for all textile wastes; adequate treatment of sewage and the connection of sewage outfalls to the main sewer; and enforcement of the laws prohibiting the throwing of corpses and carcasses into the river. Tabulated and graphical data are given for coliform bacteria, chloride, BOD, dissolved-oxygen content, and tannin. Ref: *J-46 8,:270-285, 1966.*

3.0 - 487
Schafer, Charles T. (1968). DISTRIBUTION, POLLUTION RESPONSE, TEMPORAL VARIATION OF FORAMINIFERA AND SEDIMENTATION IN WESTERN LONG ISLAND SOUND AND ADJACENT NEARSHORE AREAS

--Forty-seven stations in western Long Island Sound were sampled during June of 1965 and May of 1966. The concentrations of nitrates and total phosphates in bottom waters, and of coliform bacteria in surface waters, are higher than average at the extreme western end of the Sound. Local dumping of treated sewage apparently is responsible for these higher concentrations. Specimens of *Elphidium clavatum, E. incertum* 'complex', and *Buccella frigida* are among the most abundant species of Foraminifera in both the living and the total populations (living plus dead tests) in the upper four cm. of sediment in western Long Island Sound. Industrial pollution probably is responsible for a westward decrease in the number of species of living Foraminifera and Ostracoda. Marshes adjacent to western Long Island Sound support large living populations of *Trochammina inflata, Elphidium tisburyense,* and *Miliammina fusca*. The distribution of living marsh species also appears to be influenced by pollution. Ref: *New York Univ. Thesis 130 p., 1968.*

3.0 - 488
Schaumburg, Grant W., Jr. (1967). POLLUTION CONTROL MODELS AND THEIR RESULTS

--Various types of pollution abatement schemes for the Delaware Estuary were compared. Equity consideration of all the schemes were discussed, and tabled for comparison. Ref: *Water Pollution Contribution in the Delaware Estuary. Harvard Water Program. Chapt. IV p. 74-150, May 1967. 23 refs.*

3.0 - 489
Schink, D. R.; Fanning, K. A. and Piety, J. (1966). SEA-BOTTOM SAMPLER THAT COLLECTS BOTH WATER AND SEDIMENT SIMULTANEOUSLY

--An illustrated description is given of the design and operation of a combined deep-water and sediment sampler which enables samples to be taken simultaneously from the ocean bed and the water column immediately above. The apparatus incorporates 6 Frautschy bottles which are mounted at 1-m intervals on a PVC pipe and close automatically when the base of the pipe strikes the ocean floor, the core sampler being released at the same instant. Ref: *J-20 24(3):365-373, Sept 15, 1966.*

3.0 - 490
Schoop, E. Jack (1969). SAN FRANCISCO BAY SHORELINE: BALANCING OF DEVELOPMENT AND CONSERVATION PROPOSED

--A three-year study found that high-priority uses of the bay and shoreline are: ports, water, related industry, some airports, water-related parks, marinas, beaches and fishing piers, and perhaps some freeways. It was recommended that filling should be minimized and the bay's marshes, mudflats and adjacent salt ponds should be preserved because they are vital to the bird and fish populations and also because mudflats help oxygenate the bay waters. The bay's surrounding lands have their temperature moderated by its water and temperature inversions (smog-producing) would be prevented. The study recommends that a regional agency be created and given power to exercise controls over shoreline development. Ref: *J-49 39(5):54-58, May 1969.*

3.0 - 491
Schryver, George W. (1969). PROCESS FOR CONTROLLING STREAM AND WATERWAY POLLUTION BY TREATING SEWAGE AT THE SOURCE AND APPARATUS THEREFOR

--Apparatus for treating waste material has a receptacle that houses a comminuting chamber with comminuting means, an effluent receiving chamber communicating with the latter, and a biodegrading furnace communicating with said effluent receiving chamber that sterilizes said material before it is discharged. A process breaks up the waste material, reduces it to an effluent and sterilizes it. Ref: *U. S. Patent No. 3,458,140 not assigned. 1969.*

3.0 - 492
Schubel, J. R. (1968). TURBIDITY MAXIMUM OF THE NORTHERN CHESAPEAKE BAY

--Summarizes results of a study of the turbid zone from head Chesapeake Bay at Turdey Point seaward for 32 km. The turbidity maximum is produced mainly by local resuspension of bottom sediments, and by the estuarine 'sediment trap' formed in the upper part of the estuarine circulation regime by the net nontidal circulation. Ref: *J-6 161 (3845):1013-1015, Sept 6, 1968. 10 refs.*

3.0 - 493
Scott, A. L. and Gifford, S. E. (1968). REMOVAL OF OIL FROM HARBOR WATERS

--This report outlines the physical methods and equipment used to remove oil from harbor waters at various Navy installations and describes a prototype oil skimmer developed by NCEL. Ref: *U. S.*

Naval Civil Engineering Laboratory, Port Hueneme, Calif. Tech Note N-964 31 p., Feb 1968.

3.0 - 494
Selleck, Robert E. (1968).   MODEL OF MIXING AND DISPERSION IN SAN FRANCISCO BAY
--The author develops a method of predicting distributions of soluble substances throughout a system under a variety of hydrologic and wastewater discharge conditions. A one-dimensional diffusion analogy was used as the basis of the model, with one of the terms, coefficient of dispersion, determined from the halogen ion (Chlorosity) and dissolved silica concentrations.   Examples of steady- and unsteady-state, conservative and non-conservative systems are given. Observed and calculated results were comparable, with the dispersion coefficient, E, proportional to the 3/4 power of the net advective velocity, μ.   Chlorosity at Chipps Island was found to range from 2.0 to 5.0 g/l, with a decay rate, k, in the South Bay of 0.20 day $^{-1}$. Ref: *J-1   40(1 Part 1):1873-1876, Nov 1968. 5 refs.*

3.0 - 495
Shapiro, J. and Ribeiro, R. (1965). ALGAL GROWTH AND SEWAGE EFFLUENT IN POTOMAC ESTUARY
--Experiments were made using various mixtures of Potomac River water and waste water treatment plant effluent, with river water alone serving as control, to determine whether phosphorus level of river water was sufficiently high that addition of sewage phosphorus would result in no substantial increase of algae; results show, among other things, that addition of secondary waste water treatment plant effluent to Potomac River water greatly increases growth of both green and blue-green algae in proportion to quantity of effluent added. Ref: *J-1   37(7):134-143, July 1965.*

3.0 - 496
Sheets, T. J.; Jackson, M. D. and Phelps, L. D. (1970). WATER MONITORING SYSTEM FOR PESTICIDES IN NORTH CAROLINA
--Samples of sediment and water were routinely taken from the river and from selected sites in estuaries and sounds and analyzed by electron-capture gas chromatography. Systems for sampling and analyzing water and sediment for chlorinated hydrocarbons, organic phosphate, phenoxy acetates, and trifluroline were outlined; and personnel and equipment needs for operation of the monitoring system were listed. Ref: *North Carolina Water Resources Research Institute, Raleigh. Rept. No. 19   109 p., Jan 1970.*

3.0 - 497
Shuval, H. J.; Cohen, N. and Furer, Y. Y. (1968). DISPERSION OF BACTERIAL POLLUTION ALONG THE TEL-AVIV SHORE
--To improve the bacteriological condition of beaches and water along the Tel-Aviv shoreline, Israel, sewage was diverted from numerous short outfall sewers to a temporary outfall constructed to the north of the town, at Reading, discharging 800m from the shore. Data showing numbers of coliform bacteria and presence of faecal matter before and after the diversion are tabulated. Although pollution of the beaches and bathing waters was reduced to an acceptable level, it was considered that conditions at beaches adjacent to the new outfall would deteriorate as the volume of sewage increased and that utilization of all sewage on the land, after treatment, would be a more satisfactory solution. Ref: *P-19 and J-59 9,:107-121, 1968. 6 refs.*

3.0 - 498
Sieburth, J. M. (1965).   ROLE OF ALGAE IN CONTROLLING BACTERIAL POPULATIONS IN ESTUARINE WATERS
--Reviews previous work on antibacterial activity and reports experiments in Narragansett Bay, Rhode Island, to investigate the possibility that peaks in anticoliform activity might be associated with some seasonal component of the phytoplankton. Related studies were also made on the characteristic microflora of the bay, which was compared with that of other marine areas. A check of each species of phytoplankton showed no close association between maximal anticoliform activity and the maximal growth of any particular species; the best association appeared to be with the termination of the blooms of *Skeletonema costatum* which was the predominant diatom in the bay. Anticoliform activity was not associated with variations in salinity, but was increased by illumination and was affected by the presence of organic matter. Ref: *P-1   p. 217-233, 1965. 87 refs.*

3.0 - 499
Sieburth, J. M. (1967).   SEASONAL SELECTION OF ESTUARINE BACTERIA BY WATER TEMPERATURE
--Observations on seasonal changes in heterotrophic planktonic bacteria in Narragansett Bay, showed that the growth range of the natural bacterial population varied with water temperature but lagged 2 months out of phase. All the thermal types of bacteria detected could be isolated and their population trends were observed by surface inoculation and re-incubation of plates pretempered at 0°, 18°, and 36°C. A few isolates of several taxonomic groups exhibited a tendency for multiple temperature optima. The seasonal selection of thermal types according to water temperature occurred in all taxonomic groups. There was no apparent suppression or enhancement of any taxonomic group attributable to temperature. Ref: *J-96   1,:98-121, 1967.*

3.0 - 500
Simmons, Henry B. (1969).   USE OF MODELS IN RESOLVING TIDAL PROBLEMS
--Describes a comprehensive hydraulic model of the Delaware Estuary and its use in studies of: factors affecting salt water intrusion; flushing characteristics; new navigation facilities; improved methods for waste disposal; need for rehabilitating new dikes; and the effects of reservoir operation on salt water intrusion. Ref: *J-18 95(HY1 Paper 6345):125-146, Jan 1969.*

3.0 - 501
Singer, Fred S. (1969).   FEDERAL INTEREST IN ESTUARINE ZONES BUILDS
--Pollution and landfill are rapidly destroying estuaries. The multiple use of the estuarine zone requires the full cooperation of state and federal governments to produce a workable management system. Interim measures must be developed to prevent further degradation of this valuable resource.

Ref: *J-5   3(2):124-131, Feb 1969.*

3.0 - 502
Singer, J. and Lewis, D. C. G.   (1966).
PROPORTIONAL-FLOW WEIRS FOR AUTOMATIC SAMPLING OR
DOSING
--A comprehensive mathematical analysis of the
Sutro Proportional-flow weir is made and coefficient data for the standard design are presented
in tabular form. The results of experiments carried out on non-standard proportional weirs are
given, with particular reference to the crestless
weir which prevents the accumulation of solids upstream. With new designs and production methods,
this type of weir will be useful as a control device, especially in chemical dosing and sampling.
Ref: *J-101   70,:105-111, 1966.*

3.0 - 503
Sinha, Evelyn (1970). OCEANOGRAPHY FROM SPACE AND
AIRCRAFT
--428 informative abstracts provide direct references to literature sources representing the state-
of-the-art in the technology and applications of
oceanography from space and aircraft. Passive and
active sensing devices and techniques are reported
with applications in biology and fisheries, coastal zone engineering and resources, geodesy, geology, geophysics, ice surveillance, interaction between ocean and atmosphere, marine meteorology,
navigation and communication, oceanology, pollution detection and monitoring and salvage operations. Various geophysical devices are related to
exploration potentials. The importance of the
uses of transponding buoys and telemetry is suggested. References are also given to problems involved in data processing and in computer programming. Ref: *Ocean Engineering Information
Service. La Jolla, Calif. Ocean Engineering Information Series Vol. 2, 1970.*

3.0 - 504
Skulberg, O. M. (1967).   ALGAL CULTURES   AS A
MEANS TO ASSES THE FERTILIZING INFLUENCE OF
POLLUTION
--Assays were carried out on water from Oslo Fjord,
a threshold fjord with pronounced brackish-water
stratification. Water from the inner fjord could
support more algal growth than could water from
the outer fjord. Investigations are still in progress to determine the relative importance of various factors such as the incoming sea water, the
run-off from the catchment area, the bottom waters,
and the discharges of sewage and other pollutants,
on the eutrophication of the fjord. Ref: *P-9
1,:113-138, 1967.*

3.0 - 505
Slanetz, L. W.; Bartley, C.H. and Metcalf, T.G.
(1965).   CORRELATION OF COLIFORM AND FAECAL
STREPTOCOCCAL INDICES WITH THE PRESENCE OF
SALMONELLAE AND ENTERIC VIRUSES IN SEA WATER AND
SHELLFISH
--Using samples of water and oysters from the
estuaries and bay region of New Hampshire, which
receive untreated sewage from a population of
about 12,000, studies are being carried out to
compare and develop laboratory procedures for the
detection and enumeration of coliform bacteria,
faecal streptococci, salmonellae, and enteric viruses in sea waters and shellfish, and also to

evaluate the comparative efficiency of coliform,
faecal coliform, and faecal streptococcal organisms as indicators of the hygienic quality of
shellfish waters and shellfish, and to correlate
the numbers of these organisms in such samples
with the presence of salmonellae and enteric viruses. Ref: *P-10   3,:27-41, 1965.*

3.0 - 506
Slanetz, L. W.; Bartley, C. H. and Stanley, K. W.
(1968).   COLIFORMS, FAECAL STREPTOCOCCI AND
SALMONELLA IN SEA WATER AND SHELLFISH
--In continuation of previous work on the establishment of standards for shellfish waters in New
Hampshire which receive untreated sewage from
several towns and cities, results are given of
counts of coliform bacteria and faecal streptococci and of the detection of *Salmonella* in water and
oysters from the area, collected between 1964 and
1966. *Salmonella* sp. or serotypes were isolated
from approved growing areas meeting MPN standards
for coliform bacteria, showing that revised test
procedures may be needed to establish standards.
Ref: *J-65   5,:66-78, 1968.*

3.0 - 507
Slinn, D. J. (1968).   SOME HYDROLOGICAL
OBSERVATIONS IN AUCKLAND AND OTAGO HARBOURS
--Hydrologic data are presented for both harbors.
There appears to be little chemical evidence of
organic pollution in either harbor. Auckland Har-
bor is described as vertically well-mixed as a
result of tidal currents; this may apply to Otago
Harbor as well. Ref: *J-50   2(5):79-97, Jan 1968.
32 refs.*

3.0 - 508
Slowey, J. F.; Hayes, D. and others   (1966).
DISTRIBUTION OF GAMMA-EMITTING RADIONUCLIDES IN
THE GULF OF MEXICO
--The results are given of preliminary studies on
the distribution of some gamma-emitting isotopes
in the Gulf of Mexico. Manganese-54, was found in
all the samples of water examined and its concentration factor in algae was higher than that of
other isotopes. Particulate matter contained
higher concentrations of manganese-54 than of
stable manganese-55, suggesting that the chemical
form in which manganese-54 reaches the sea is different from that of stable manganese. It is probable that some of the manganese-54 enters as manganese dioxide which is relatively insoluble in
sea water and would tend to form a colloid or precipitate out as particulate matter. The studies
also showed that 50 per cent of zirconium-95-nio-
bium-95, 66 per cent of ruthenium-106, and 33 per
cent of cerium-144 occur in the soluble form even
18 months after the last nuclear test. Antimony-
125 was found for the first time in surface sea
water, the concentration being higher near the
shore than in the open Gulf, but it was not found
in organisms or in particulate matter. It is
thought that antimony may be washed down from land
surfaces and concentrated in the surface waters of
the ocean. Ref: *J-97   13,:784, 1966*

3.0 - 509
Smith, A. N. (1968).   EFFECTS OF OIL POLLUTION
AND EMULSIFIER CLEANSING ON SHORE LIFE IN
SOUTH-WEST BRITAIN
--Discusses the effects on shore life of various

episodes of oil pollution, followed by treatment with emulsifier, which have occurred off southwest Britain between 1960, when the Esso Portsmouth caught fire and released its cargo of crude oil at Milford Haven, and 1967, when the Torrey Canyon struck a reef off Land's End. The reported toxicities of crude oil, emulsifiers, and their active constituents, are reviewed and, based on a range of observations, common littoral plants and animals are placed in a rough order of susceptibility to oil and emulsifiers. Ref: *J-51 5,:97-107, 1968.*

3.0 - 510
Smith, D. B.; Parsons, T. V. and Wearn, P. L. (1967). FURTHER INVESTIGATION OF SILT MOVEMENT IN THE EBB CHANNEL, FIRTH OF FORTH, USING RADIOACTIVE TRACERS, 1966
--The use of Scandium-46 as a radioactive tracer for continued studies on spoil movement in the Firth of Forth enabled the labelled material to be followed for 4 months. Previous investigations into short-term movement of spoil dumped in the Ebb Channel spoil ground showed that the principal movement was downstream. In the present investigation the movement along the line of the Ebb Channel was confirmed, and only very limited upstream drift occurred; after 1 month traces of material had reached the southern edge of the main channel. Ref: *U. K. Atomic Energy Authority Res. Gr. Rept. AERE-R5523 8 p., 1967.*

3.0 - 511
Smith, Ethan T. and Morris, Alvin R. (1969). SYSTEMS ANALYSIS FOR OPTIMAL WATER QUALITY MANAGEMENT
--Describes the formulation of the comprehensive plan for water quality control on the Delaware Estuary. Optimality was sought by using techniques from operations research. The methods of systems analysis were used to identify and model the cause and effect relationships between water pollution and water quality. The final program that was selected is included. Ref: *J-1 41(9):1635-1646, Sept 1969. 3 refs.*

3.0 - 512
Smith, J. Wardley (1968). PROBLEMS IN DEALING WITH OIL POLLUTION ON SEA AND LAND
--There are a number of apparent alternative ways which might be used to deal with oil floating on the sea. The first, which is frequently suggested for crude oil, is to set fire to the oil; however, if one excludes burning the oil when it is contained in a wrecked ship, the problem of burning oil which is floating on the surface of the sea can be considered practically insoluble. The other methods of dealing with floating oil are: (1) to collect it; (2) to skim it off the surface; (3) to absorb it; (4) to make it into a jell and pick it up; (5) to sink it to the bottom; and (6) to emulsify or disperse it. Each of these are separately examined. Ref: *J-8 54(539):358-366, Nov 1968. 2 refs.*

3.0 - 513
Smith, Lowell Kent (1968). ROLE OF BENTHIC MARINE PLANTS IN THE LITTORAL PHOSPHATE CYCLE
--The role of attached macrophytic marine plants - chiefly marine algae - in the uptake, release and regeneration of phosphates was investigated along

Monterey Peninsula in California. Considered also were the disintegration of dead plants, upcast and detached plants. Ref: *Stanford University. Thesis 330 p., 1968.*

3.0 - 514
Smith, Richard H. (1969). DEEP SEA REFUSE DISPOSAL
--The invention relates to disposal at sea of material such as mixed trash and refuse of the character commonly collected in a community as household rubbish. More particularly, the invention relates to a method for collecting mixed rubbish in one location, transporting it out to sea and submerging the rubbish to a depth sufficient to render it non-buoyant, and there dumping it so that the material will then sink to the ocean bottom. Ref: *U. S. Patent No. 3,456,824. Not assigned. 1969.*

3.0 - 515
Snook, W. G. G. (1968). MARINE DISPOSAL OF TRADE WASTES
--A paper presented originally at a symposium on 'Discharges to the Sea' in London, March 1968 by the Industrial Water and Effluents Group. Outlines the design, construction and economic aspects of the disposal of trade wastes by a submarine pipeline with a diffuser system. Ref: *J-21 46,: 1593-1598, Nov 16, 1968.*

3.0 - 516
Synder, George R. (1969). HEAT AND ANADROMOUS FISHES AND DISCUSSION
--This discussion, on how the problems of thermal pollution at Hanford, Washington fit into the general problem of thermal pollution of the Columbia River, suggests that tangible evidence is needed on the investigation of predator stomach contents or results from traps that are being carried out now by Battelle to establish the magnitude of mortalities that are caused by the thermal pollution. Data are presented on changes in water temperature and river flow. Ref: *P-30 p. 318-353, 1969. 10 refs.*

3.0 - 517
Society for Underwater Technology. (1969). OCEANOLOGY INTERNATIONAL 69. CONFERENCE: TECHNICAL SESSIONS DAY I
--This volume, covering the first day of the conference on oceanology held in Brighton, Eng. Feb, 1969, contains 18 papers on oceanographic instrumentation and data handling and 9 papers on offshore minerals technology. Among the instruments described are, by BURR, P., an underwater towed vehicle designed as a complete instrument package with a continuous plankton recorder (or other type of sensor, for example for tracking the diffusion of contaminants), sensors for measuring temperature, depth, and salinity, data recorder, and its own power supplies, and capable of undulating between depths of 26 and 382 ft with 1 cycle per 5 miles when towed behind a ship at 8-16 knots; by GAFFORD, R.D., and GREEN, M.W., a modification of the diffusion-limited polarographic sensor for determination of dissolved oxygen, which is suitable for oceanographic use; by LINES, R.W., the Coulter counter as used to measure the particle size of suspended matter and sediments and to determine the numbers and sizes of algal cells in fresh and

sea water and to study the effects of changes in salinity on estuarine phytoflagellates; and, by KREY, J., and HEMPEL, G., a multiple plankton sampler, with sensors for temperature, irradiation, and turbidity, which has been developed as a time-saving instrument for sampling plankton in ecologically well-defined depths. Ref: P-21 300 p. 1969. (See also Technical Session Day 4 - following)

3.0 - 518
Society for Underwater Technology (1969). OCEANOLOGY INTERNATIONAL 69. CONFERENCE: TECHNICAL SESSIONS DAY 4
--This volume, covering the 4th day of the conference on oceanology held at Brighton, England. Feb, 1969 contains papers presented at the session on underwater observation and communications; diving technology, pollution; and submarine vehicles and operations. Ref: P-21 384 p., 1969.

3.0 - 519
Sood, Ravinder K. (1969). METHOD OF DEAERATING SEA WATER
--In this method of removing dissolved gases from sea water, two adjacent deaeration chambers are provided both of which are maintained at subatmospheric pressures. Sea water heated in the final condenser of an evaporator system is introduced into a first chamber where a portion of it flashes to vapor, providing an atmosphere which facilitates the removal of dissolved gases. Cold sea water is introduced into the second chamber, wherein it is contacted with steam from the first chamber. Deaerated waters from both chambers are collected in a common sump and removed. Ref: U. S. Patent No. 3,458,972. Assigned to U.S.A. Atomic Energy Commission. 1969.

3.0 - 520
Sport, M C. (1969). DESIGN AND OPERATION OF GAS FLOTATION EQUIPMENT FOR THE TREATMENT OF OILFIELD PRODUCED BRINES
--This paper presents an evaluation of the gas flotation process as a method of treating produced oil field brine for the control of pollution. Shell Oil Company's Delta Production Division has designed and installed the first phase of a $1.8 million produced water treating facility on the Southwest Pass of the Mississippi River. This facility removes oil from produced brine. Ref: P-13 1,:145-152, May 1969. 2 refs.

3.0 - 521
Stafford, Donald Bennett (1968). DEVELOPMENT AND EVALUATION OF A PROCEDURE FOR USING AERIAL PHOTOGRAPHS TO CONDUCT A SURVEY OF COASTAL EROSION
--Presents a procedure developed to utilize existing aerial photographs of a coastal area to conduct a survey of coastal erosion. The use of the procedure is illustrated by data from Onslow and Carteret Counties in North Carolina and a preliminary evaluation of the results obtained in these two counties is given. The most important types of errors in aerial photographs are discussed and techniques for minimizing the errors are proposed. A preliminary evaluation of the composite error present in the measurement techniques and aerial photographs is given for the different types and scales of aerial photographs. An extensive review of the literature concerning the application of

aerial photographs to investigations of coastal phenomena is included. Ref: North Carolina State Univ., Raleigh. Thesis 230 p., 1968.

3.0 - 522
Stann, E. J. and Ringwood, R. J. (1969). SYSTEMS ENGINEERING APPROACH TO WATER QUALITY MANAGEMENT
--The proposed region-wide solution for the San Francisco Bay area includes quality and effectiveness, cost feasibility, geo-economic influences, and social and esthetic requirements. Two new parameters of waste disposal and waste effects--toxicity and biostimulation--were employed. Three mathematical models of the area and system were used. Ref: J-49 39(6):74-79, June 1969.

3.0 - 523
Steed, D. L. and Copeland, B. J. (1967). METABOLIC RESPONSES OF SOME ESTUARINE ORGANISMS TO AN INDUSTRIAL EFFLUENT
--The chronic and sub-lethal toxic effects of petrochemical waste water on estuarine fish and crustaceans were studied, taking changes in the rate of oxygen consumption to indicate physiological stress. The rate of metabolism of the test fish (Cyprinodon variegatus, Lagodon rhomboides, and Micropogon undulatus) decreased in concentrations of waste waters of less than half the TL$_m$ value, but increased in higher concentrations, representing limiting and loading stresses, respectively. Chronic low-level effects on C.variegatus were found to be similar to short-term effects at higher concentrations. In tests with the crustaceans, Penaeus duorarum and P. aztecus, the former exhibited loading stress and the latter limiting stress in low concentrations of the waste water. Physiological differences are responsible for the different reactions of these two crustaceans. The long-term consequences to fish and invertebrate populations of discharging toxic effluents to their environment are discussed. Ref: Univ. of Texas. Institute of Marine Science Contr. 12 p. 143-159, 1967.

3.0 - 524
Stehr, E. (1967). ABOUT OIL POLLUTION ON THE HIGH SEAS, CAUSED BY TANKER ACCIDENTS
--The author reviews existing literature on the protection of sea water from oil pollution, including accidental pollution from oil tankers, in connection with an accident which occurred in February 1966 near Heligoland. Based on experiences gained from this accident the urgent need arose for first-aid measures and the availability of information for the immediate removal of oil in cases of emergencies and for the most effective methods to prevent the spreading of oil, including the use of binding agents, both in calm and rough waters. Ref: J-98 108,:53-54, 1967.

3.0 - 525
Stephan, Edward C. (1969). LONG ISLAND'S APPROACH TO COASTAL ZONE PLANNING
--Nassau and Suffolk Counties, Long Island, have begun a joint research and development program to develop a regional planning system for the management of the marine environment and resources of Long Island. This paper describes the major problems that forced county officials into action and discusses the establishment of the Regional Marine Resources Council of the Nassau-Suffolk Regional

Planning Board and the initiation of a research program to ascertain the adequacy of the scientific base for marine environment management. Ref: *J-52   3(6):71-72, Nov/Dec 1969.   3 refs.*

3.0 - 526
Stevenson, Robert E. (1969).   SOME TIME AND SPACE RESOLUTION REQUIREMENTS FOR SPACE OCEANOGRAPHY
--Analyses of photographs from manned space flights and the related oceanography have led to determinations of the spatial resolution and intervals of repetition necessary for the optimum utilization of space-derived, remotely sensed data of certain ocean-surface features. Coastal waters, both continental and insular, place the greatest demands on the space system. In these inshore waters, ocean-surface features of 25 square kilometers or larger must be viewed once every 24 hours, on a temperature grid of 10 kilometers, with a feature-boundary definition of 100 meters. These requirements must be applied only to precise geographic localities, if excessive data handling is to be avoided. Coastal eddies that form sequences of van Karman vortices are examples of ocean-surface features that have periods, sizes, and sufficient energy to contribute significantly to local environments. A cost-benefit study of three submarine outfalls that carry 1 billion gallons of sewage to the sea indicated a $1 million per year advantage if daily data were available on the near-shore eddy system. Ref: *P-20 Vol. 24, Part 3   4 p., 1969.   7 refs.*

3.0 - 527
Stirn, J.   (1968).   POLLUTION OF TUNIS LAKE
--The author described the physical features of Tunis Lake, a shallow, almost stagnant, saline lagoon separating the town of Tunis from the sea. Enrichment by sewage and sewage effluents from the town has caused marked eutrophication in the lagoon, and decomposition of algae results in hydrogen sulphide production and death of fish. It was proposed that all but a small part of the town's sewage shall be discharged to the Mediterranean by a new submarine outfall, the remainder to receive biological treatment at the existing plant and the effluent to be used for irrigation. Algae will be harvested and used as fertilizer, and sea water will be pumped to the lagoon through artificial channels in the sand barrier that separates it from the sea, establishing constant circulation in the lagoon, with return flow via the navigation channel. Ref: *P-19 and J-59   9,:99-106, 1968.*

3.0 - 528
Stoertz, George E.; Hemphill, W. R.; and Markle, D. A. (1969).   AIRBORNE FLUOROMETER APPLICABLE TO MARINE AND ESTUARINE STUDIES
--An experimental Fraunhofer line discriminator detected solar-stimulated yellow fluorescence (5890 A) emitted by Rhodamine WT dye in aqueous solutions. Concentration of 1 part per billion was detected in tap water 1/2 meter deep. In extremely turbid San Francisco Bay, dye was monitored in concentrations of less than 5 parts per billion from helicopter and ship. Applications include studies of current dynamics and dispersion. Potential applications of the technique could include sensing oil spills, fish oils, lignin sulfonates, other fluorescent pollutants, and chlorophyll

fluorescence. Ref: *J-52   3(6):11-26, Nov/Dec 1969.   16 refs.*

3.0 - 529
Stoltenberg, David H. and Sobel, Mathew J. (1965). EFFECT OF TEMPERATURE ON THE DEOXYGENATION OF A POLLUTED ESTUARY
--A systems analysis technique was presented for describing the space and time variations of DO in a body of water. Because of a lack of sufficient data for the deoxygenation constant for the Delaware Estuary comprehensive study, the following work was done to determine its values in the estuary. The decay coefficient was related empirically to stream temperatures after the effect on the coefficient of organic matter concentration and other factors were tested. Ref: *J-1   37(12):1705-1715, Dec 1965.   12 refs.*

3.0 - 530
Storrs, P. N. and others (1968).   ESTUARINE WATER QUALITY AND BIOLOGICAL POPULATION INDICES
--Describes the quantitative relationships defined between water and sediment quality parameters and two biological indices in San Francisco Bay. Ref: *P-8 and J-12   p. 128, 1968.*

3.0 - 531
Strawn, Kirk and Dunn, James E.   (1967). RESISTANCE OF TEXAS SALT-AND FRESH WATER-MARSH FISHES TO HEAT DEATH AT VARIOUS SALINITIES
--Heat resistance and effects of various salinities were studied on 10 species of fishes living in or near the salt marshes of the Texas coast utilizing response surface diagrams. It was found that each species reacted differently to the combined stresses of salinity and high temperatures. As temperature decreased optimum salinities for survival decreased for freshwater fishes and increased for saltmarsh fishes. In general some salt in the water afforded protection from heat shock. Ref: *J-53   19(1):57-76, April 1967.   17 refs.*

3.0 - 532
Strickland, J. B. (1969).   REMARKS ON THE EFFECTS OF HEATED DISCHARGES ON MARINE ZOOPLANKTON
--Brief remarks on the present lack of information on the effects of heated discharges on marine zooplankton. Ref: *P-30   p. 73-79, 1969.*

3.0 - 533
Strobel, Gerald A. (1968).   COLIFORM-FAECAL COLIFORM BACTERIA IN TIDAL WATERS
--Studies were made on the occurrence of coliform organisms and faecal coliform organisms in several embayments on Long Island, N.Y., which receive different types of organic pollution. The results indicated that the relation between coliform and faecal coliform bacteria varies with the source of pollution, degree of waste treatment provided, characteristics of the receiving waters, and precipitation on the watershed. The suggested faecal coliform stantard (median MPN of 7.8 per 100 ml) did not compare with observed values in waters with a median coliform MPN of 70 per 100 ml, which ranged from 15 to 67 faecal coliform organisms per 100 ml. In view of the present limited knowledge of the risks of eating shellfish from moderately polluted waters, complementary standards should be based on correlations with existing standards that have been shown to be adequate, and these

correlations should be specific for each area. Ref: *J-3   94(SA4 Paper 6068):641-656, Aug 1968.* *22 refs.*

3.0 - 534
Sugiki, Akinori (1968).   POLLUTION FORECASTING IN AN ESTUARY (Japanese).
--The Sumida Estuary was used as an example and the study presented an analysis of the factors affecting the oxygen balance of polluted waters. A mixing theory developed for the Thames River Estuary was the most reliable for forecasting pollution in a strongly mixed estuary. Discussions included: deoxygenation, reaeration, and oxygen consumption by bottom deposits. Forecasts for 1975 and 1985 are presented. Ref: *J-54 Series A. Annual Report No. 6:12-13, 1968.   2 refs.*

3.0 - 535
Suner, J. and Pinol, J. (1967).   COLIFORM BACTERIOPHAGES AND MARINE WATER CONTAMINATION
--Sewage from the city of Barcelona, Spain, is discharged without treatment into the Mediterranean through 4 short outfalls and this causes severe pollution of the water and the beaches. The authors report the results of bacteriological investigations of the coastal waters with particular reference to the use of bacteriophages as an index of pollution. The results confirmed the polluted condition of the water, the polluted area extending for a distance of 6 km offshore. Direct counts of total bacteria and of *Esch. coli* were made, and coliform bacteriophages were detected using *Esch. coli* strain C-5; this strain was always found in the sewage discharges and was the dominant strain in the polluted water. It was concluded that the bacteriophage index could give useful information, particularly in the study of pathogenic species that are difficult to isolate, such as *Salmonella*. One unexpected result obtained was the fact that the counts of *Esch. coli* and of bacteriophage in most of the samples were similar. Ref: *P-9 3,:105-120, 1967.*

3.0 - 536
Swift, W. H.; Touhill, C. J. and others (1969). OIL SPILLAGE PREVENTION, CONTROL, AND RESTORATION. STATE OF ART AND RESEARCH NEEDS
--This is a report on research to evaluate current state of technology of prevention and control of major oil spillage on water, restoration of shore face and waterfowl, and on effects of oil pollution and defensive measures on aquatic life. Detailed research and development recommendations for prevention, control and restoration are made. Ref: *J-1   41(3 Part 1):392-412, March 1969.*

3.0 - 537
Talbot, G. B. (1966).   ESTUARINE ENVIRONMENTAL REQUIREMENTS AND LIMITING FACTORS FOR STRIPED BASS
--A review of factors affecting the development of the striped bass is based on a bibliography of 67 references. Adequate spawning areas are necessary for the survival of this fish, with suitable degrees of stream flow, water quality, turbidity, and temperature. Degradation of estuaries by dredging, filling, pollution, and agricultural drainage and erosion may have an adverse effect on striped bass populations, and aspects on which research is required for proper management of this

species are indicated. Ref: *P-5 and J-23   95(4): 37-49 (Spec. Pub. No. 3), 1966.   67 refs.*

3.0 - 538
Taylor, James I. and Stingelin, Ronald W. (1969). INFRARED IMAGING FOR WATER RESOURCES STUDIES
--Applicability of infrared remote sensing in water resources studies, applications include studies of interaction of river and seawater and attendant current patterns in tidal estuary, and current patterns and pollution studies in Great Lakes. Explains how informational content of infrared imagery can be improved for special purposes through various enhancement techniques, including variable detector-filter configurations, provision for manual gain control, signal differentiation, and development of calibrated line-scan imaging system. Ref: *J-18   95(HY1 Paper 6331): 175-189, Jan 1969.   8 refs.*

3.0 - 539
Teal, J. M. and Wieser, W. (1966).   DISTRIBUTION AND ECOLOGY OF NEMATODES IN A GEORGIA SALT MARSH
--In studies on the distribution of nematodes in a coastal salt marsh in Georgia, very high population densities were found, particularly near the low-tide boundary, but since individuals were small the greatest biomass recorded was 0.76 mg per cm^2 (wet weight), which coincided with a point at which nematodes penetrated to the greatest depth (14 cm below the mud surface). The respiration rate of 15 species taken from the marsh was shown to be related to their buccal cavity size, with the exception of *Odontophora, Bolbella,* and the predators. It was estimated that nematodes are responsible for only 3 per cent of the total uptake of oxygen in the mud. Ref: *J-41   11(2): 217-222, April 1966.   10 refs.*

3.0 - 540
Templeton, W. L. and Preston, A.   (1966). TRANSPORT AND DISTRIBUTION OF RADIOACTIVE EFFLUENTS IN COASTAL AND ESTUARINE WATERS OF THE UNITED KINGDOM
--The authors summarize available data on the transport and distribution of radioactive waste waters discharged to estuaries and coastal waters of the United Kingdom. The principal surveys have been concerned with the discharge into the Irish Sea of the waste waters from the fuel-element reprocessing plant at Windscale, Cumb., and information is given on the accumulation of radioactive isotopes by algae, invertebrates, fish, bottom deposits, and beach material in the area, indicating that contamination from this source spreads for 75-100 miles. Studies have also been carried out in Blackwater Estuary, Essex, on the distribution of zinc-65 originating from a nuclear power plant; these showed that although the outfall is in the mouth of the estuary, in the ebb channel, much of the radioactive material is carried upstream and is accumulated by oysters. Ref: *P-4 p. 267-289, 1966.*

3.0 - 541
Teresi, J. D. and Newcombe, C. L.   (1968). EVALUATION OF HAZARDS FROM IMMERSION OF PLUTONIUM IN THE MARINE ENVIRONMENT
--Studies were made to evaluate the potential hazards from the contamination of the California coastal environment with plutonium following an

instantaneous release upon immersion. The hazards were evaluated on the basis of the possible incorporation of plutonium into marine food chains. Using published concentration factors for fish and marine algae, the expected body burdens resulting from ingestion of fish, agar, algin, and *Porphyra* were calculated, on the basis of conservative assumptions, and compared with the recommended permissible body-burden for large populations. Using various mathematical diffusion models, details of which are given in an appendix, the diffusion parameters were calculated for instantaneous release of plutonium and were used to predict the area of the sea which would become contaminated with a hazardous concentration of plutonium and the duration of the hazardous concentration. Ref: *P-7 p. 673-680, 1968.*

3.0 - 542
Thomann, Robert V. (1965). RECENT RESULTS FROM A MATHEMATICAL MODEL OF WATER POLLUTION CONTROL IN THE DELAWARE ESTUARY
--Presents an application of a mathematical model to the control of DO in the Delaware Estuary. The model was based on the classical dissolved oxygen sag equation. Equations describing the time and space variability of DO are set forth and their usefulness discussed. Two programs were written. Ref: *J-16 1(3):349-359, July/Sept 1965. 4 refs.*

3.0 - 543
Thomann, Robert V. (1968). OPTIMUM WATER QUALITY MANAGEMENT OF STREAM AND ESTUARINE SYSTEMS
--Discussion of the use of a dynamic water pollution control model using illustrations from the Green River, Washington and the Delaware River. Ref: *American Water Resources Conference. Fourth. New York. p. 115-122, Nov 1968. 3 refs.*

3.0 - 544
Thomann, Robert V. and Marks, D. H. (1967). RESULTS FROM A SYSTEMS ANALYSIS APPROACH TO THE OPTIMUM CONTROL OF ESTUARINE WATER QUALITY
--Details are given on the use of systems analysis to determine optimal conditions for controlling water quality in the Delaware Estuary. The results of the analysis indicate the variability of the cost of achieving a water quality goal in relation to given estuarine conditions such as different diffusion and re-aeration levels. It was found that for fixed waste loads and costs, the solutions are particularly sensitive to the reaeration coefficient and are considerably less sensitive to the diffusion and decay terms. In the case of the Delaware Estuary, a definitive change occurs in the convexity of the functional relation between the cost of a programme and the dissolved-oxygen objective; this results in a 'break-point' in the quality goal beyond which it becomes increasingly expensive to achieve higher dissolved-oxygen levels by removal of carbonaceous oxygen-demanding material. Ref: *P-9 3,:29-48, 1966. Also in J-1 39(3):, March 1966. (abstract only).*

3.0 - 545
Thomann, Robert V.; O'Connor, Donald J. and DiToro, Dominic M. (1968). MANAGEMENT OF TIME VARIABLE STREAM AND ESTUARINE SYSTEMS
--This paper is concerned primarily with the first step, that is, the forecasting of future water quality conditions on a weekly or seasonal basis.

In many cases, the dissolved oxygen of the water body is used as the primary indicator of water quality. A survey of observed time variable water quality data is presented first. This is followed by a review of the theory used in modeling stream and estuarine systems. The extension of the steady state water quality control forecasting problem to include time variability and the relative differences in the responses of streams and estuaries to environmnntal fluctuations are discussed. The potential for time variable waste reduction is reviewed in the light of this forecasting ability. Ref: *American Institute of Chemical Engineers. Chemical Engineering Progress Symposium Series. Water. 64(90), 1968.*

3.0 - 546
Thomas, M. L. H. and White, G. N. (1969). MASS MORTALITY OF ESTUARINE FAUNA AT BIDEFORD, P.E.I. ASSOCIATED WITH ABNORMALLY LOW SALINITIES
--Following a gale in May 1967, a deep layer of fresh water occurred in the Bideford River, Prince Edward Island, and salinities of less than one per thousand were found at depths of 3 m in the inner part of the estuary. The reduced salinity caused extensive mortality of a variety of fauna, including *Anguilla rostrata, Asterias vulgaris, Macoma balthica, Tellina agilis,* and *Yoldia limatula.* Mortalities of *A. rostrata* and *M. balthica,* which are typical of brackish waters could not be easily explained. A rising temperature, increasing the activities of species, as well as lack of time for acclimation to lower salinities, may have contributed to many cases of mortality. Ref: *J-32 26,:701-704, 1969.*

3.0 - 547
Thomson, D. A.; Mead, A. R. and Schreiber, J. R. (1969). ENVIRONMENTAL IMPACT OF BRINE EFFLUENTS ON GULF OF CALIFORNIA
--The possible effect of introducing large volumes of brine effluent from large size desalting plants on the ecology of the Gulf of California was investigated. An examination was made of the literature containing references to the subject. Heat budget calculations show annual mean temperature increases above ambient values resulting from the mixing of brine effluent with gulf water. Biological effects were assessed. Ref: *Office of Saline Water Research and Development Progress Rept. No. 387. 196 p., March 1969. numerous refs.*

3.0 - 548
Tibby, R. B.; Foxworthy, J. E.; Oguri, M. and Fay, R. C. (1965). DIFFUSION OF WASTES IN OPEN COASTAL WATERS AND THEIR EFFECTS ON PRIMARY BIOLOGICAL PRODUCTIVITY
--In the vicinity of the submarine outfall of Orange County, Calif., investigations were made on the dispersing effluent field, with regard to physical diffusion, primary productivity of pelagic phytoplankton, and certain chemical properties. At the Hyperion and Orange County treatment plants, the filtered effluents were found to have an unusually high optical absorbance in the ultraviolet region. Since this absorbance, high in the boil, decreased progressively with time and distance along the trajectories of the dispersing effluent field, following the general trend of the changes in chemical characteristics, further studies are in progress to determine the usefulness of optical

measurements for assessing the extent and concentration of the field, and also to identify the substances responsible for the unusual optical characteristics. <u>Ref</u>: *P-1 p. 95-113, 1965.*

3.0 - 549
Tichenor, Bruce A. and Cawley, William A. (1969).
RESEARCH NEEDS FOR THERMAL POLLUTION CONTROL
--The authors spell out the research needed for better control of thermal pollution, and indicate the items of high national priority. The needs are dealt with in three categories: (1) transport and behavior of heat in water, (2) treatment processes, (3) non-treatment controls. Four items having the highest priority for research are outlined: Development of non-empirical stochastic temperature-prediction models; development of three-dimensional mathematical models for determining temperature distributions of complex hydraulic conditions on both macro and micro scales; improvement of the effectiveness of cooling devices for handling large thermal loads; development of methods for effectively utilizing waste heat, including industrial and agricultural use.
<u>Ref</u>: *P-30b Chapter 12 p. 329-340, 1969.*

3.0 - 550
Tilton, R. C. (1968). DISTRIBUTION AND CHARACTERIZATION OF MARINE SULPHUR BACTERIA
--During an investigation of marine thiobacilli in Central and North American waters, the greatest number (275 per 100 ml) was isolated in surface waters of the Caribbean Sea. The numbers found were much lower than expected from concentrations of reduced sulphur compounds present in these waters. Membrane-filter and enrichment-culture techniques were used for enumeration and isolation, and tables were produced to show the effects of salinity, initial pH value of the medium, and form of sulphur substrate on growth of the bacilli.
<u>Ref</u>: *P-19 and J-59 9,:237-253, 1968.*

3.0 - 551
Tokuomi, H. (1969). MEDICAL ASPECTS OF MINAMATA DISEASE
--A discussion of the medical aspects of the minamata disease common to persons eating fish and shellfish taken from the Bay of Minamata, Japan. The disease is caused by a mercury compound discharged along with industrial wastes. <u>Ref</u>: *J-59 13/14,:5-35, 1969.*

3.0 - 552
Torpey, Wilbur N. (1967). RESPONSE TO POLLUTION OF NEW YORK HARBOR AND THAMES ESTUARY
--Presents a historical analysis of the relationships between BOD loading and dissolved oxygen content of the waters in New York Harbor and the Thames Estuary in England. For both, the curve defining the relationship of organic loading rate to dissolved oxygen is considerably distorted. It does not follow the smooth path of the oxygen-sag formulations. The relationship to human population in the area is pointed out. <u>Ref</u>: *J-1 39(11): 1797-1809, Nov 1967.*

3.0 - 553
Torpey, Wilbur N. (1968). EFFECTS OF REDUCING POLLUTION OF THAMES ESTUARY
--Study has been made relating to effects of reducing polluting discharges to Thames Estuary by

comparing water quality data for summer months prior to (1950-59) and after (1964-65) use of extensive new activated sludge treatment facilities. It was demonstrated that nitrogenous matter was oxidized after and separately from carbonaceous matter before use of new treatment facilities; carbonaceous and nitrogenous matter were oxidized concurrently when new treatment facilities were operated; nitrate production assumed auto-catalytic pattern both before and after use of new treatment facilities. <u>Ref</u>: *J-4 115(7):295-301, July 1968. 3 refs.*

3.0 - 554
Townson, J. M. (1968). TRANSDUCER FOR OPEN CHANNEL FLOW
--Following an explanation of the theory on which an instrument has been designed to enable simultaneous values of water level, current velocity, current direction to be measured remotely, the practical details of the apparatus and its calibration are described. An application to on-line control of a tidal model by coupling the instrument to an analog or digital computer is suggested.
<u>Ref</u>: *J-55 6(1):45-68, 1968. 5 refs.*

3.0 - 555
Tsai, C. (1968). EFFECTS OF CHLORINATED SEWAGE EFFLUENTS ON FISHES IN UPPER PATUXENT RIVER, MARYLAND
--A study was made to determine the effects of chlorinated sewage effluents on the abundance and species diversity of fish in the Patuxent River, Md., and two of its tributaries. Immediately below sewage outfalls numbers of fish were drastically reduced even when the dissolved oxygen and pH values were at acceptable levels. As the numbers of fish increased with distance below the outfall a species shift was noted. Dissolved oxygen and pH values, which are the parameters generally recognized for pollution assessment, are not necessarily the decisive factors in depletion of fish populations below points of discharge of chlorinated sewage effluents. <u>Ref</u>: *J-25 9(2): 83-93, June 1968.*

3.0 - 556
Tsuruga, H. (1965). SEQUENTIAL ANALYSIS OF RADIONUCLIDES IN MARINE ORGANISMS
--Details are given of the method developed for determining radioactive iron, cobalt, zinc, zirconium, ruthenium, and cerium in marine organisms. Carriers are added to the ashed biological samples and the mixture is fused with a mixture of potassium hydroxide, potassium carbonate, and potassium nitrate; the product is leached with water, and zirconium and ruthenium are precipitated as the sulphides, and isolated. The water-insoluble residue is leached with hydrochloric acid after silica dehydration, and the acidic solution is passed through a column of Amberlite CG; cerium, cobalt, and iron are eluted with different strengths of hydrochloric acid, and isolated. Finally, the precipitates are counted. The radioactivity of plankton samples collected off the Pacific coast of Japan in 1962 and 1964 was found to be due mainly to cerium-144, with some ruthenium-106. <u>Ref</u>: *J-99 31,:651-658, 1965.*

3.0 - 557
Tully, Paul R. (1969). REMOVAL OF FLOATING OIL

SLICKS BY THE CONTROLLED COMBUSTION TECHNIQUE
--A product called CAB-O-SIL ST-2-0 and method of application of the material to the surface of the slick is described. After burning, a non-tacky, hardened residue, similar in appearance to tar paper, remains in a collectible form. The oil combustion produces a smoke column - a form of pollution which represents only a small fraction of the damage caused by oil pollution. Ref: P-14 p. 81-91, 1969. 3 refs.

3.0 - 558
Turekian, K. K. (1966). TRACE ELEMENTS IN SEA WATER AND OTHER NATURAL WATERS. ANNUAL PROGRESS REPORT, DECEMBER 1, 1965 - NOVEMBER 30, 1966.
--A neutron activation technique has been developed for the determination of trace elements in stream waters; it involves addition of a carrier salt (high-purity sodium carbonate), freeze drying, irradiation of the recovered residue, and separation and counting of the desired radioactive nuclide. Ref: U. S. Atomic Energy Commission, YALE-292-12 60 p., 1966.

3.0 - 559
Turekian, K. K. and Scott, M. R. (1967). CONCENTRATIONS OF CR, AG, MO, NI, CO, AND MN IN SUSPENDED MATERIAL IN STREAMS
--There are regional differences in concentrations of chromium, silver, molybdenum, nickel, cobalt, and manganese in suspended sediments of streams; sediments of Mississippi, and rivers west of it draining into Gulf of Mexico, as well as Rhone River resemble average shale in composition, while rivers of United States east of Mississippi are considerably higher in concentration; this difference is not due to differences in cation-exchange capacity but rather perhaps to greater amount of trace-element rich soil component and industrial contamination in eastern rivers. Ref: J-5 1(11):940-942, Nov 1967.

3.0 - 560
Turner, Charles H.; Ebert, E. E. and Given, R. R. (1965). SURVEY OF THE MARINE ENVIRONMENT OFFSHORE OF SAN ELIJO LAGOON, SAN DIEGO COUNTY
--An illustrated report of an ecological survey offshore from San Elijo lagoon in San Diego County, Calif., carried out during March-April 1964 to provide background data for environmental changes which might occur following the discharge of sewage effluent through a submarine outfall, and to enable an assessment to be made of the adequacy of the standards for the effluent. Observations were made along 3 transects from the intertidal area out to depths of 80 ft, and 239 plants and animals were recorded, only 16 being from sand areas. Four appendices list the biological and physical data obtained, the latter including records of bottom temperature and visibility. Ref: J-14 51(1):81-112, 1965.

3.0 - 561
Turner, Charles H.; Ebert, E. E. and Given, R. R. (1966). MARINE ENVIRONMENT IN THE VICINITY OF THE ORANGE COUNTY SANITATION DISTRICTS OCEAN OUTFALL
--Reports that a biological survey in the area of a sewer outfall showed that there was generally a typical faunistic assemblage for the depths and substrates examined. Two exceptions were noted: (1) a reduced number of species encrusting the

last 100 feet of the outfall pipe as compared to the central portion and (2) considerably fewer kinds and numbers of organisms on an artificial reef in the area as compared to other artificial reefs exposed for the same time at the same depth. Ref: J-14 52(1):28-48, 1966.

3.0 - 562
Turner, Charles H.; Ebert, Earl E. and Given, Robert R. (1968). MARINE ENVIRONMENT OFFSHORE FROM POINT LOMA, SAN DIEGO COUNTY
--This is the third in a continuing series of marine environment surveys conducted by the California Department of Fish and Game in cooperation with the State's Regional Water Quality Control Boards. Data from this ecological study are to be used in evaluating the effects of a submarine outfall discharge on the marine life in the vicinity of Point Loma, San Diego County. Ecological studies should be carried out at least annually to record biotic changes which may be relative to the outfalls operation. Ref: California. Dept. of Fish and Game. Fish Bulletin 140 85 p., 1968.

3.0 - 563
Turner, Charles H. and Strachan, Alec R. (1969). MARINE ENVIRONMENT IN THE VICINITY OF THE SAN GABRIEL RIVER MOUTH
--During April and May 1966, California Department of Fish and Game biologist-divers conducted an ecological assessment of the benthic biota in the vicinity of the San Gabriel River Mouth. This study, gathered data which will be used in evaluating the effect waste discharges and proposed waste discharges into the San Gabriel River will have on the nearshore area. The 11 stations included such habitats as sand bottom, river bottom, and rock jetties. The area was 'healthy' in 1966, and a wide variety of organisms was present. But lack of fleshy brown algae on the jetty rocks indicates that conditions are not yet optimal. Ref: J-14 55(1):53-68, Jan 1969. 9 refs.

3.0 - 564
Uyeno, Fukuzo (1966). NUTRIENT AND ENERGY CYCLES IN AN ESTUARINE OYSTER AREA
--The nutrient circulation and microbial abundance of oyster producing waters in the Malpeque Bay area, Prince Edward Island, were followed at 2 stations through an open season, and the efficiency of carbon assimilation and dissimilation was estimated. Ref: J-32 23(11):1635-1652, 1966. 24 refs.

3.0 - 565
Vaccaro, R. F.; Hicks, S. E. and others (1968). OCCURRENCE AND ROLE OF GLUCOSE IN SEA WATER
--Glucose concentrations in the Atlantic Ocean from Bermuda to Dakar were measured by an enzymatic method, and by a modification of the bio-assay procedure of HOBBIE, J. E., and WRIGHT, R. T. Results obtained by both methods generally agreed; marked concentrations of glucose occurred in nearshore waters, concentrations found being 60-80 μg of glucose-carbon per litre in the Bermuda area, and 5-25 μg of glucose-carbon per litre off the African Coast. At most locations where glucose was present there was a decrease in concentration with depth. Glucose could not be detected in a mid-ocean area. Ref: J-41 13(2):356-360, April 1968. 12 refs.

3.0 - 566
Vacelet, E. (1965). CHEMICAL ASPECTS OF THE POLLUTION OF COASTAL SEA WATER IN THE BAY OF MARSEILLES. INFLUENCE ON THE PLANKTON POPULATIONS
--Physio-chemical data obtained for water in the Bay of Marseilles, in a zone close to the shore and situated between the Endoume Islands and the Cuivres Cove, showed that water close to the shore is extremely rich in minerals, compared with the open water; there are corresponding increases in the total count of bacteria, in the concentrations of chlorophyll a, b, and c (of vegetable origin) and in the concentration of astacine-carotenoid pigments (of animal origin). Although some plankton species requiring very pure water have disappeared from the coastal region, the conditions favor increased growth of other species. These conclusions resemble those obtained by SANTINI, D.B., for benthic organisms in the same zone of the Gulf; certain species of algae disappeared, being replaced by fungi characteristic of polluted water, and this was accompanied by an increase in the biomass. Ref: *P-1 p. 89-93, 1965.*

3.0 - 567
Vaillan-court, G. (1968). INDICATORS OF POLLUTION OF THE WATERS OF THE RIVIÈRE DES PRAIRIES
--Studies were carried out on the Rivière des Prairies, which flows along the north shore of the island of Montreal, to determine the relative efficience of various indicators of pollution. In Rivière des Prairies the concentration of dissolved oxygen and the numbers of *Gammarus* decreased downstream, while the BOD and coliform count increased. The results indicate that this river is seriously polluted along two-thirds of its course. Ref: *J-100 95,:979-1029, 1968.*

3.0 - 568
Van Dam, G. C. (1965). HORIZONTAL DIFFUSION IN NORTH SEA NEAR NETHERLAND'S COAST IN CONNECTION WITH WASTE DISPOSAL
--Experiments have been performed to study horizontal spreading of dissolved matter in Netherlands' coastal areas. The problem cannot be entirely separated from the vertical mixing process, but it was found that especially for large scales of time and space a two-dimensional approach leads to usable results. Application to waste spreading problems is possible insofar as waste behaves as dissolved matter. Horizontal diffusion problem tracer studies with Rhodamine-B on a natural scale were performed; the tracer was monitored by continuous sampling by boat and by aerial photography. Ref: *P-18 5,:129-133, 1965.*

3.0 - 569
Van Dam, G. C. (1967). DISCHARGE OF WASTE WATER TO THE SEA. CONCENTRATION DISTRIBUTIONS OF WASTE WATER IN MARINE AREAS
--Research, using intermittent and continuous injection of Rhodamine-B to determine the distribution of sewage discharged to the coastal waters of the Netherlands, is described. A mathematical model which is used for the interpretation of results on a digital computer is presented. Ref: *J-102 51,:128-129, 1967.*

3.0 - 570

3.0 - 570 (right column)
Van Lopik, J. R.; Rambie, G. S. and Pressman, A.E. (1968). POLLUTION SURVEILLANCE BY NONCONTACT INFRARED TECHNIQUES
--Airborne infrared mapping techniques and their application to identification and monitoring of pollutants in streams and other bodies of water are described and illustrated. Thermal, organic and inorganic pollution can be determined and monitored providing for rapid measurement and synoptic assessments of pollution parameters. Activities in the study of Galveston Bay, Texas are used to illustrate. Proper selection of wavelengths allows identification of contaminants by their spectral emissivity characteristics. Ref: *J-1 40(3 Part 1):425-438, March 1968. 10 refs.*

3.0 - 571
Van Lopik, Jack R.; Pressman, Albert E. and Ludlum, Roger L. (1968). MAPPING POLLUTION WITH INFRARED
--The utility of 8- to 14- micron imagery in thermal pollution and hydrographic investigations is exemplified by data obtained during an aerial infrared survey of the Galveston Bay, Texas area. Discharge into water bodies either warmer or colder than the debouching water can be located and the resulting surface thermal patterns delineated. Ref: *J-56 34(6):561-564, June 1968. 7 refs.*

3.0 - 572
Van Uden, N. (1967). OCCURRENCE AND ORIGIN OF YEASTS IN ESTUARIES
--Estuarine waters contain not only more yeast per volume but also more yeast species than the adjacent sea. Critical differences in salinity tolerance may account for some differences. Sewage pollution may be the source of yeasts. Ref: *In Book Estuaries, p. 306-310, 1967. 21 refs. See also 3.0 - 421.*

3.0 - 573
Vaughan, J. W. and Miles, M. E. (1966). DISPOSAL OF RADIOACTIVE WASTES FROM U.S. NAVAL NUCLEAR-POWERED SHIPS AND THEIR SUPPORT FACILITIES
--Radioactivity in harbor water and sediments due to waste discharge from U.S. nuclear-powered ships was found not to be above normal background level; only low-level radioactivity from cobalt-60 around piers in bases and shipyards constantly used for maintenance was detected. Total radioactivity discharged in any harbor from such veseels was less than 2 c per year. Ref: *J-103 7,:257-262, 1966.*

3.0 - 574
Waldichuk, Michael (1965). WATER EXCHANGE IN PORT MOODY, BRITISH COLUMBIA, AND ITS EFFECT ON WASTE DISPOSAL
--Port Moody is a comparatively shallow appendage of the Burrard Inlet-Indian Arm system on the southern coast of British Columbia. Although highly stratified, it receives little direct run-off, its oceanography being strongly influenced by the properties of contiguous waters. Wastes from various industries surrounding the harbor have altered the natural characteristics and created mildly polluted conditions. Exchange occurs mainly by turbulent diffusion and advection arising out of tidal action. From current measurements at the entrance to Port Moody, taken on a number of surveys since 1957, net currents were evaluated for periods of a tidal day. A layer of no net motion

near 10 m corresponded to a dissolved oxygen minimum. Volume transport through different layers of the harbor was estimated from current data and compared with transport derived from predicted tide heights. The ratios of predicted to measured transport averaged 0.77 on both flood and ebb but ranged from 0.71 to 1.01 on the flood and from 0.55 to 1.00 on the ebb. Estimates of flushing rates, based on exchange ratios in different layers of Port Moody, show that for a survey in September 1962 slightly more than 50% of an introduced contaminant was removed from the upper 12.5-m layer, 83% from the 12.5-17.5-m layer, and 74% from the near-bottom layer, in one tidal day. Ref: *J-32   22(3):801-822, May 1965. 19 refs.*

3.0 - 575
Waldichuk, Michael (1965).   ESTIMATION OF FLUSHING RATES FROM TIDE HEIGHT AND CURRENT DATA IN AN INSHORE MARINE CHANNEL OF THE CANADIAN PACIFIC COAST
--Northumberland Channel, a tidal passage between Gabriola and Vancouver Islands, B. C. can be classified as a partially-mixed tidal system having rapid replacement of its waters. Sewage from Nanaimo is discharged to the channel and there is a threat of increased pollution by trade waste waters, particularly from an expanded Kraft pulp mill and a new chemical works producing chlorine and caustic soda from brines. A study was therefore carried out on the mechanisms and rate of flushing in the system; and a hypothetical model was set up in which the water of the upper layer funnels through the channel into the Narrows. At this discharge point accurate current measurements were made over an extended period to permit the evaluation of tidal transport. Flushing rates, calculated by various methods, were used to predict the maximal amount of kraft pulping waste waters which could be discharged safely from the points of view of BOD and toxicity to fish. With the present volume of waste waters, there is no serious depletion of dissolved oxygen in Northumberland Channel. Ref: *P-10   3,:133-166, 1965.*

3.0 - 576
Waldichuk, Michael (1966).   EFFECTS OF SULFITE WASTES IN A PARTIALLY ENCLOSED MARINE SYSTEM IN BRITISH COLUMBIA
--Sulfite-mill wastes discharged into the inner basin of a series of shallow marine embayments in British Columbia depresses the DO by as much as 8 mg/l. Wastes are flushed from the basin chiefly by turbulent diffusion as a result of tidal action. Over 50 per cent of the water is replaced in 2 and 3 tides, respectively, in the outer and inner basins, and 90 percent in 5 and 8 tides. The flux of DO is close to the daily oxygen demand of the mill wastes. DO was restored to normal concentrations during a week of mill shutdown and declined after resumption of production. A BOD loading of 14 percent of that imposed in July 1962 would allow adequate DO for fish life. Ref: *J-1   38(9):1484-1505, Sept 1966. 8 refs.*

3.0 - 577
Waldichuk, Michael (1967).   CURRENTS FROM AERIAL PHOTOGRAPHY IN COASTAL POLLUTION STUDIES
--The author describes the application of aerial photographic methods for investigating coastal currents in the vicinity of Vancouver and Victoria,

B. C. It was found possible to trace the discharge from the Fraser River owing to the high load of silt carried by the river water; the results obtained with the aerial photographs were in good agreement with float studies and showed that, to prevent effluent from the Vancouver primary sewage works on Iona Island, in the Fraser River, from being carried northward into English Bay, it would be necessary to construct a dike just north of the effluent channel. In studies on currents in Cordova Bay, one of the areas being considered as the site of an outfall for the Greater Victoria region, various possible target objects were considered and it was finally decided to use long strips of paper; the tracing procedure and the method used to translate the data obtained into current charts are described and the predicted dispersion of sewage from the proposed outfall site is discussed. Aerial photographs were also used to estimate the rate of dilution in the area. Although aerial photography can give useful information, it has certain limitations, being particularly dependent on the weather. Ref: *P-9   3,263-294, 1967.*

3.0 - 578
Waldichuk, Michael (1969).   EUTROPHICATION STUDIES IN A SHALLOW INLET ON VANCOUVER ISLAND
--Sampling was carried out at 13 stations in the system comprising Victoria Harbor, the Gorge Narrows, Portage Inlet, and the estuaries of the Colquitz River and Craigflower Creek, Vancouver Island, B.C., to assess the change in various water-quality characteristics from the relatively uncontaminated Juan de Fuca Strait to the heavily polluted Portage Inlet and tributary waters. Results are given graphically, showing variations over a period of 15 months; the individual characteristics are discussed; and the flushing effects of freshwater displacement and tidal exchange are outlined. Particular emphasis is placed on the marked seasonal variations in the concentrations of nutrients; the principal source of nutrients is waste waters discharged into the Colquitz River and its tributaries, including the seasonal discharge of effluent from a winery; and in summer phosphates may also enter the system from fertilized and irrigated land. Although the waste waters contribute only a small amount of nutrients, the volume of the system is so small, and flushing is so poor, that nutrients tend to accumulate, particularly during the summer months; phosphates and nitrates are absorbed by plankton and deposited on the bottom by the dying organisms. Suggestions are made for solving the problem of nutrient enrichment. Ref: *J-1 41(5):745-764, May 1969. 14 refs.*

3.0 - 579
Waldichuk, Michael (1969). EFFECTS OF POLLUTANTS ON MARINE ORGANISMS, IMPROVING METHODOLOGY OF EVALUATION - A REVIEW OF THE LITERATURE
--This is a review of the literature of studies made at Nanaimo, B. C. devoted largely to the marine environment and with particular attention called to the effects of pollutants on marine organisms. Ref: *J-1 41(9):1586-1601, Sept 1969. 83 refs.*

3.0 - 580
Walkup, Paul C.; Peterson, P. L.; Polentz, L.M.; Phinney, E. H.; and Smith, J. D.   (1969).

STUDY OF EQUIPMENT AND METHODS FOR REMOVING OIL FROM HARBOR WATERS
--A cost effectiveness analysis was performed for equipment, materials, and techniques for the removal of spilled petroleum products from the surfaces of ports and harbor waters used by U.S. Naval craft. Effectiveness criteria included speed, completeness, ease of operation, effect on marine life, and availability. Parameters for the effectiveness study were based on the petroleum products now in use or planned for future use and a detailed review of the geographic, hydrographic, physical, and environmental characteristics of ports used by the U. S. Navy. It was found that the two most cost effective systems for broad application were mechanical recovery of spilled material by surface suction devices supplemented by mechanical containment and the application of chemical dispersants by pier or vessel mounted high pressure spray equipment. Ref: *Battelle Memorial Institute. Richland, Wash. Pacific Northwest Labs. NCEL-CR-70.001 189 p., Aug 1969.*

3.0 - 581
Wallace, D. H. (1966). OYSTERS IN THE ESTUARINE ENVIRONMENT
--Oyster production in U.S.A. has been reduced owing to several factors, including chemical and biological pollution, dredging of estuaries, and alteration of current and salinity patterns, in addition to over-fishing. Ways of overcoming these difficulties are discussed briefly, with particular reference to the advantages of scientifically-controlled artificial culture systems. Ref: *P-5 and J-23 95(4):68-73 Special Publication 3, 1966.*

3.0 - 582
Wallhausser, K. H. (1967). OIL DECOMPOSING MICROORGANISMS IN NATURE AND TECHNIQUE
--Experiments on oil degradation by microorganisms were conducted. Possibilities of assisting nature by adding cultures of bacteria to oil polluted waters are discussed. Ref: *J-106 16(4):328-335, Dec 1967.*

3.0 - 583
Walsh, Don (1968). MISSISSIPPI RIVER OUTFLOW, ITS SEASONAL VARIATIONS AND ITS SURFACE CHARACTERISTICS
--This investigation provides a tentative description of mean seasonal and monthly outflow patterns together with an analysis of the factors that shape them. Three ship cruises and ten aircraft overflights were conducted from 1966 to 1968. Data from these surveys were combined with older data to establish mean conditions for the Mississippi Delta region. Ref: *Texas A & M Univ. Thesis, 1968.*

3.0 - 584
Walsh, Raymond (1968). SAN FRANCISCO BAY - DELTA WATER QUALITY CONTROL PROGRAM
--San Francisco Bay and the Sacramento-San Juaquin Delta area comprise one of the most rapidly developing areas in the country. Existing and planned water project developments together with agricultural drainage waters all have an effect on the area. The program, to be completed in 1969, will develop the basic features of a comprehensive plan for the control of water pollution including a system for the collection, reclamation, treatment, and disposal of waste and drainage water discharges. Ref: *J-1 40(2):241-251, Feb 1968.*

3.0 - 585
Ward, B. Q.; Carroll, B. J.; Garrett, E. S. and Reese, G. B. (1967). SURVEY OF THE U.S. GULF COAST FOR THE PRESENCE OF *CLOSTRIDIUM BOTULINUM*
--An extensive survey of the coast of the Gulf of Mexico was made on the occurrence of *Clostridium botulinum*; bottom samples of mud, sand and coral, plant materials and animals, including fish, 4 ducks and a sea turtle, were taken at random in summer and winter. Tabulated results of 1414 samples tested and maps of the collecting areas are given. All known types of botulism are present in the Gulf of Mexico from the tip of Florida to the Mexican border and seasonal fluctuations occur. A comparative evaluation of the mouse assay and fluorescent-antibody techniques of detection was made. Ref: *J-31 15(3):629-636, May 1967.*

3.0 - 586
Ward, B. Q.; Carroll, B. J. and others (1967). SURVEY OF THE U.S. ATLANTIC COAST AND ESTUARIES FROM KEY LARGO TO STATEN ISLAND FOR THE PRESENCE OF *CLOSTRIDIUM BOTULINUM*
--Results are given of a survey for *Clostridium botulinum* in coastal waters from Key Largo, Fla., to Staten Island, N.Y. Of 717 samples collected, 11 summer and 4 winter samples were positive; overall incidence of *C. botulinum* seemed to be lower than along the Gulf Coast, although there were concentrations in several areas. It was observed that oysters, considered to possess some inhibitory influences, could still possibly act as vectors of contamination, since *C. botulinum* type D, which was found in 6 samples in the Gulf of Mexico, was also found in Atlantic coast animals. Ref: *J-31 15(4):964-965, July 1967.*

3.0 - 587
Warinner, J. E. and Brehmer, M. L. (1966). EFFECTS OF THERMAL EFFLUENTS ON MARINE ORGANISMS
--Studies reported were undertaken by Virginia Institute of Marine Science in 1963 and are divided into primary productivity and effects on benthic invertebrates. Field investigations were made at Virginia Electric & Power Co's steam electric generating plant at Yorktown, Va. It is shown that assimilation of carbon by natural phytoplankton populations of York River is affected by artificial increase in water temperature and that community composition and abundance of marine benthic invertebrates in the river were affected by thermal discharge over a distance of 300 to 400 m from discharge. Ref: *J-57 10(4):277-289, April 1966. 10 refs.*

3.0 - 588
Warner, Richard E. (1967). BIOASSAYS FOR MICROCHEMICAL ENVIRONMENTAL CONTAMINANTS
--A detailed review of bioassay procedures in the study of actual and potential contaminants. Consideration is given to the selection of appropriate tests, the problem of sequential concentration, and the establishment of response syndromes. Ref: *J-15 36,:181-207, 1967. 221 refs.*

3.0 - 589
Wasserman, Larry P. (1968). MARINE POLLUTION ON

THE CONTINENTAL SHELF - HELPFUL OR HARMFUL?
--Planning and control, coupled with research can turn a potential threat into a great asset. Using proper disposal techniques, wastes can serve as a source of nutrients, shelter, and breeding grounds for the plant and animal life presently found on the shelf areas. The oceanographic community should be organized to control disposal in marine waters. Ref: P-25 p. 339-343, March 19-20, 1968.

3.0 - 590
Wastler, T. A. (1969). MEASURING ESTUARINE POLLUTION
--Describes briefly the basic elements of estuarine pollution and the prevailing techniques used for detecting and mapping the pollutants. It is suggested that the increasing sophistication of instrumentation and data analysis procedures, combined with the current awareness offers hope that a viable national basic data collection system may be developed to survey the coastal zone. Ref: J-109 4(3):43-45, May/June 1969.

3.0 - 591
Wastler, T. A. and de Guerrero, L. C. (1968). NATIONAL ESTUARINE INVENTORY: HANDBOOK OF DESCRIPTORS
--The handbook is a skeleton for the recording of information. It consists of a set of tables for the organization of information and data. It is designed for the National Estuarine Pollution Study. The appendix contains a list of all estuaries in the U.S. Ref: Federal Water Pollution Control Administration. Office of Estuarine Studies Report 105 p., June 1968. Revised Sept 1968.

3.0 - 592
Wastler, T. A. and Walter, Carl M. (1968). STATISTICAL APPROACH TO ESTUARINE BEHAVIOR
--Data analysis techniques used in a study of Charleston Harbor, South Carolina, show how spectral analysis can be used to characterize hydraulic interactions within the estuary. The technique was used to establish the water quality and hydraulic patterns existing during the field study period and to predict future water quality and hydraulic structure under conditions of greatly reduced river inflow. Methods of calculating cross-spectra and associated statistics are presented, and the use of these techniques in carrying out the data analysis is shown. Results of the study show that every strong vertical stratification exists at high river discharges, and that the stratification breaks up as river discharge decreases. Ref: J-3 94(SA6 Paper 6311):1175-1194, Dec 1968. 6 refs.

3.0 - 593
Water Pollution Research Steering Committee. London (1968). WATER POLLUTION RESEARCH 1967
--An annual report on the result of work at the Water Pollution Research Laboratory in London during 1967. Subjects studied: coastal pollution, estuaries, freshwater streams, effects of pollution on fish, aerobic biological treatment processes, methods of chemical analysis, and instrumentation. Lists of publications of the staff are included. Ref: Water Pollution Research Pub. Annual Report 1967. London. 213 p., 1968.

3.0 - 594
Welander, A. D. (1969). DISTRIBUTION OF RADIONUCLIDES IN THE ENVIRONMENT OF ENIWETOK AND BIKINI ATOLLS, AUGUST 1964
--To assess the impact on the environment of the numerous atomic and nuclear tests at Bikini and Eniwetok atolls in the period 1946-1958, samples of animals and plants, sea and ground water, and soils and bottom deposits were analyzed in August 1964. Results are tabulated and discussed for the individual isotopes, distinguishing between the land and marine areas. In general, the highest radioactivity was still to be found near test sites and along the westerly path of fallout from the tests. Cobalt-60 was usually the dominant gamma-emitting nuclide in marine samples and was the best measure of the distribution of radioactivity in the aquatic environment. At most localities, the highest values for cobalt-60 were found in clam kidney; and large sedentary invertebrates such as clams are concluded to be the best biological indicators, and perhaps the best measure, of radioactivity in an aquatic area. Caesium-137 was present in sea water and sediments and strontium-90 was present in ground water, but very little of these isotopes was found in marine animals or algae. Ref: P-3 p. 346-354, 1969.

3.0 - 595
Welch, Eugene (1969). FACTORS INITIATING PHYTOPLANKTON BLOOMS AND RESULTING EFFECTS ON DISSOLVED OXYGEN IN DUWAMISH RIVER ESTUARY, SEATTLE, WASHINGTON
--Phytoplankton productivity, standing stock, and other environmental factors were studied during the period 1964-1966 in the Duwamish River Estuary to determine which factors affect phytoplankton growth. The field data suggest that a 46% increase in effluent discharge between 1965 and 1966 did not increase the estuary's phytoplankton biomass significantly. Ref: U. S. Geological Survey. Water Supply Paper 1873-A 62 p., 1969. 45 refs.

3.0 - 596
Welch, Eugene B. (1968). PHYTOPLANKTON AND RELATED WATER-QUALITY CONDITIONS IN AN ENRICHED ESTUARY
--Investigations were carried out on the effect of nutrients in the effluent from Renton Sewage Works on the standing crop and productivity of phytoplankton in the Duwamish Estuary in Seattle, Wash. Results, which are given graphically for periods before and after the sewage works began operation, indicate that; although the sewage effluent produced significant increases in the concentrations of ammonia, soluble phosphate, and total phosphate; algal blooms were also dependent on other factors, particularly the hydrographic conditions. Ref: J-1 40(10):1711-1721, Oct 1968. 27 refs.

3.0 - 597
Welch, Eugene B. and Isaac, G. W. (1967). CHLOROPHYLL VARIATION WITH TIDE AND WITH PLANKTON PRODUCTIVITY IN AN ESTUARY
--At the new Renton Sewage Works of Seattle, investigations were planned to determine the effect of the effluent on production and standing crop of plankton. The results show that the concentration of chlorophyll a is inversely related to tidal stage at most periods when there is an inverse relation between chlorophyll a and the specific con-

ductance of the water. This inverse relation is most marked in the central part of the estuary, during periods when river discharge is low enough to permit considerable tide-induced changes in specific conductance. Chlorophyll a is a reliable indicator of phytoplankton standing crop, as shown by a highly significant correlation between chlorophyll a and gross productivity, except during periods of high river discharge, when the scouring effect in the upstream channel can introduce chlorophyll that is photosynthetically inactive and is, therefore, not a reliable measure of phytoplankton. In areas of highly variable river discharge and relatively great tidal range, any sampling program to investigate standing crop of plankton, chlorophyll, and productivity should include sampling to determine the effect of the tide. Ref: *J-1 39(3):360-366, March 1967.*

3.0 - 598
Werner, A. E. and Hyslop, W. F. (1967). DISTRIBUTIONS OF KRAFT MILL EFFLUENT IN A BRITISH COLUMBIA HARBOUR
--Concentrations of kraft mill effluent in Alberni Harbor were measured on three occasions; (a) after a period during which no effluent had been discharged; (b) during the influx of effluent into the almost-clean harbor, and (c) after a year of regular effleunt discharge. Optical methods were used to measure concentrations. A simple formula was developed to estimate the concentrations of currently or recently discharged effluent. Another pollution source contributed to the water color in at least one area. The transient pattern of effluent patches which formed when the mill renewed operations was followed, from the sewer outfall, several miles down the inlet. It resembled the distribution obtained with a hydraulic model of Alberni Harbor developed in the 1940's by another worker. Effluent concentrations after a year of normal operation were recorded; their distribution is discussed. Ref: *J-32 24(10):2137-2153, Oct 1907. 8 refs.*

3.0 - 599
Wicker, Clarence F. (1965). EVALUATION OF PRESENT STATE OF KNOWLEDGE OF FACTORS AFFECTING TIDAL HYDRAULICS AND RELATED PHENOMENA
--Hydraulic model studies including studies on dispersion and flushing of pollutants are reviewed. Ref: *U.S. Army Corps of Engineers, Vicksburg, Miss. Rept. No. 3 257 p., May 1965.*

3.0 - 600
Wicker, Clarence F. (1969). NEW HORIZONS IN THE FIELD OF TIDAL HYDRAULICS
--The states of knowledge in the subdivision of this broad field of engineering are analyzed, and the needs, for new knowledge are determined. Ref: *J-18 95(HY1 Paper 6346):147-160, Jan 1969. 9 refs.*

3.0 - 601
Wilder, Hugh B. (1968). ESTUARIES AND SOUNDS OF NORTH CAROLINA
--The estuaries and sounds are described in terms of tides, river flow, saline water intrusion, and use. It is suggested that planning is necessary to preserve their esthetic values. Ref: *J-58 4(4): 28-38, Dec 1968.*

3.0 - 602
Willeke, Gene E. (1968). EFFECTS OF WATER POLLUTION IN SAN FRANCISCO BAY
--A 914-case sample survey was conducted in San Francisco Bay area to measure attitudes toward and perception of water pollution in the Bay and to determine what effects these attitudes and perceptions have on it's use for recreation. Policy implications include need for better public information programs and more use of qualitative quality parameters. Ref: *Stanford University. Program in Engineering-Economic Planning. Rept. EEP-29, Oct 1968.*

3.0 - 603
Willeke, Gene E. (1969). EFFECTS OF WATER POLLUTION IN SAN FRANCISCO BAY
--A sample survey was conducted in the San Francisco Bay Area to measure attitudes toward and perception of water pollution in San Francisco Bay and to determine what effects these attitudes and perceptions have on individual use of the Bay for recreational activities. Patterns of information-seeking, credibility of sources, and the influence of five private conservation organizations were also studied. Demographic characteristics of respondents were obtained. Attitudes toward government, time perspectives, and esthetics were studied to some degree through a battery of Likert-type items. Ref: *Stanford Univ. Thesis. 1969.*

3.0 - 604
Williams, R. B.; Murdoch, M. B. and Thomas, L. K. (1968). STANDING CROP AND IMPORTANCE OF ZOOPLANKTON IN A SYSTEM OF SHALLOW ESTUARIES
--The taxonomic composition and standing crop of zooplankton were studied for a year in estuaries in the Beaufort area of North Carolina and simultaneous observations were made on phytoplankton production. Copepods predominated, followed by meroplanktonic larvae; abundance of zooplankton varied widely between sampling stations, volumes being generally greatest in the winter and least in late summer and early autumn; and the annual average standing crop was 0.114 ml per m^3. Such small standing crops appear to be typical of shallow areas. Phytoplankton production was similar to that in the open sea; consumption by zooplankton was estimated to be small, and it is thought that such consumption becomes less important with decreasing depth in areas shallower than 100 m. Ref: *J-25 9(1):42-51, March 1968. 41 refs.*

3.0 - 605
Wilson, Douglas P. (1968). LONG-TERM EFFECTS OF LOW CONCENTRATIONS OF AN OIL-SPILL REMOVER ('DETERGENT'): STUDIES WITH THE LARVAE OF *SABELLARIA SPINULOSA*
--The effect of the 'detergent' BP 1002 on the larvae of the marine worm, *Sabellaria spinulosa,* was examined. It was found that concentrations of 1 p.p.m. caused a violent irritation reaction in the larvae and although they appeared to recover after a few hours they died several weeks later. Larvae subjected to 2.5 p.p.m. of the surface-active and stabilizer fractions died within 2 days. The reaction to the different fractions of the 'detergent' varied, that caused by the solvent being most violent. Ref: *J-2 48(1):177-183, Feb 1968.*

3.0 - 606
Wilson, Douglas P. (1968). TEMPORARY ADSORPTION ON A SUBSTRATE OF AN OIL-SPILL REMOVER (DETERGENT): TESTS WITH LARVAE OF *SABELLARIA SPINULOSA*
--Sand was soaked for 90 min. in sea water containing the detergent BP 1002 in concentrations of 1000 and 100 p.p.m. (=mg/1) and then washed. Larvae obtained from Plymouth Sound in March 1967 were observed crawling on the sand and were damaged but the toxic effect disappeared shortly afterwards. Ref: *J-2 48(1):183-186, Feb 1968.*

3.0 - 607
Wilson, James F., Jr. (1968). IMPROVED DYES FOR WATER TRACING
--Dye manufacturers are beginning to tailor the properties of certain fluorescent dyes for water-tracing purposes. Various solutions of Rhodamine B are now available with specific gravities in the range 1.00 to 1.03. Rhodamine WT, a new dye, exhibits low sorptive tendency and is proving to be an excellent tracer, especially for discharge measurements. Selection of fluorometer filters appropriate to the particular dye used is a critical factor in instrument sensitivity. Ref: *Selected Techniques in Water Resources Investigation, 1966-67. U.S. Geological Survey Water-Supply Paper 1892 p. 5-8, 1968. 3 refs.*

3.0 - 608
Wilson, James F., Jr.; Cobb, Ernest D. and Yotsukura, N. (1969). MOVEMENT OF A SOLUTE IN THE POTOMAC RIVER ESTUARY AT WASHINGTON D.C. AT LOW INFLOW CONDITIONS
--In the study the average net rate of downstream movement of the solute was less than 0.6 mi/day. The average inflow was 900 cfs. Tidal action was fairly efficient in dispersing the solute longitudinally. Lateral diffusion was a slow process and the lateral distribution of the solute was far from uniform 6 1/2 days after release. Ref: *U.S. Geological Survey Circular 529-B 14 p., 1969. 3 refs.*

3.0 - 609
Wiseman, William J., Jr. (1969). ON THE STRUCTURE OF HIGH-FREQUENCY TURBULENCE IN A TIDAL ESTUARY
--As part of a comprehensive program to study naturally occurring fluid motions in the marine environment at all time scales a meter has been developed which is capable of sensing high-frequency turbulence. This meter introduces a number of new features to the field of current measurement techniques. It does not disturb the fluid at the point of measurement. It measures the entire velocity vector. It takes a vector average of its measurements. The meter has been laboratory tested and used in the field. It was demonstrated that the current meter has the capability of operating effectively in the presence of a wave field and may be useful in the study of such types of fluid motion. Ref: *Johns Hopkins Univ., Baltimore, Md., Chesapeake Bay Institute Rept. Nos. TR-59, Ref-69-12 85 p., Nov 1969.*

3.0 - 610
Wood, P. C. (1965). EFFECT OF WATER TEMPERATURE ON THE SANITARY QUALITY OF *OSTREA EDULIS* AND *CRASSOSTREA ANGULATA* HELD IN POLLUTED WATERS
--Flat oysters (*Ostrea edulis*) and Portuguese oysters (*Crassostrea angulata*) were exposed to flowing sea water containing a known number of *Esch. coli*, at temperatures in the range 3°-17°C, and samples of both water and oysters were examined bacteriologically after various periods of exposure. Results were analyzed statistically, showing that the numbers of *Esch. coli* in the oysters depended on both the number of organisms in the water and the temperature. Ref: *P-1 p. 307-317, 1965.*

3.0 - 611
Woodwell, G. M.; Wurster, C. F. and Isaacson, P.A. (1967). DDT RESIDUES IN AN EAST COAST ESTUARY: A CASE OF BIOLOGICAL CONCENTRATION OF A PERSISTENT INSECTICIDE
--Measurement of DDT residues in the soils of a brackish marsh at the mouth of Carmans River, on the south shore of Long Island, N.Y., and in various organisms in the area showed a high concentration of residues in the marsh and a systematic increase in DDT residues with increase in trophic level. The highest concentrations were found in scavenging and carnivorous fish and birds, although birds had 10-100 times more than fish. In many cases the concentrations approached those found in organisms known to have died of DDT poisoning, suggesting that many natural populations are now being affected, and possibly limited, by DDT residues. The authors conclude that water analyses are of limited value in evaluating the effects of DDT residues on aquatic populations, since water can be expected to have a lower concentration of DDT than other components of the ecosystem; risks of DDT pollution can be best evaluated by analysing carnivores or other organisms that concentrate the residues. Ref: *J-6 156(3776):821-823, May 12, 1967.*

3.0 - 612
Wurster, C. F. (1968). DDT REDUCES PHOTOSYNTHESIS BY MARINE PHYTOPLANKTON
--Experiments were carried out to determine the effect of DDT on the photosynthetic activity of marine phytoplankton. DDT in concentrations of a few parts per 1000 mil. reduced photosynthesis in laborabory cultures of 4 species of coastal and oceanic phytoplankton representing 4 major classes of algae, and also in a natural phytoplankton community collected near Woods Hole, Mass. The toxic effect increased as the numbers of algal cells decreased. The ecological significance of these results is discussed, including the possibility that selective toxic stress by DDT on certain algae could alter the species composition of a natural phytoplankton community and the resulting imbalance could result in blooms of species normally suppressed by others, particularly in waters enriched with sewage or other sources of organic pollution. Ref: *J-6 159(3822):1474-1475, March 29, 1968.*

3.0 - 613
Yamagata, N. and Iwashima, K. (1965). RADIOACTIVE CONTAMINATION IN THE HARBOURS OF SASEBO AND YOKOSUKA
--Concentrations of various radioactive elements in 2 Japanese harbors were determined before and after visits from nuclear-powered submarines; no significant effects were observed as a result of the visits. Ref: *J-104 14,:183-193, 1965.*

3.0 - 614
Yamazaki, M. (1965). PROBLEMS IN USING SEA WATER FOR CONDENSER COOLING IN THERMAL POWER STATIONS
--Tabulated data are given on the chemical quality of sea water in Tokyo Bay, Japan, indicating the occurrence of pollution, particularly at Shin-Tokyo and Shinagawa where the concentration of dissolved oxygen is low, the chlorine and chemical oxygen demands are high, and sulphides sometimes occur, owing to the influx of sewage and trade waste waters from the Sumida and Meguro Rivers, respectively. The polluted sea water contains 10^2-10^3 times as many general and sulphate-reducing bacteria as ordinary sea water. Examples are given of the difficulties caused when such polluted water is used for cooling purposes in power stations on the shores of this bay and other polluted bays in Japan; methods for overcoming these problems have been investigated. Ref: *P-10 3,: 117-132, 1965.*

3.0 - 615
Yee, Y. E. (1967). OIL POLLUTION OF MARINE WATERS
--A selected list of references to the literature on oil pollution of marine waters covering the period 1950 to Nov 1967. Ref: *U.S. Dept. of the Interior. Library Bibliography No. 5 32 p., Nov 1967.*

3.0 - 616
Young, D. R. and Folsom, T. R. (1967). LOSS OF ZINC-65 FROM THE CALIFORNIA SEA MUSSEL, *MYTILUS CALIFORNIANUS*
--Colonies of the California mussel, *Mytilus californianus*, collected near the mouth of the Columbia River, where they had taken up zinc-65, were transferred to coastal waters of southern California where much lower levels of zinc-65 occur, and were subsequently sampled at intervals for one year. During this period the concentration of zinc -65 in the soft tissues (after allowing for radioactive decay) decreased by more than 97 per cent. This decrease appears to be described satisfactorily by a single exponential function, with a biological half-life for growing organisms of 76±3.5 days; if radioactive decay is not excluded the observed rate of loss of zinc-65 is described by an effective half-life of 58±2.7 days. Ref: *J-105 133,:438-447, 1967.*

3.0 - 617
Young, Robert G. (1968). ENZYMATIC DEGRADATION OF DDT BY AQUATIC ORGANISMS
--Reports research to determine whether a number of mammals, fish and microorganisms had enzymatic capabilities to degrade DDT to DDE. It was found that fish possess the necessary enzymes to give some degree of protection in DDT contaminated water. Preliminary tests were made to determine whether metabolic conversion of DDT could be observed in pure cultures of some common algae. Conclusive evidence was not found. Ref: *Cornell Water Resources and Marine Sciences Center OWRR Rept. A-015NY. 7 p., Aug 1968.*

3.0 - 618
Zachariasen, Fredrik (1968). OIL POLLUTION IN THE SEA: PROBLEMS FOR FUTURE WORK
--It is estimated that about one million tons of non-volatile petroleum products are dumped into the ocean every year. Typically, these products congeal into slowly hardening lumps which are only gradually oxidized, and which can therefore drift for long distances. Technical problems associated with the enforcement of pollution control laws are discussed, and possible means are given for solving these problems, and for providing defenses against pollution. Data requirements for further studies are specified. Enforcement of preventative legislation would be facilitated if it were possible to identify unequivocally the source of the pollutant. A scheme for doing this is discussed. Potential health hazards, cost and instrumentation considerations, and other aspects of the use of additives are surveyed. It is concluded that the technique poses no foreseeable health hazard, that it is economically feasible, and that the investment required for identification instrumentation is nominal. Ref: *Institute for Defense Analyses, Arlington, Va. Rept. No. RP-P-432 IDA/HQ-68-8914, 32 p., June 1968.*

3.0 - 619
Zats, V. I. (1965). EFFECT OF OCEANOGRAPHIC FACTORS ON THE CONTAMINATION OF COASTAL WATERS (A BRIEF REVIEW OF SOVIET AND NON-SOVIET LITERATURE)
--Presents a review of the international literature dealing wihh the effects of oceanographic factors on the contamination of coastal waters. The thesis presented is that an oceanological solution should explain how the sea copes hydrodynamically with impurities and contaminants. Important factors affecting the behavior of sewage are said to be: currents, waves, density stratification, tidal phenomena, horizontal turbulent diffusion and vertical mixing. Ref: *J-66 5(3):1-9, 1965. in English, May 1966. 57 refs.*

3.0 - 620
Zeitoun, M. A.; Mandelli, E. F. and McIlhenny, W.F. (1969). DISPOSAL OF THE EFFLUENTS FROM DESALINATION PLANTS INTO ESTUARINE WATERS
--It was found that the disposal of effluents from desalination plants into estuarine waters can produce changes in the temperature, salinity, copper concentration, oxygen content, hardness and other minor parameters of the environment. The proper design of an outfall system will minimize environmental changes. Pretreatments that may be necessary before discharge are aeration to increase its content of dissolved oxygen or copper removal. Ref: *Office of Saline Water R. & D Progress Rept. No 415 140 p., March 1969.*

3.0 - 621
Zeitoun, M. A.: Mandelli, E. F.; McIlhenny, W. F. and Reid, R. O. (1969). DISPOSAL OF THE EFFLUENTS FROM DESALINATION PLANTS: THE EFFECTS OF COPPER CONTENT, HEAT AND SALINITY
--Criteria for outfall designs were established based on the copper concentration in the effluent from a desalting plant, its concentration after dispersion in the environment and the ecological effects of heat, salinity and copper on the planktonic organisms in the water column. The use of diffusers to mix the effluent with sea water to reach safe copper concentration by dilution is believed to be a more practical solution than chemical removal or inactivation. Ref: *Office of Saline Water, R & D Progress Rept. No. 437 192 p., March 1969. numerous refs.*

3.0 - 622
Ziebell, Charles D. (1966).   FLOATING FIELD
LABORATORY FOR ESTUARINE FISH TOXICITY STUDIES
--Describes the materials used and construction of
a floating field laboratory used for estuarine
fish toxicity studies. It is essentially a raft
with a center well. This device makes it possible
to take water samples during mortality episodes.
Ref: *J-26   28(3):180-182, July 1966. 2 refs.*

(Received too late to enter
in alphabetical sequence)

3.0 - 623
Edgerton, A. T. and Trexler, D. T.   (1970).
RADIOMETRIC DETECTION OF OIL SLICKS
--Laboratory and airborne measurements were made
of a variety of oil base pollutants under various
atmospheric and low sea state conditions including
several at night. Investigations included microwave response as a function of oil film thickness,
physical temperature of the oil-water system, pollutant type sensor wavelength, antenna polariza-
tion, and observation angle. The results were
used to select the most suitable microwave radiometer for the airborne measurements by the U.S.
Coast Guard. Ref: *Aerojet General Corp., El
Monte, Calif. Rept. No AGC-SD-1335-1   127 p.,
Jan 1970.*

3.0 - 624
Federal Water Pollution Control Administration
(1969).   OIL SAMPLING TECHNIQUES
--Several basic 'dip-stick' techniques, which are
primarily applicable for sampling slicks with a
thickness of greater than 2 mm, as well as suggested methods for sampling thin oil slicks are
discussed and illustrated. Preliminary results on
oil entrapment by solid adsorbents, and various
types of sampling equipment and materials used
by foreign and U.S. researchers are reported.
Ref: *FWPCA. Edison, N.J. Water Quality Lab. Water
Pollution Control Research Series 62 p., Dec
1969.*

3.0 - 625
Heinle, Donald R. (1969).   TEMPERATURE AND
ZOOPLANKTON
--All metabolic rates of zooplankton are dependent
on temperature. Rates generally rise in a linear
fashion, with inflection points when plotted on a
semi-log scale, and fall at higher temperatures.
The upper limits of thermal tolerance for two
species of copepods from Chesapeake Bay were found
to be near the normal temperature of the habitat
during the summer. Acclimation temperature had
little effect on the upper limits of thermal tolerance. Estuarine copepods were killed by passage
through the condensers of a power plant, although
temperatures encountered were generally below the
upper limits of thermal tolerance. Chlorine gas
was applied at relatively high rates at that particular power plant and is suspected to be the
cause of mortalities. The operation of the power
plant did not alter the seasonal patterns of distribution or production of estuarine copepods.
Ref: *J-25   10(3/4):186-209, Sept/Dec 1969.*

3.0 - 626

Lindenmuth, W. T.; Scherer, J. O. and Van Dyke, P.
(1970).   ANALYSIS AND MODEL TESTS TO DETERMINE
FORCES AND MOTIONS OF AN OIL RETENTION BOOM.
--This two part document presents a theoretical
analysis of the loads and motions of a continuous,
elastic, oil retention boom of arbitrary configuration. The boom is subjected to loads of wind,
current, and an irregular sea. The analytical
method was programmed for an IBM 1130 computer
and used to generate data for a variety of oil
booms. Towing tank tests were conducted on selected boom configurations and serve to check the
theoretical analysis. Ref: *Hydronautics Inc.,
Laurel, Md. Rept TR-948-1(I) and (II)   267 p.
and 300 p., Jan 1970.*

3.0 - 627
Mitchell, Charles T.; Anderson, E. K.; Jones L.G.
and North W. J. (1969).   ECOLOGICAL EFFECTS OF
OIL SPILLAGE IN THE SEA
--Ecological consequences following oil spillage
vary with oceanographic conditions, character of
the liberated substance, and nature of any clean-
up activities that may follow. A spillage of
diesel fuel in a small cove on the open coast of
Mexico in 1957 produced definable changes for a
distance of about five miles. The recent spillage
of crude oil in the Santa Barbara Channel affected
certain bird species profoundly but did not initially cause significant mortalities among intertidal and shallow subtidal organisms. After several weeks of exposure, however, losses appeared
among certain attached species such as barnacles
and mussels. Various criteria for assessing ecological consequences are described and findings of
field observations after the two   spillages
are explained in terms of literature on biological
effects of exposure to oil. Ref: *Water Pollution
Control Federation. 42nd Annual Conference held
October 5-10, 1969, Dallas, Texas 10 p., 8 refs.
(Preprint).*

3.0 - 628
Montgomery, Suzanne (1970).   COAST GUARD HAS NEW
TOOL TO COUNTER TANKER OIL SPILLS
--The system basically involves the air-drop of
pumping equipment and huge collapsible plastic
bags next to a stricken tanker. The oil cargo is
transferred to the 500-ton-capacity bags, which
are then towed by surface craft to pier facilities. Ref: *J-111   11(5):32-34, May 1970.*

3.0 - 629
North, Wheeler J. (1969).   BIOLOGICAL EFFECTS
OF A HEATED WATER DISCHARGE AT MORRO   BAY,
CALIFORNIA
--Abundance and diversity of plant and animal
species were affected by a heated effluent over a
distance of approximately 200 meters from the ter-
minus of a discharge canal. Seaweeds were almost
completely lacking within the discharge canal and
solid surfaces were densely colonized with sessile
invertebrates. The principal algae were unicellular symbionts in the tissues of sea anemones. Ten
seaweed species were distributed sparsely in the
transitional region lying between the canal and
areas considered to be normal. Densities and numbers of animal and plant species were reduced.
Substantial temperature fluctuations were observed
and may have contributed to the observed conditions. Recovery to normality occurred in a rela-

tively short horizontal distance of ten meters at the outer border of the region. The flora appeared to be affected more than the fauna. Several ways in which seaweeds might be affected were discussed but it was not possible to evaluate the importance of each. Ref: P-27 6,:275-286, 1969. 6 refs.

3.0 - 630
North, Wheeler J. and Adams, James R. (1969).
STATUS OF THERMAL DISCHARGES ON THE PACIFIC COAST
--This report attempts to assess the impact of cooling water discharges on the surface water temperatures of tidal areas on the Pacific Coast, U.S.A. both for present conditions and for conditions expected in 1980. Ref: J-25 10(3/4): 139-144, Sept/Dec 1969. 13 refs.

3.0 - 631
North, Wheeler J. and Pearse, John S. (1970).
SEA URCHIN POPULATION EXPLOSION IN SOUTHERN CALIFORNIA COASTAL WATERS
--A brief note indicating that many luxuriant kelp beds have all but disappeared during the past few decades and in the place of the holdfasts are barren areas supporting extremely dense populations of sea urchins. The sea urchins seem to be responding to unexpected and unpredictable events that follow environmental change by man. High population densities may be the result of destruction of their main predators, sea ottors, depletion of the abalone and enrichment of coastal waters with sewage effluent. Ref: J-6 167,:209, Jan 9, 1970. 5 refs.

KEYTERM INDEX

specific subjects

AUTHOR   INDEX